THE NEURAL BASIS OF BEHAVIOR

Lloyd S. Woodburne
University of Washington

Charles E. Merrill Books, Inc.
Columbus, Ohio

MERRILL'S INTERNATIONAL PSYCHOLOGY SERIES

under the editorship of

Donald B. Lindsley
University of California at Los Angeles

and

Arthur W. Melton
University of Michigan

Library of Congress Catalog Card Number: 66-23649

Printed in the United States of America

1 2 3 4 5 6 7 8 9 10 11 12 / 75 74 73 72 71 70 69 68 67

To

Agnes M. and Elizabeth O. Woodburne

Preface

The present volume has grown out of the need for an introduction to the nervous system on the part of first-year graduate students in physiological psychology. The treatment followed has been found useful also for senior premedical students, as well as for those majoring in biology and speech pathology. This review of the nervous system is intended to be followed by a course in physiological psychology, and if possible one in the sensory basis of behavior as well. Only in this context can the volume be considered an adequate introduction.

The need for a new treatment of this subject seems indicated by two factors. The first is the gap that exists between the very elementary texts and the medical compendiums. The second factor is the difficulty of finding in one volume enough of both neuroanatomy and neural physiology for real understanding. Finally, very few of the volumes available at present include in their treatment any substantial indication of the behavioral significance of either neural function or interference with neural function by reason of accident or disease.

As the table of contents makes clear, this volume is organized on the basis of the functional input of sensory information and its coordination and "processing" by higher centers. The sections progress, therefore, from receptors to spinal cord to brain, with an attempt to examine structure, function, and behavioral significance at each stage. The section on the autonomic nervous system interrupts this upward flow of sensory information, but it had to be kept in close conjunction to the consideration of the hypothalamus.

One of the most important considerations in the study of the nervous system is that it functions as a unit rather than as the successive addition of a series of separable parts. Thus, while the following sections are examined separately, the full significance of the spinal tracts, for instance, does not become apparent until one reaches the cerebellum or even the thalamus, for it is there that sensation from the face joins sensation from the body. So the separation into discrete parts for study purposes creates a false impression which is not borne out by normal functional activity.

It is my hope that this volume will increase the student's understanding of neural action as an integral component of human and animal behavior. I am indebted to a number of colleagues and students for criticisms and suggestions, and to my brother Russell, to Donna Schram, and to Gerald Stinson for most careful reading.

LLOYD S. WOODBURNE

Contents

One

ROLE OF THE NERVOUS SYSTEM IN BEHAVIOR

PSYCHOLOGICAL PROCESSES AND THE NERVOUS SYSTEM

The student who is interested in human or animal behavior frequently wishes to plunge immediately into the fascinating details of personality development or psychopathology, or methods of efficient learning. At a particular point in each subfield he discovers with some astonishment and disappointment that his study is blocked by gaps in our information and knowledge. In the field of learning, for instance, we know much about the effect of inhibition, the progress of sensorimotor skill, and the strongly motivated "one shot" learning. But we do not yet know how memory is stored or, indeed, what changes occur in the nervous system to constitute memory of past events. It was once thought that the concept of the declining resistance at the synapse would explain learning and memory, but this, clearly, is totally inadequate.

One set of experiments may demonstrate the problem of memory. Hamsters were taught a simple maze pattern of three or four turns. Some of them were given electrical shock four hours after each learning run, others were shocked after one hour, and still others were shocked one minute after each learning run. Those which were shocked after a four-hour wait learned the maze in the fewest learning trials; the hamsters with an hour interval before the shock required a larger number of trials than the four-hour group; the group which was shocked one minute after each trial never learned the maze better than chance performance. The conclusion from this experiment is clear. A four-hour wait before shock has no detrimental effect on learning or memory, a one-hour interval before shock results in a slight deficit in learning and memory, while a one-minute interval followed by shock makes learning and memory impossible. It seems evident then that the fixing of memory takes time to accomplish. From this experiment, fixing of memory is not completed before one hour has elapsed, and, presumably, successively shorter periods produce greater and greater deficit in both learning and memory. Memory then has a time dimension, for during the time interval of approximately an hour some process supremely important for learning and memory takes place. This may be a growth process, or it may be a different metabolic process, or it may be purely nervous conduction—we do not know.

In another experiment an attempt was made to test whether memory was dependent on continuous activity of the nervous system. Hamsters were used again, and their normal spontaneous brain-wave patterns were recorded on an electrical recorder. Then they were subjected to progressively lower temperatures, with the brain-wave pattern recorded at each stage. Finally, at about 40° F the spontaneous pattern of brain waves completely disappeared. After being held at this low temperature for several hours the animals were brought back to normal living temperature. On a test of running a previously learned maze, the animals' records showed very few errors and, as a result, no loss of memory. Memory, then, is not a function of continuous activity of the nervous system. This drop in temperature is analogous to that experienced by hibernating animals; and, if continuous activity at a particular level were essential for any memory, the hibernating animals would be at a distinct disadvantage.

These two experiments should demonstrate how dependent a complete understanding of such everyday topics as learning and memory is upon an increasing knowledge of the nervous system. They also illustrate the fact that, while we know that the brain is essential in the recording and organizing of past experience, we are as yet unable to say precisely how and where learning and memory take place and are stored for future use.

The same essential relationship holds true when we examine the field of perception. For perception, in its simpler forms, entails the identification and rectification of incoming sensory information by means of previously stored memory of the same or similar objects. A door set at an angle records in the eye a series of acute and obtuse angles, and yet we never mistake the door's square-cornered shape. This process of correction or rectification is so fixed in our perceptive behavior that some of the standard illusions could not occur without assurance that this rectification would take place. In addition, any serious study of perception begins with a knowledge of the particular sense organ, whether this be eye, ear, or touch corpuscle, and of its unique characteristic of transforming light waves, sound waves, or pressure into nervous impulse, and of coding the nervous impulse so as to represent the features of a particular stimulus environment.

A thorough understanding of learning, memory, and perception, as well as other aspects of behavior, depends on a knowledge of how the nervous system contributes to these important psychological functions. The same relationship holds for most aspects of behavior, since the nervous system, together with the sensory receptors, is the major information input-output system which the animal kingdom possesses.

NERVOUS SYSTEM AS INPUT-OUTPUT SYSTEM

All plants and animals live in an environment providing for variations in light, in warmth, and in nourishment. In evolutionary history those forms which survived were able to adjust to changes in all of these variables, while those forms which died out were unable to adjust to these same changes. This process of adjustment required an integrated input-output system of substantial complexity. The animal forms, at least, had to be sensitive to the changes which were occurring in the external environment and respond to those changes by some adjustment which allowed them to continue to exist. The various animal forms are responsive only to a limited number or percentage of the forms of physical energy. The skin, aside from the location of specific sensory endings or free nerve endings, is an impervious covering, and very little information about the outside can get through except at those receptive points. For this reason, when we look at the input-output systems of the animal kingdom, we must realize that the first step in information input is performed by sensory endings which transmit coded information about the particular external condition to which they are sensitive, to the nervous system. The information about the external environment coded by the sensory endings requires a transmission system for its utilization in adaptive response by the animal. That transmission system is the nervous system. The nervous system can serve in relatively simple reflex levels of adjustment, in which few synaptic connections are needed. At the simple reflex level of the knee-jerk, or the reflex withdrawal of a finger from pain, the integrating function of the central nervous system is at its lowest level. As the reflexes become more complex the integrating function of the central nervous system increases in importance, the number of synaptic connections increases, and the circuitry of the transmission system becomes very involved. The posturing of a dog or cat in urination or defecation illustrates a fairly complex reflex response, in this case to internal rather than external changes.

But the central nervous system is more than a transmission system which merely integrates bodily functions. It becomes, above the reflex level, a system which is flexible in response, modifiable because of previous experience, and retentive of that past experience. To provide for these more complex functions the central nervous system has increased in complexity. This complexity involves multiple branchings of axons and dendrites, more intricate and numerous synaptic junctions, alternate pathways, excitatory and inhibitory mechanisms, and expansion and elaboration of cortical association areas on which learning, reasoning, and imagination depend so heavily.

NERVOUS SYSTEM IN EVOLUTION

This gradual shift from simple reaction levels to the most complex has spanned most of the period of life on earth as the evolutionary development of newer forms of life unfolded. It is also illustrated by those forms which survived the changes in environmental conditions. The insects, for example, illustrate a level of activity almost wholly at the reflex level, aside from the social organization of the ants and bees. One aspect of this reflex level of activity is that in some forms the sexual activity of procreation kills the individual male, while at the same time assuring the continuation of the species. Among the vertebrates even a brief examination of the nervous system of fishes, amphibians, birds, mammals, primates, and man shows a steady progression into more complex and larger nervous systems. This progression in size and complexity is paralleled very precisely by an increasing complexity, plasticity, and selectivity of behavior. As the nervous system becomes more complex and more proliferated the behavior becomes more variable in response, for the animal is able to select one course of action from a number of alternatives.

Fish and Amphibians

If we begin by examining the brain of a fish we find that the various lobes into which it is divided have as their function primarily the reception of sensory information and some coordination. The olfactory lobe is anterior to the optic lobe, which is followed posteriorly by the acoustico-lateral area and the skin area, as illustrated in Fig. 1–1. Thus

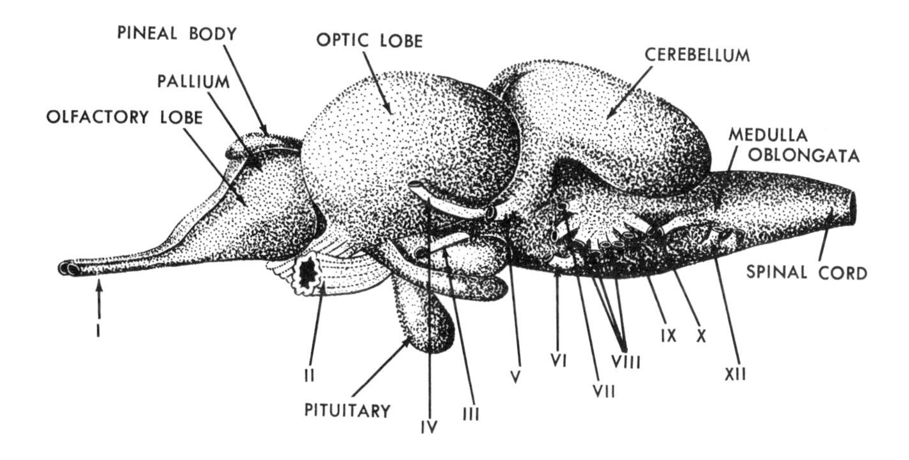

Drawing by Brenda Sutherland

Figure 1–1. Brain of Salmon

we see that the fish brain is made up of nose brain, eye brain, auditory brain, skin and visceral brain. It is clear also from the illustration that, while there is a very rudimentary cerebellum for adjustments of equilibrium, there is no higher center of coordination comparable to the cerebral cortex which makes possible the variability of response of the higher forms. It sometimes surprises students to realize that animals as low in the evolutionary scale as fish have the entire complement of cranial nerves for sensory input to the brain and for motor outflow which are possessed by man—with the exception of spinal accessory, XI[1]—without having the cerebral cortex of the higher forms.

[1] Cranial nerves will be considered in Chapter 9.

In terms of behavior the fishes are limited to rather simple reactions to their environment and "instinctive" and unvarying behavior patterns such as migratory return to the stream of their spawning.

As we move upward in the evolutionary scale we find an increase in complexity of the nervous system accompanied by more complex and selective behavior.

In the fishes and the amphibians one of the dominant sensory departments in migration is olfaction, and the coordination of this—in fishes at least—with lateral-line-equilibratory system and vision comprises much of the incoming sensory data which is basic to the animal's behavior. In the amphibians there begins a marked change in cerebellar function for equilibrium and posture, with a greater development in the tailless than in the tailed forms. This is certainly related to the needs of balance and equilibrium and to the use of the tail in this static function. In these forms there is an increase in the receptive centers for tactile and cutaneous sensation without any real reduction of the importance of the olfactory system as one of the dominant sensory departments. The amphibians show no cerebral cortex, but there is a significant development of the highest correlation centers for olfactory information in the hippocampus and amygdaloid complex.

In terms of behavior again, the amphibian is characterized by unvarying, built-in responses of a reflexive or "instinctive" sort to sensory information.

Birds

One of the first major changes in neural mechanisms and related behavior occurs in birds.[2] In the avian forms, for the first time, the visual sensory information begins to become dominant, and the olfactory sense declines markedly. The changes which show up in the avian over the reptilian nervous system reflect this shift in the dominant sensory department. There is an enlargement of the roof of the subcortical brain stem which is a reflection of the need for coordination between visual, cutaneous, and proprioceptive (muscle-tendon-joint) information. As might be expected, the dynamics of flight brings about a great increase in the size and extent of fissures in the cerebellum, which is the center for posture and equilibrium. This is the result of the enhanced need for delicate equilibrium, not merely because of two-legged support in

---

[2] It is recognized that birds are not in the direct line of development from amphibians to mammals, but are an end line.

relation to a stable earth, but in relation to air horizons during flight as well. There is a centralization of the cerebellar coordinating centers. This is accompanied by an increase in the number of fibers in the spinocerebellar tracts, bringing muscle-tendon-joint information to the cerebellum. The spinal cord of birds has both the cervical and lumbar enlargements for innervation of wings and legs respectively. The cervical enlargement is larger in "good fliers," while the lumbar enlargement is larger in the ostrich, which doesn't fly, but runs. With the birds also begins the channeling and integration of visceral, tactile, and other sensations such as temperature into the final subcortical coordination center, the ventral thalamus. It follows, therefore, that there should be a great increase in the somatic receptive centers of the cortical hemispheres. The cerebral cortex begins to develop, then, as this increased sensory input is elaborated and as the need increases for a higher center of correlation between different sensory modalities. (See Fig. 1–2.)

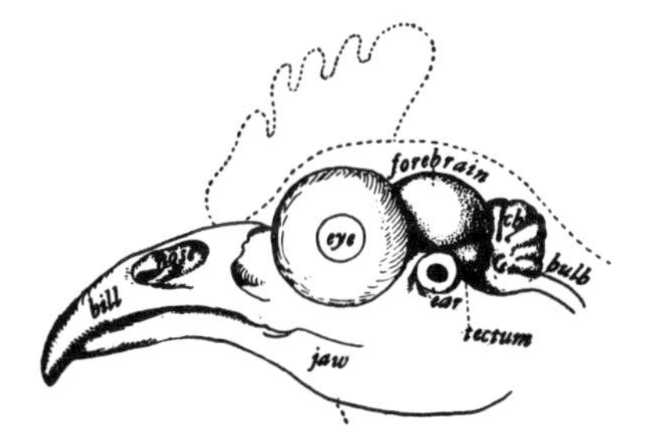

Source: James W. Papez, *Comparative Neurology* (New York: Hafner Publishing Company, 1964), p. 411.

Figure 1–2. Brain of Bird

Mammals

When we study the mammals, we see the further elaboration of many of the structures mentioned in connection with the lower phylogenetic forms. The mammalian cerebellum, for instance, is largely expanded by the addition of the hemispheres, which arise because of the great increase in connections between the cerebral cortex and cerebellum, allowing voluntary control of the machinery of equilibrium and posture. This is accompanied by a vast increase in the size and activity of the thalamus as the way station for sensory information to reach the center of coordination and choice in the cerebral cortex. The simple, primitive cortex called the piriform cortex, which carries out correlation of olfactory and visceral messages, is relatively unchanged from the level of the reptile and bird. The dominant characteristic of the mammalian brain, accompanied by a quantum jump in the potential complexity of behavior, is the overlaying of all the lower centers by the highly fissured neocortex. (See Fig. 1–3.) This provides for voluntary control, a wider range of choice of response, and makes possible the higher learning processes.

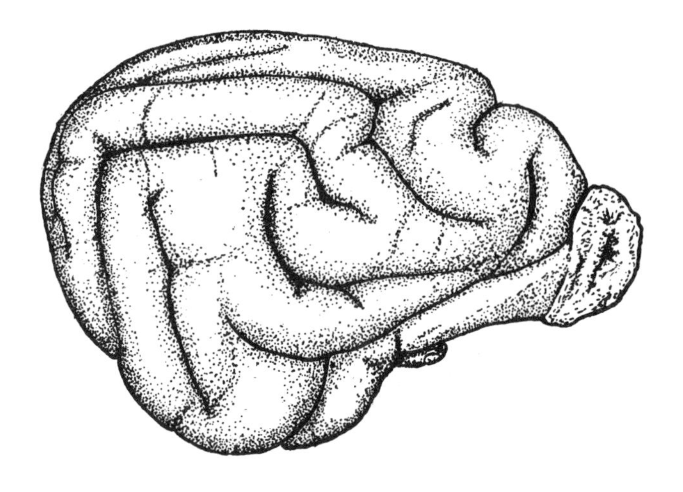

Source: Papez, *Comparative Neurology,* p. 13.

Figure 1–3. Cerebrum of Cat

Primates

In the higher mammals the more automatic behavior patterns of lower forms do not apply, because of the dominance of the cortical mechanisms governing learning and choice of response. As the subcortical centers become more differentiated one from another, the need for correlation increases. So the cerebral cortex as the highest center of correlation and integration gains predominance in direct proportion to the elaboration and differentiation of subcortical centers. Finally, the largest area of the cerebral cortex is composed of association areas which are essential for learning, reasoning, and imagination. (See Figs. 1–4 and 1–5.)

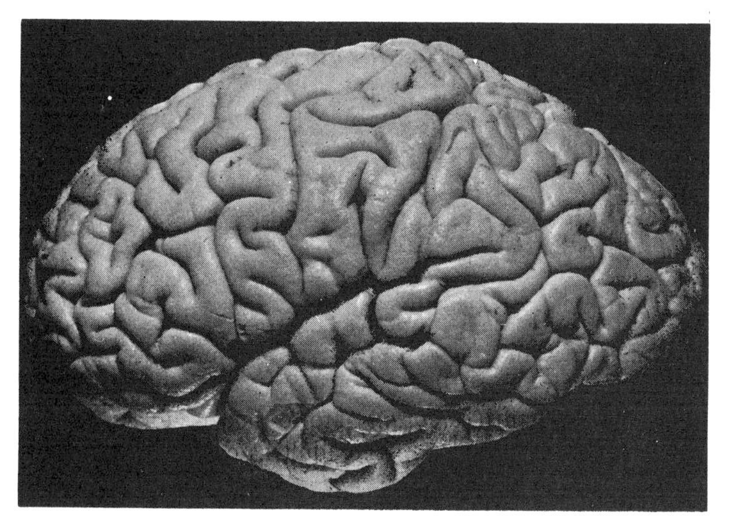

Source: Ernest Gardner, *Fundamentals of Neurology* (4th ed.; Philadelphia: W. B. Saunders Company, 1963), p. 12.

Figure 1–4. Lateral Hemispheres of Human Brain

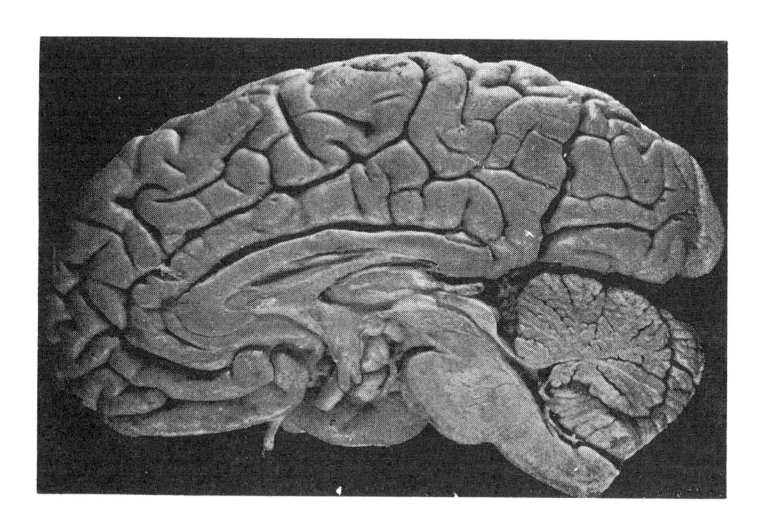

Source: Gardner, *Fundamentals of Neurology,* p. 19.

Figure 1–5. Medial Section of Human Brain

It should be clear then how closely the development of the nervous system in the various vertebrate forms is paralleled by the increasing complexity in behavior, the introduction of voluntary choice, and the higher mental processes. The increased complexity of the nervous system is not the cause, but the necessary substratum, for this increased complexity of behavior.

Some readers may be disturbed by terms which impute purpose to the activity of the nervous system. The use of such terms is meant to imply the adaptation of an animal to its environment, or the natural selection of certain subfamilies which possess neural structures allowing better adjustment to particular environmental conditions. For further justification of such terminology the reader is referred to the last chapter of the *Handbook of Physiology,* Sec. I, Vol. I. In this chapter Dr. Robert Livingston discusses the central control or selective modulation of sensory input. In this central modulation of sensory input no other basis has been found for the selective monitoring of the input which is allowed through to higher centers than what appears to be significant to the individual at that moment. This meaningful significance is certainly a teleological mechanism.

SOURCES AND ADDITIONAL READING

Gerard, R., "What Is Memory?" *Sci. American,* Sept. 1953.

Handbook of Physiology, Sec. I, Vol. I. Washington, D. C.: American Physiol. Soc., 1959.

Herrick, C. J., *Neurological Foundations of Animal Behavior.* New York: Hafner Publishing Company, 1962.

Kappers, C. U. A., G. C. Huber, and E. C. Crosby, *Comparative Anatomy of the Nervous System of Vertebrates* (3 vols.). New York: Hafner Publishing Company, 1960.

Papez, J. W., *Comparative Neurology.* New York: Hafner Publishing Company, 1964.

Ranson, S. W. and S. L. Clark, *The Anatomy of the Nervous System* (10th ed.), Chap. 1. Philadelphia: W. B. Saunders Company, 1959.

Two

GROSS ANATOMY AND FUNCTION OF THE PARTS OF THE NERVOUS SYSTEM

ANATOMICAL ORIENTATION

The student who is beginning a study of the nervous system will find, without some preliminary orientation, a bewildering array of terms for parts of the body or nervous system which must be learned for any accurate description or identification. *Dorsal* indicates a location toward the back of a four-footed animal, *ventral* a location toward the belly. Because of upright posture in man, these terms have been changed to *posterior* and *anterior* respectively. Thus the *dorsal* portion of the spinal cord is also spoken of as the *posterior* columns, and the *ventral* motor cells as the *anterior* motor cells. *Cranial*, or *rostral*, which means the same, indicates a location toward the head end, while *caudal* indicates a location toward the tail end. The *median* plane is a vertical plane exactly through the midline of the body or brain. Thus if a structure is medial of another it is more toward the midline than the second. The *sagittal* plane, by contrast, is any dorsal-ventral, or posterior-anterior, plane parallel to the median plane. Thus the *mid-sagittal* plane is another term for the median plane, and divides the nervous system into symmetrical halves. The *coronal* plane is a vertical plane from side to side, and therefore at right angles to any sagittal plane. The *horizontal* plane is transverse to the vertical plane, and is therefor a longitudinal section. See Fig. 2–1 for the graphic relations of these terms. In four-footed animal anatomy this cross section goes from dorsal to ventral sides of the spinal cord. *Ipsilateral* means on the same side;

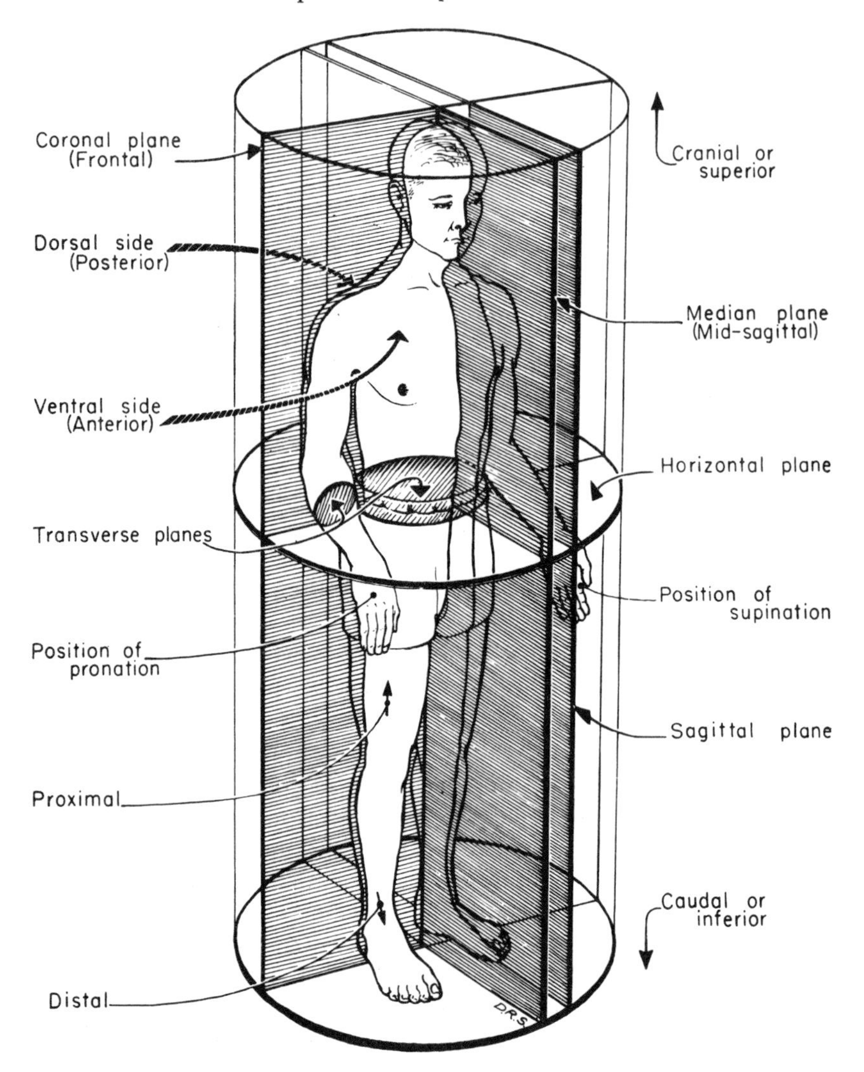

Source: Russell T. Woodburne, *Essentials of Human Anatomy* (3d ed.; New York: Oxford University Press, 1965), p. 4.

Figure 2–1. Planes of Body and Terms of Orientation

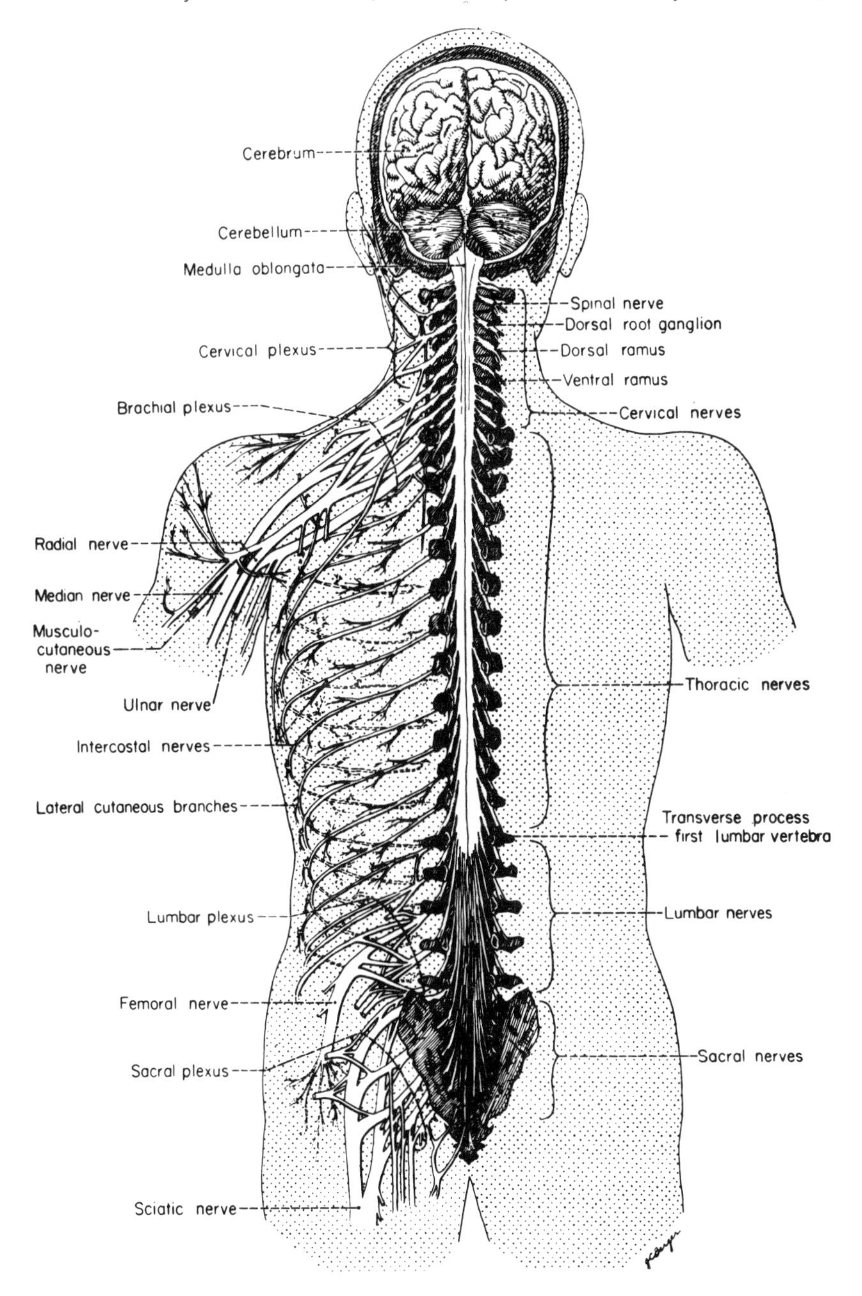

Source: Russell T. Woodburne, *Essentials of Human Anatomy*, p. 25.

Figure 2–2. Brain and Spinal Cord in Situ

contralateral means on the opposite side; while *homonymous* structures are those exactly corresponding nerves or muscles on the two sides of the body.

The nervous system has traditionally been divided into 1) central nervous system, 2) peripheral nervous system, and 3) autonomic nervous system. The central nervous system is composed of those divisions lying entirely within the vertebral column and skull. The peripheral nervous system is composed of the other segments which lie outside the vertebral column and skull, and which connect the central nervous system with skin and muscles, both for sensory impulse moving toward the central nervous system and for motor impulse moving toward muscle or gland as indicated in Fig. 2–2. The autonomic nervous system lies adjacent to the spinal cord and brain stem and serves visceral organs, blood vessels, and glands. It is composed mainly of a pair of sympathetic trunks alongside the vertebral column or of peripheral ganglia close to the organs (largely visceral) innervated.

PERIPHERAL NERVES

The peripheral nervous system includes mainly, then, spinal and cranial nerves. The spinal and cranial nerves are composed entirely of afferent fibers bringing into the spinal cord and brain sensory impulses about external or internal stimuli, or of efferent fibers sending motor impulses out to muscle and gland effectors. It may be of interest to note at this point that there are no other effectors in the body except various kinds of muscles and glands. The impulses in spinal nerves may be somatic afferent from the sense organs of temperature, touch, etc. in the skin or proprioceptive afferent from sense organs in muscle, tendon, and joint. The afferent fibers also include small fibers bringing visceral sensation to the central nervous system for coordination and interconnection. The motor fibers carry impulses to voluntary striated muscle of hand or foot, to cardiac muscle of the heart, and to smooth muscle of the viscera and blood vessels, as well as to salivary and other glands. For the most part, the visceral organs, blood vessels, sweat glands, adrenal glands, etc. are innervated by the autonomic fibers from sympathetic trunks or peripheral ganglia of the parasympathetic division, or both.

Essentially, the peripheral nervous system represents lines of communication, whereas the central nervous system is the center of coordination and the place of determination of the most appropriate response to incoming impulses. As we will see later, no choice of response is possible without synaptic connections between nerve cells, and these connecting points are contained—aside from those in autonomic ganglia—entirely in the central nervous system.

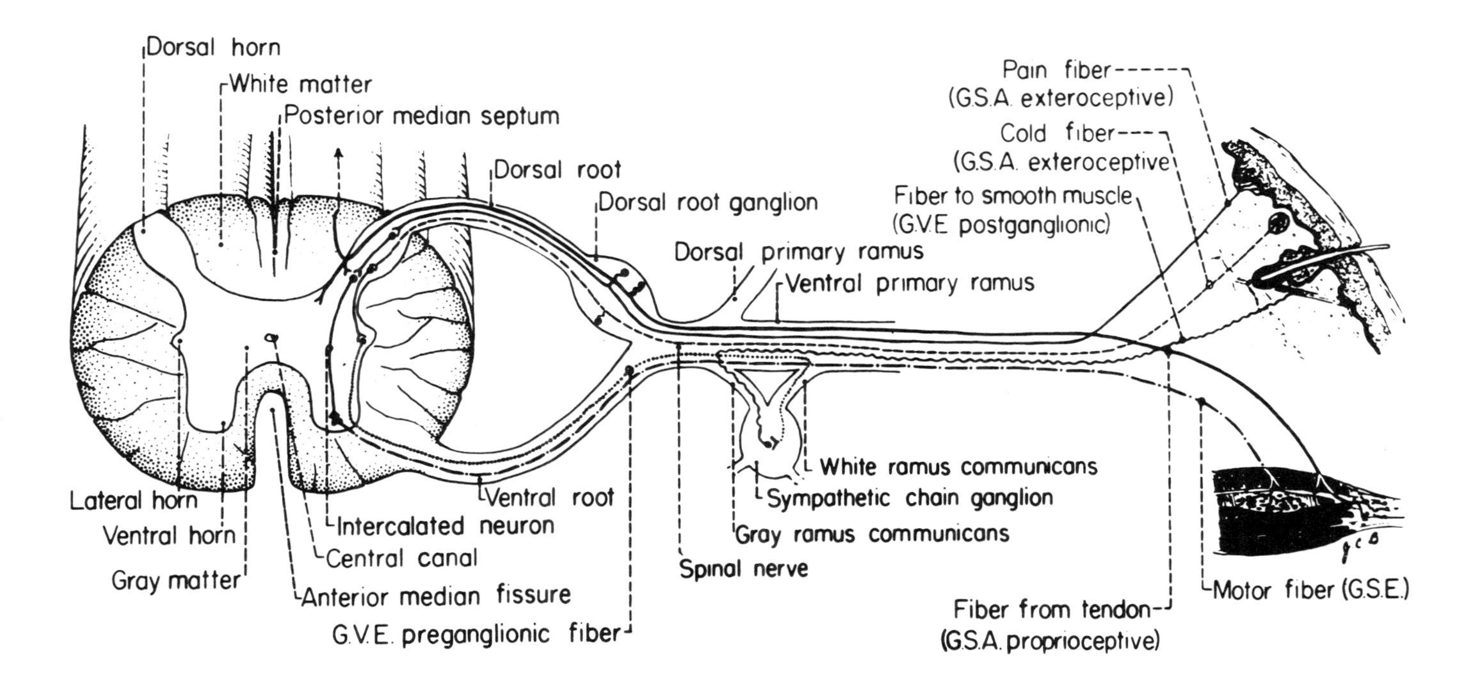

Source: Russell T. Woodburne, *Essentials of Human Anatomy*, p. 25.

Figure 2–3. Components of Typical Spinal Nerve

SPINAL CORD

Most of the peripheral nerves enter or leave the spinal cord. We will begin our examination of the central nervous system, therefore, with the spinal cord. The spinal cord occupies the canal which is enclosed by the vertebral column. It is from 40-45 cm long, and reaches from the base of the skull to the second lumbar vertebra. At each vertebral level there is an intervertebral foramen through which the spinal nerves emerge.

There are, then, spinal nerves both afferent and efferent connecting the spinal cord at each vertebral level with the corresponding dermatome segment of the body, as will be made clear by reference to Fig. 2–3. The spinal cord and nerves represent a segmental relationship between the central nervous system and the body which is not shown so clearly elsewhere in the nervous system. The spinal cord is not uniform in size or shape down its whole length. It is small in cross section at the sacral level, since few fiber pathways have accumulated at that stage, or descend to this level.

It generally becomes larger in cross section through the lumbar, thoracic, and cervical segments as the ascending and descending fiber pathways and nerve cells in the central gray substance increase in number, as indicated in Fig. 2–4. At the cervical and lumbar regions there

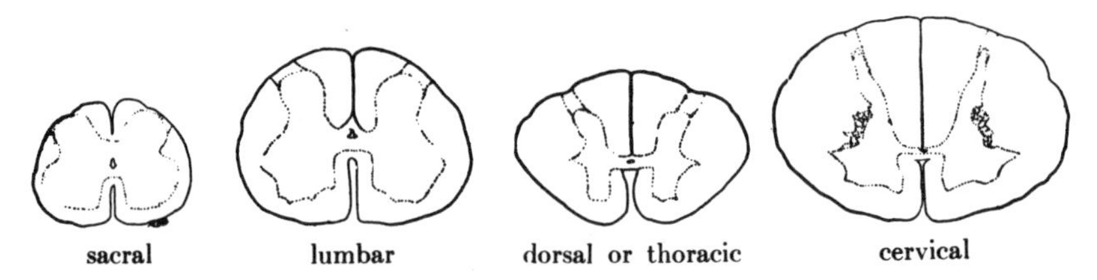

Source: S. W. Ranson and S. L. Clark, *The Anatomy of the Nervous System: Its Development and Function* (10th ed., Philadelphia: W. B. Saunders Company, 1959), p. 171.

Figure 2–4. Sacral, Lumbar, Thoracic, and Cervical Segments of Human Spinal Cord

are, in addition, very noticeable enlargements which have been produced by the additional number of nerve cells and fibers supplying the muscles and skin of the arms and legs. There are in all thirty-one pairs of spinal nerves divided into eight cervical, twelve thoracic, five lumbar, five sacral, and one coccygeal.

At the caudal end of the spinal cord is a *filum terminale* which continues into the filum of spinal dura mater, which in turn is attached to the coccygeal end of the vertebral canal. The spinal cord, like the brain, is protected by two sheets of tissue: a) the *dura mater* (with the arachnoid underneath), which is next to the bony covering and is very tough; and b) the *pia mater* underneath the dura and arachnoid and adhering to the nervous tissue. (See Fig. 2–5.)

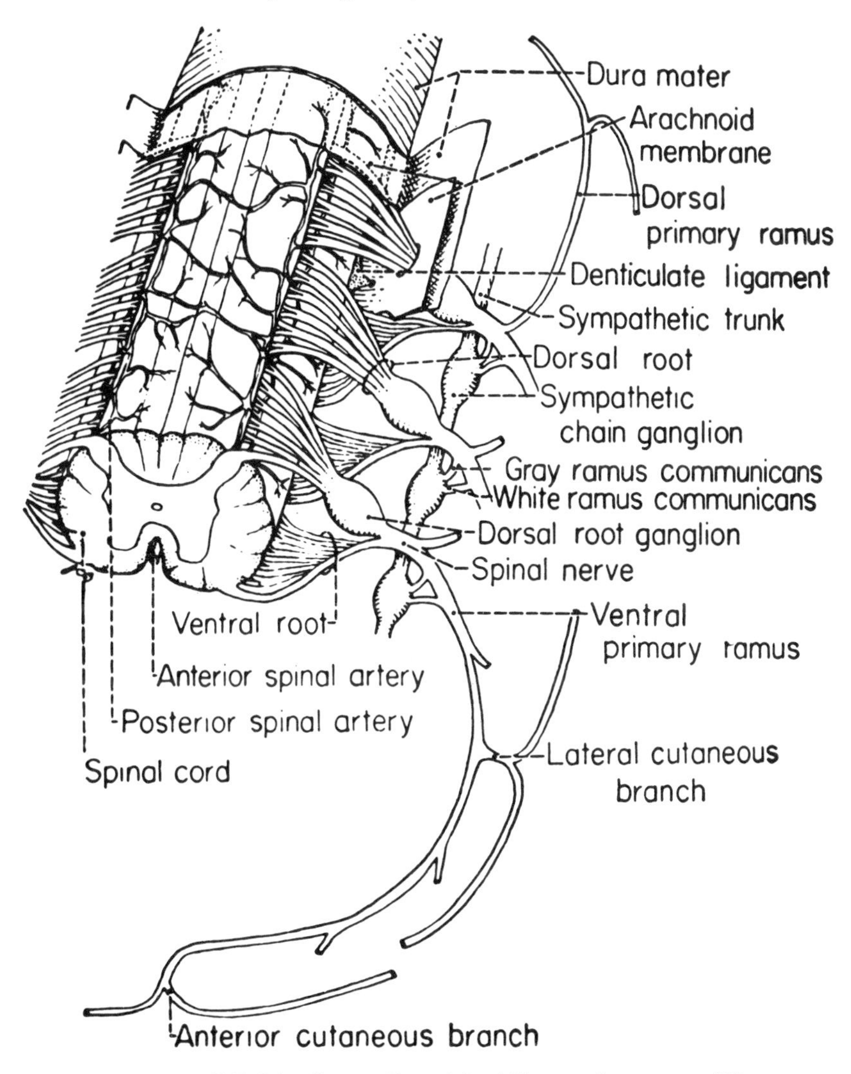

Source: Russell T. Woodburne, *Essentials of Human Anatomy*, p. 327.

Figure 2–5. Spinal Cord Showing Dura, Arachnoid, and Spinal Nerve Branching

The blood vessels supplying the brain and cord are just above the pia. In general, the cervical nerves supply the diaphragm and the cervical muscles and muscles of arm and hand; the thoracic nerves supply the trunk and intercostal muscles; lumbar and upper sacral nerves supply abdominal muscles and those of legs and feet; and the lower sacral nerves supply the anal and perineal muscles.

MEDULLA

Above the level of the spinal cord the first level of brain proper is the medulla oblongata. At this point the segmentation of nerve supply to the body ceases and there begins the functional specialization of the cranial nerves. The medulla shows four prominences on its ventral and lateral surfaces. The medullary pyramids form substantial bulges on the ventral surface on each side of the midline. Above and lateral to these are the bulges of the inferior olives. (See Fig. 2–6.) Aside from these

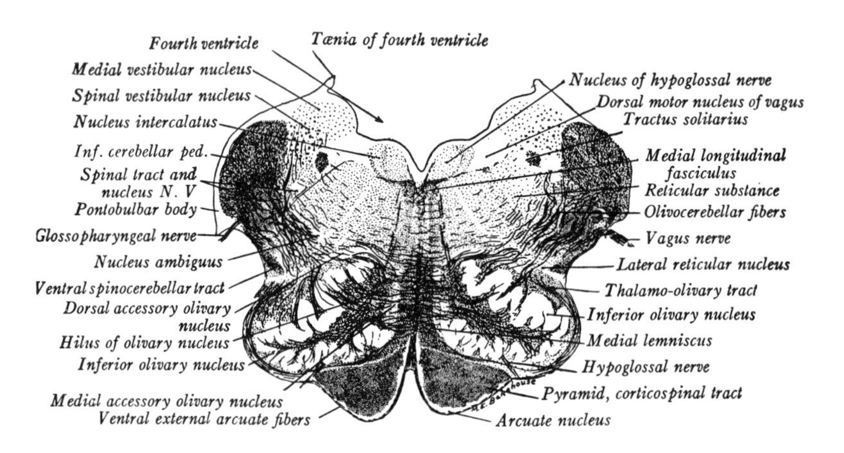

Source: S. W. Ranson and S. L. Clark, *The Anatomy of the Nervous System*, p. 213.

Figure 2–6. Section through the Medulla Oblongata of a Child

bulges the medulla is somewhat wedge shaped in appearance, tapering from rostral to caudal end. Functionally the medulla is dominated by visceral centers such as those for respiration and digestion, as well as for heart action. In addition the vestibular nuclei appear near the rostral border of the medulla for coordination of equilibrium. Roughly half the cranial nerves terminate in the medulla, while some of the others have nuclei which extend into the medullary area.

PONS

As we proceed rostrally on the ventral surface of the brain, the end of the medulla is marked sharply by a prominent bulge on the ventral surface, and covering both halves of the brain stem, which is known as the *pons*, or bridge. This bulge is made up of descending corticospinal fibers and of corticopontine fibers carrying impulses to the cerebellum, allowing coordination of voluntary and involuntary influences on automatic movement and posture. (See Fig. 2–7.) This broad band of fibers

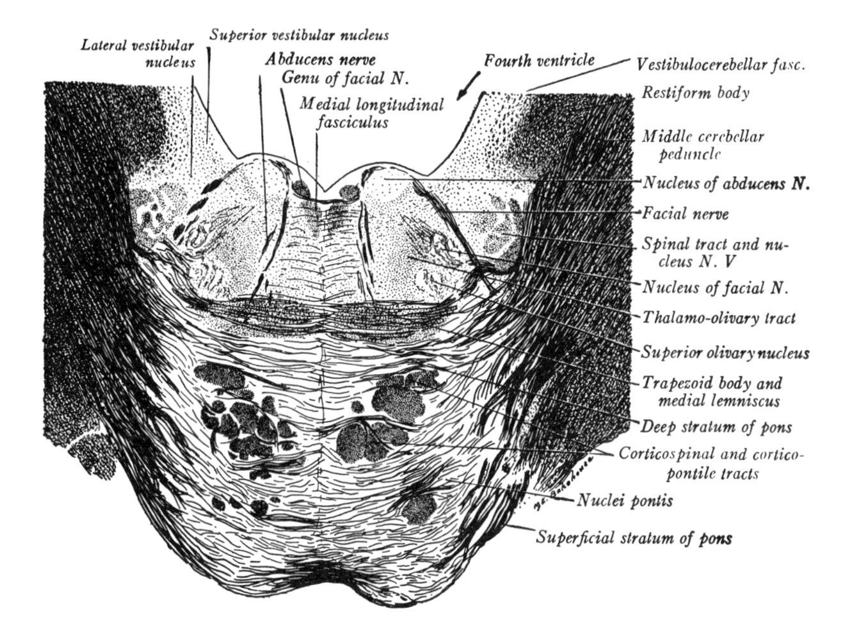

Source: S. W. Ranson and S. L. Clark, *The Anatomy of the Nervous System*, p. 219.

Figure 2–7. Section through Pons and Middle Cerebellar Peduncle

connecting the pons with the cerebellum, which lies dorsal to both pons and medulla, is known as the middle cerebellar peduncle. The tegmental portion of the pons, dorsal of the fibers just mentioned, is in some ways a continuation of the pathways in the medulla. Aside from this function it contains the nuclei of several cranial nerves for the face, eye movement (the abducens nerves), vestibular nuclei, and the auditory pathway.

CEREBELLUM

The cerebellum, which lies dorsal to both pons and medulla, is separated from them by the IV ventricle. (See Fig. 2–8.) The cerebellum is

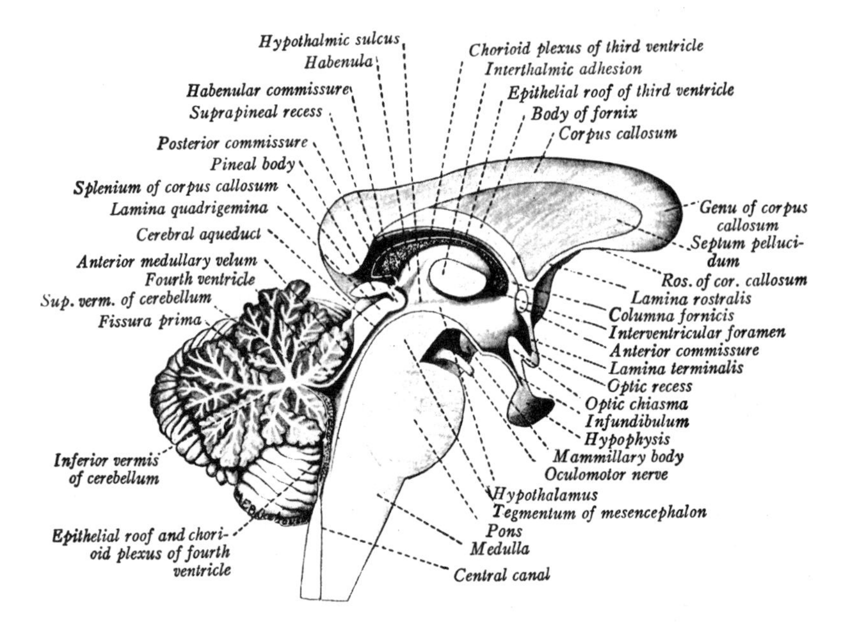

Source: S. W. Ranson and S. L. Clark, *The Anatomy of the Nervous System*, p. 50.

Figure 2–8. Median View of Brain Stem Showing Relation of Cerebellum, IV Ventricle, Pons, and Medulla

profusely fissured, with much of the surface, or cortex, in the folds. It is estimated that only one-sixth of the surface, or cortex, of the cerebellum is exposed; the rest is in the sulci, or folds, of the mantle. The function of the cerebellum is the maintenance of muscle tone and balanced or upright posture, and the synergy of action of voluntary muscles. Because of this complex and varied function the cerebellum has connections with all parts of the body and many of the sensory modalities. Control of muscle action must be based on information about the current state of contraction or relaxation of muscle fibers and tendons. One of the largest inputs to the cerebellum, therefore, is proprioceptive, or muscle-tendon-joint impulses from all the bodily musculature. Several of the large spinal pathways serve this proprioceptive function.

The primary function of the cerebellum is the coordination and integration of many types of nerve impulses. Muscle-tendon sensory impulses are not responded to alone, but must be combined with vestibular impulses for equilibrium. And, in upright posture, these two must be combined with visual data to maintain the body in an upright postion. The cerebellum, lying above the pons and medulla, must have connections to the structures below it, as well as those rostral and caudal. These

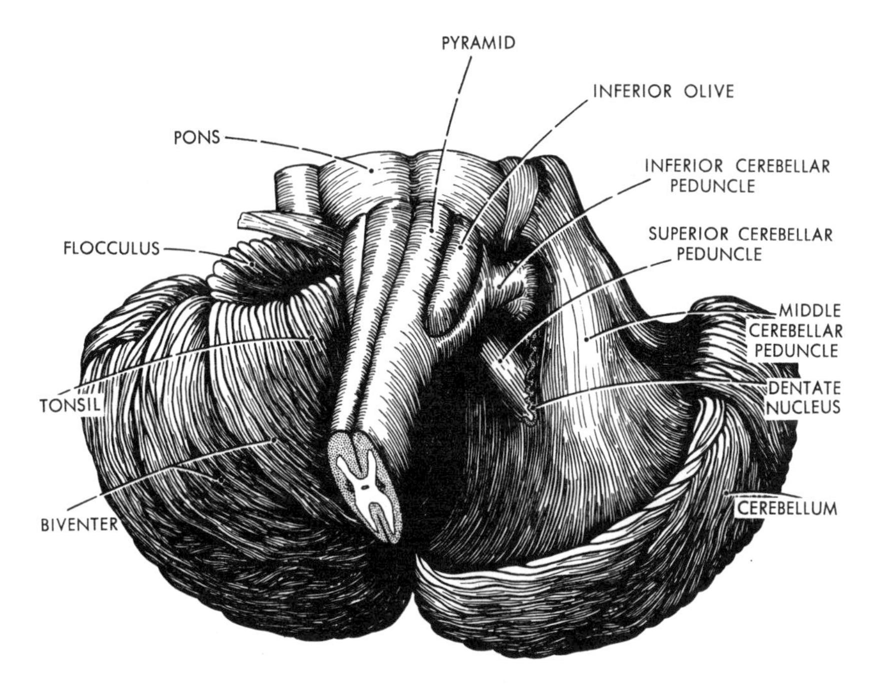

Source: Reprinted with permission of The Macmillan Company from *Correlative Anatomy of the Nervous System* by Elizabeth C. Crosby, Tryphena Humphrey, and Edward W. Lauer. © The Macmillan Company, 1962. P. 201 (labeling altered slightly).

Figure 2–9. Cerebellum and Its Three Peduncles

connections are provided by three peduncles, or stalks—the inferior, middle, and superior cerebellar peduncles, as indicated in Fig. 2–9. The inferior peduncle carries fibers from the spinal cord, from the inferior olive, and from the vestibular nuclei to the cerebellar cortex. The middle peduncle carries fibers from the pons below to the cerebellar cortex. These in turn synapse in the pons with fibers from the cerebral cortex for voluntary influence on cerebellar mechanisms. The superior cerebellar peduncle primarily carries efferent fibers out from the deep nuclei of the cerebellum to the nuclei of the more rostral midbrain and thalamus. In internal structure the cerebellum is analogous to the cerebral cortex in that the incoming fibers proceed directly to the cortical surface and thence, after synapse, to the deep nuclei. From these nuclei the impulses go out to muscle groups and to the cerebral cortex as well.

MIDBRAIN

Rostral, or upstream, from the cerebellum and pons lies a section known as the midbrain, or mesencephalon. The largest area in its ventral portion is occupied by the cerebral peduncles, which are composed of fibers coming from the cerebral cortex and going to the spinal cord via the pyramids of the medulla, or to intermediate synapse as in the pons. The middle portion of the midbrain, ventral to dorsal, contains all the pathways which are still ascending to the thalamus. (See Fig.

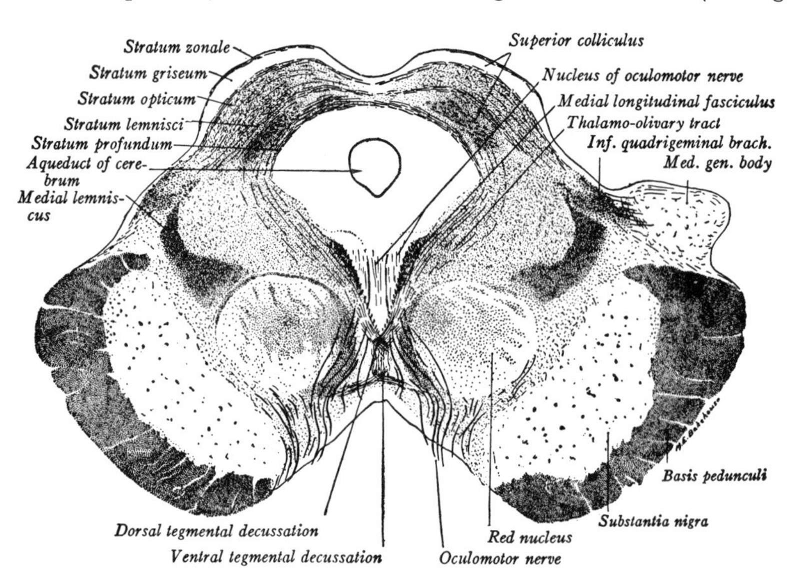

Source: S. W. Ranson and S. L. Clark, *The Anatomy of the Nervous System*, p. 229.

Figure 2–10. Section of Midbrain at Level of Superior Colliculus

2–10.) In addition the red nucleus, or ruber, occupies a central position on either side of the midline. This nucleus, as we will see, is crucially important in locomotion. The dorsal portion of the midbrain is occupied by four rounded prominences on the dorsal surface known as the inferior and superior colliculi. The inferior colliculi, one on each side, are the reflex centers for hearing; while the superior colliculi are reflex centers for vision. There are interconnections between the colliculi on the two sides, as well as connections between inferior and superior colliculi of each side. Together these four colliculi constitute the tectum, or roof, of the midbrain. This is the point of origin of the *tectospinal* pathway and of other fiber connections essential for carrying out auditory and visual reflexes.

THALAMUS (Diencephalon)

Rostral of the mesencephalon (midbrain) lies the diencephalon, whose main nuclear groups make up the thalamus. Below the thalamus, on the base of the brain, is the hypothalamus, which is essential to the carrying out of many homeostatic mechanisms. Above and posterior to the thalamus lies the epithalamus, which is composed of the pineal body and the habenular nucleus. This nucleus serves as an olfactory reflex center. The function of the pineal body, which is not nervous, is to act as one of the endocrine glands. It may be of greater importance in lower animals than in mammals, since it is larger in the lizard than in higher forms.

The main centers of the diencephalon are the thalamic nuclei. This is a major subcortical coordinating center for the afferent sensory impulses from all parts of the body surface. Refer to nuclei in Fig. 2–11. Here sensation from the face joins sensation from the body. Touch, and that portion of proprioception needed for two-point discrimination, as well as temperature, pain, and pressure are here coordinated into an integrated pattern of sensation which is projected to the somatic sensory area of the cerebral cortex. In the thalamus, in the lateral and medial geniculate bodies, lie the last synapses before projection to the cerebral cortex of visual fibers and auditory fibers respectively. In one nucleus of the thalamus, the pulvinar, there is coordination of visual and auditory impulses. In essence, then, the thalamus is a relay center, including the relay of impulses to the hypothalamus below for visceral or homeostatic reactions. But beyond this function as a relay center the thalamus has some residual function as a sensory receptive area, for children born without any cerebral cortex can exhibit simple pleasure and pain. In fact, it is sometimes difficult for doctors to tell that such children are not completely normal behaviorally up to several months of age. Finally there are midline nuclei and association nuclei which are involved in diffuse cortical and nonspecific thalamic projection respectively.

INTERNAL CAPSULE

Lateral to the mass of the thalamus is a broad band of fibers, the internal capsule, linking the thalamus with the cerebral cortex and the cerebral cortex with the spinal cord and with other centers. In the medial portions of this band are fibers connecting the ventral and anterior thalamic nuclei to various areas of the cerebral cortex; the lateral

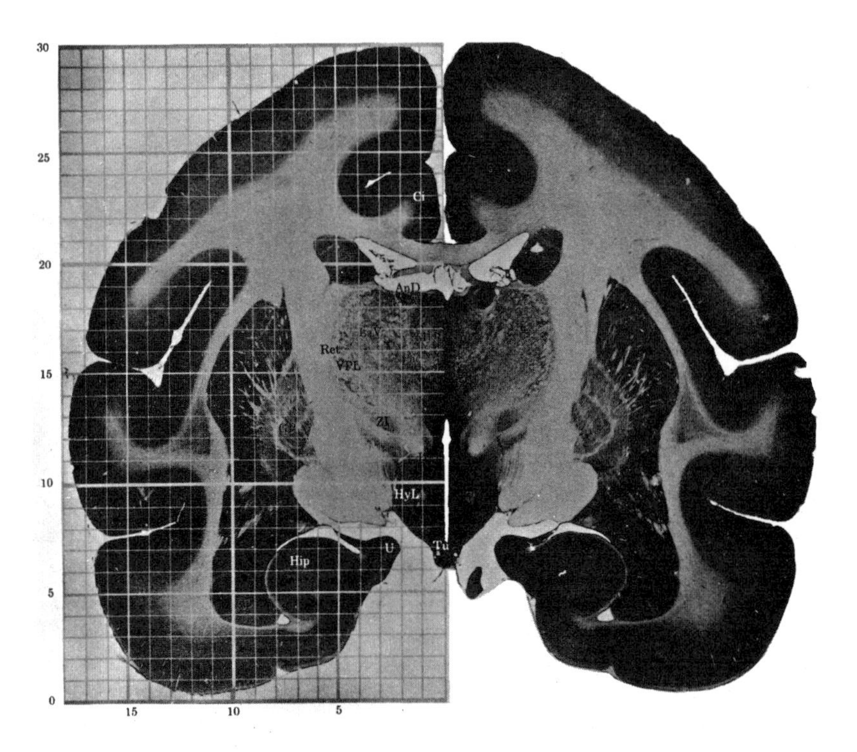

Source: John A. Gergen and Paul D. MacLean, *A Stereotaxic Atlas of the Squirrel Monkey's Brain (Saimiri sciureus)* (Health Service Publication No. 933 [Bethesda, Md.: U. S. Department of Health, Education, and Welfare, 1962]), p. 37.

Figure 2–11. Thalamus and Hypothalamus of Squirrel Monkey

portions carry fibers originating in the cerebral cortex and moving ventrally and caudally through the cerebral peduncles to the spinal cord or to pontine or other coordinating centers. It is very important clinically, since it is in this region that cerebral hemorrhages are likely to occur. Since the fibers for arms, trunk, and legs are carried in separate fascicles, the location of a paralysis can frequently suggest where the effusion of blood has occurred. For relation of thalamus, internal capsule, and basal ganglia see Fig. 2–11.

BASAL GANGLIA

Another group of subcortical centers, the basal ganglia, lies partly anterior to the thalamus and partly lateral to the internal capsule. They are fiber linked with both thalamic nuclei and with the cerebral cortex. Their function in primates and mammals is somewhat obscure but is concerned with producing and controlling automatic associated, or rhythmic, movements. It is largely a discharge center for thalamic reflexes. This is particularly true in animals without cerebral cortex. Birds, which have highly developed basal ganglia, or striatum, can carry out complex instinctive actions—such as flying, nesting, and mating—with basal ganglia alone, without cerebral cortex. The parts of the basal ganglia are three: the caudate nucleus, lying between the dorsal edge of the lateral thalamic nuclei and the lateral ventricle; the globus pallidus, lying just lateral to the internal capsule; and the putamen, lying more lateral still to the globus pallidus. The fibers from the caudate nucleus and the putamen feed into the globus pallidus, which is the major motor, or efferent, center of the basal ganglia. Anterior to the thalamus the caudate nucleus expands greatly to form the head of the caudate. Little is known about the function of any portion of the caudate except this large anterior head section. (See Fig. 2–12.)

CEREBRAL CORTEX

Covering all of the subcortical centers and dominating most of the functions of the mammalian nervous system is the cerebral mantle, or cortex, which has developed extensively in primates. The lower mammals have little frontal portion, or lobes, anterior to the motor area; whereas the development of these frontal portions has pushed out the primate brain anteriorly, placing the motor cortex nearly midway from anterior to posterior pole. The following description will apply then to the primate or human brain. (See Figs. 2–13, 2–14, and 2–15.)

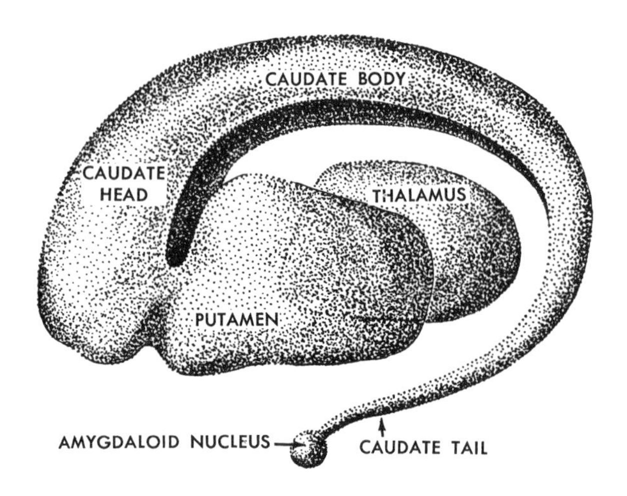

Drawing by Brenda Sutherland

Figure 2–12. Caudate Nucleus—Head, Body, and Tail

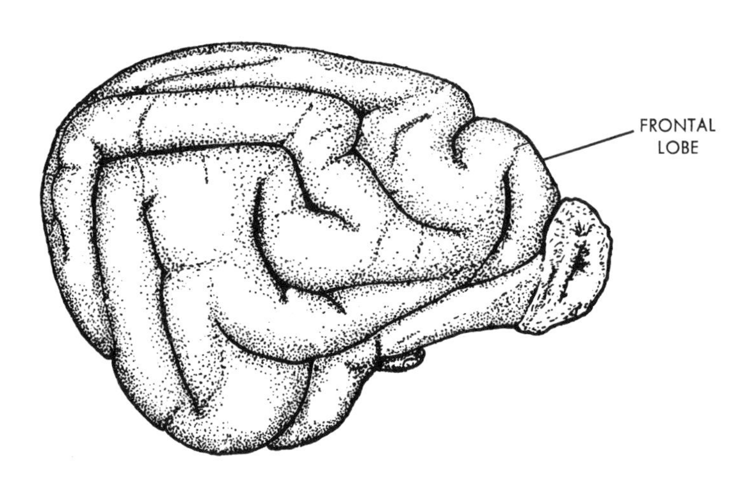

Source: James W. Papez, *Comparative Neurology* (New York: Hafner Publishing Company, 1964), p. 13.

Figure 2–13. Lateral Surface of Cat Brain

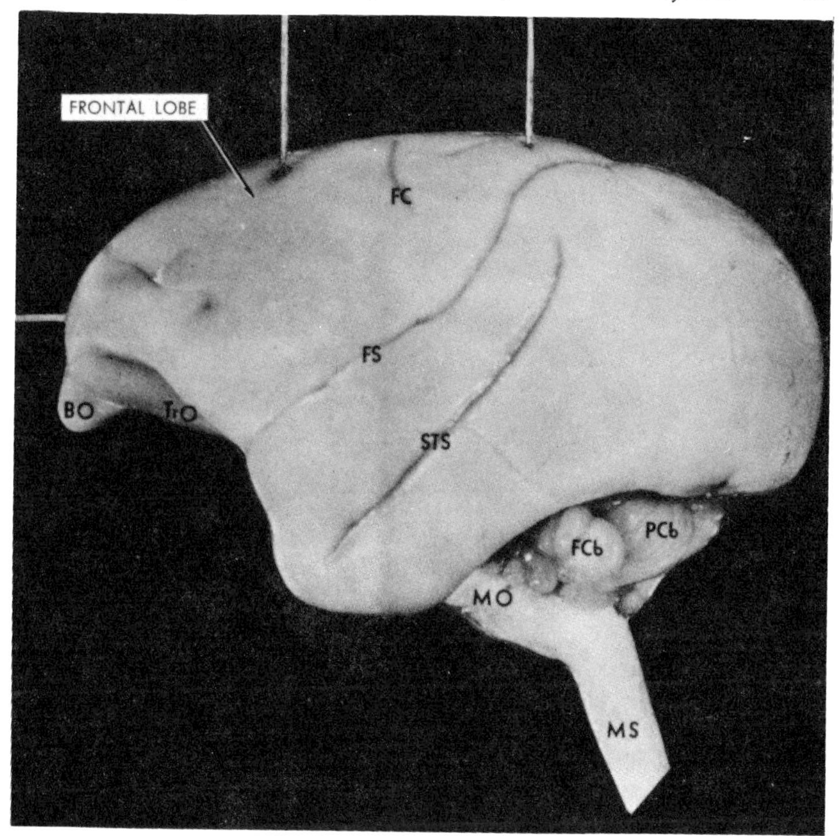

Source: Reprinted with permission of the copyright owners, the Regents of the University of Wisconsin, from Raimond Emmers and Konrad Akert, *A Stereotaxic Atlas of the Brain of the Squirrel Monkey,* The University of Wisconsin Press, 1963. P. 16.

Figure 2–14. Left Lateral View of Squirrel Monkey Brain

The primate brain is usually divided into four lobes: (1) the frontal lobe, which extends from the frontal pole, both dorsally and laterally back to the central, or Rolandic, sulcus; (2) the parietal lobe, which extends posteriorly from the central fissure to the parieto-occipital fissure, and laterally and ventrally down to the lateral cerebral, or Sylvian, fissure; (3) the occipital lobe, which covers the back of the brain from the parieto-occipital fissure on the dorsal surface to the preoccipital notch on the ventral surface; and (4) the temporal lobe, which occupies all the area of cortex lateral and ventral to the lateral cerebral fissure and extending posteriorly to the preoccipital notch. The major dividing lines are the folds of the cortex and the fissures between them. The central

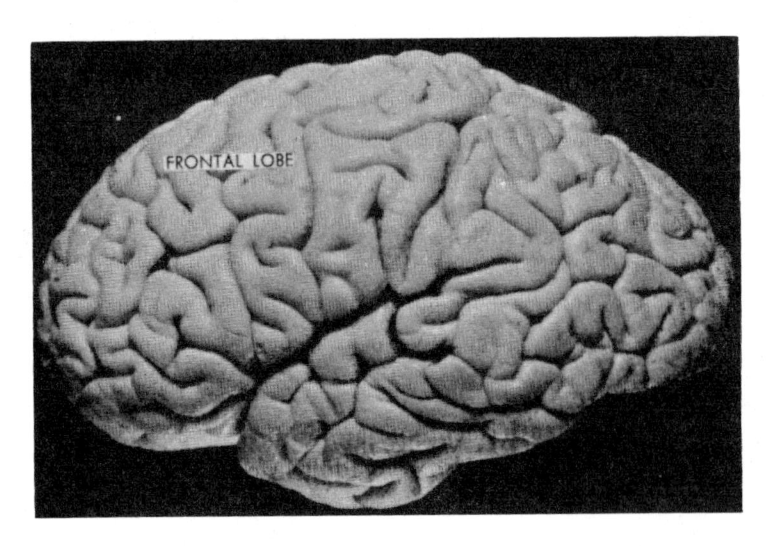

Source: Ernest Gardner, *Fundamentals of Neurology* (4th ed.; Philadelphia: W. B. Saunders Company, 1963), p. 12.

Figure 2–15. Lateral Surface of Human Cerebral Hemisphere

fissure (Rolando) runs from the dorsal midline downward and angling slightly rostrally to meet the lateral cerebral fissure. The lateral cerebral fissure (Sylvius) separates the temporal lobe from the frontal lobe and partly from the parietal lobe as well. These dividing lines are indicated on Fig. 2–16.

The subdivisions of the lobes in terms of function are as follows. The frontal lobe, starting with the anterior pole, has as its functions: (1) association cortex, (2) frontal eye fields for conjugate eye movement, (3) premotor cortex, and (4) motor cortex. The motor cortex, then, is along the precentral gyrus, or fold, just anterior to the central fissure. The functions of the parietal lobe, from central fissure posteriorly, are: (1) somatic sensory cortex along the postcentral gyrus, (2) association cortex, and (3) visual association cortex. The occipital lobe is concerned predominantly with visual reception. In some primates the visual receptive area along the lips of the calcarine fissure extends well forward into the internal folds of the parietal lobe. The temporal lobe contains the sensory receptive area for hearing on the upper rounded surface of the superior temporal gyrus, just below the lateral cerebral fissure. The remainder of the temporal lobe is association cortex and is concerned with higher mental processes.

One portion of the cortex is buried in the junctional folds of the

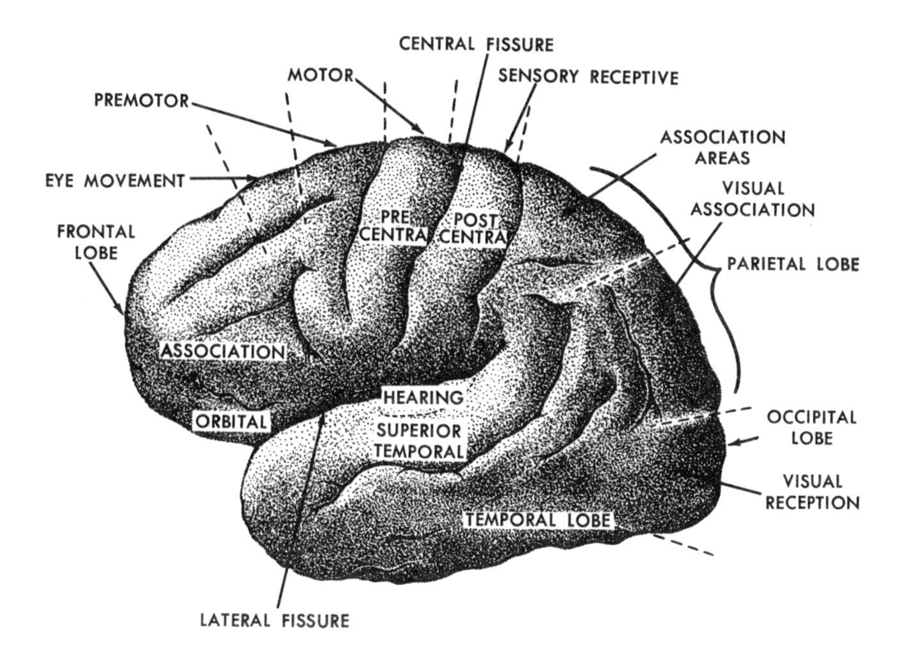

Drawing by Brenda Sutherland

Figure 2–16. Lateral Cortical Areas and Their Functions

frontal, temporal, and parietal lobes. This is called the island of Reil, or insula. It is concerned primarily with the cortical projection of taste and sensation from the alimentary canal.

The cortex is divided down the midline by the longitudinal cerebral sulcus into two hemispheres which are homologous in external appearance. Connecting these two hemispheres in their middle portion is a broad band of fibers known as the corpus callosum. The interconnecting fibers connect homologous points in the two hemispheres, and allow the two hemispheres to act as a single unit. The corpus callosum is bent double in front to form the *genu,* or knee, and is slightly curved ventrally behind to form the *splenium.*

Numerous other bands or fascicles of nerve fibers connect various portions of the cortex with each other. The details of these fiber bundles and of the cortical function generally will be reserved to a later section.

SOURCES AND ADDITIONAL READING

The CIBA Collection of Medical Illustrations, Vol. I, *Nervous System*, Sec. III. CIBA Pharmaceutical Company, 1953.

Crosby, E. C., T. Humphrey, and E. W. Lauer, *Correlative Anatomy of the Nervous System*. New York: The Macmillan Company, 1962.

Gardner, E., *Fundamentals of Neurology* (4th ed.), Chap. 2. Philadelphia: W. B. Saunders Company, 1963.

Ranson, S. W. and S. L. Clark, *The Anatomy of the Nervous System* (10th ed.), Chap. 2. Philadelphia: W. B. Saunders Company, 1959.

Three

TECHNIQUES OF STUDY OF THE NERVOUS SYSTEM

The earliest method of study of the nervous system was gross dissection based upon cadavers prepared for medical dissection, or upon bodies in which the nervous system was exposed by accident or disease. Some of the illustrations from the time of Galen in the 2nd century and of Vesalius in the 16th century exhibit this type of gross examination. Gross examination of brains is still important in preparation for certain brain operations, for the critical brain areas in any primate are not synonymous with those of a dog or cat.

The invention of the microscope opened new avenues of study of the parts of the nervous system. Much of the new knowledge which came from microscopic study depended heavily, however, on the development of new stains to show nerve fibers or cell structure. In fact, the tremendous contribution of Ramon y Cajal to neuroanatomy rested in part on his development of new stains. Similarly the contributions of Marchi and, much more recently, Nauta derive in part from their stains that bring out degenerating fibers. To identify the pathways of certain nerve bundles or the connections they make requires that we be able to differentiate these separate bundles from the mass of nervous tissue. Consequently, accidental or other damage to nervous tissue resulting in degeneration of these fibers has enabled us to see pathways or connections which were hidden and undifferentiated before such injury.

STEREOTAXIC INSTRUMENT

One of the most dramatic developments in techniques of study occurred in 1908 when Horsley and Clarke developed a stereotaxic instrument for studying the deep structure of the brain. This instrument holds the animal's head rigid in both horizontal and vertical planes. The head is fixed by ear bars inserted in the external auditory meatuses, and by the forward part of the head being clamped between the infraorbital ridge and the upper jaw. Arbitrarily, a line connecting the infraorbital ridge and the auditory meatuses has been accepted as a horizontal plane. This horizontal plane, or plane 10 mm above this level depending on the brain atlas, is identified as the zero horizontal plane from which to measure dorsal-ventral, vertical plane points in the brain space. Lateral points in space are measured from the midline, and anterior-posterior or frontal plane locations are made relative to a

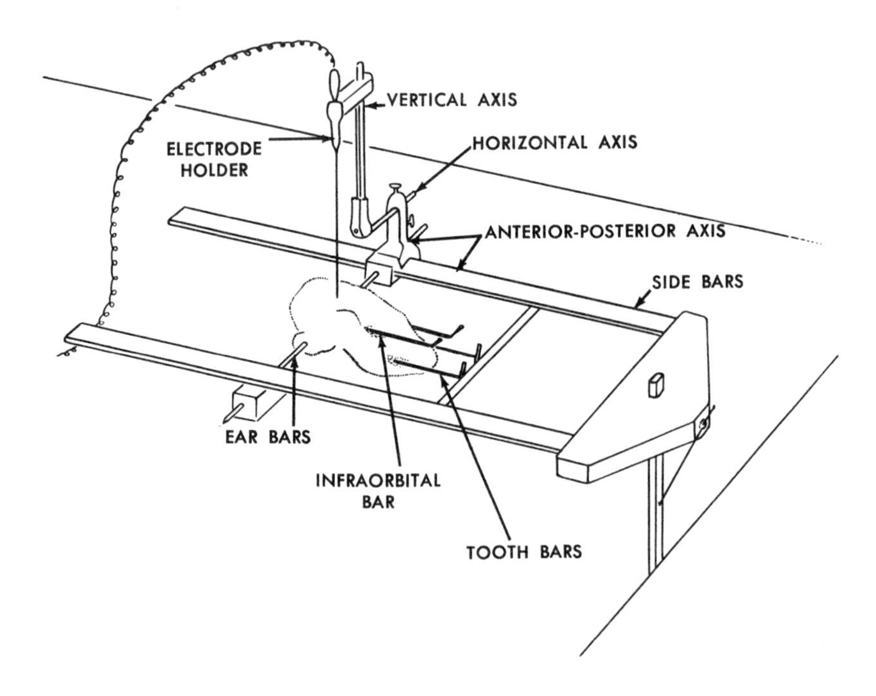

Drawing by Brenda Sutherland (after Jasper)

Figure 3–1. Drawing of Stereotaxic Instrument

vertical plane through the auditory meatuses. Thus, with the animal anesthetized and its head properly positioned in the instrument, any point in brain space may be located by the vertical, horizontal, and lateral coordinates. (See Fig. 3–1.) With the brain of the animal thus oriented it is possible to lower electrodes to almost any desired location for purposes of recording local electrical activity, for stimulating, or for making electrolytic lesions. The instrument is constructed so that adjustments in all three coordinates—lateral, anterior-posterior, and vertical—are possible by millimeter stages or, with a micrometer attachment, by hundreths of a millimeter. For each type of animal studied there must be a carefully prepared atlas of brain structures, although individual investigators make rough plates for their earlier use and these frequently lead to formal atlases. The atlas of a particular animal brain is composed of plates or microscopic sections about 0.5 mm apart from rostral to caudal. These plates, which must be true coronal sections, are marked both laterally and vertically in millimeter scales to correspond to the brain dimensions. The correspondence of the atlas to the coordinates of the stereotaxic instrument allows an investigator to make a reasonably exact placement of an electrode for electrical recording, stimulation, or lesion making.

It will be evident that the dimensions of the brains of all animals of a given species are not identical. They vary with age, body weight, and the general variability within the species. Consequently some of the recent atlases include a measure of variability which can be expected in the location of neural structures in each plate. In using the atlases, then, it is particularly important to use animals which closely approximate the size, body weight, and subspecies (as in the dog) on which the atlas is based. An examination of a brain atlas of the squirrel monkey will show the "red nucleus" to be Ant-Post-5.5 mm, Lat-2 mm, Vert-10 mm above the ear bars as indicated in Fig. 3–2. These measurements, transferred to the animal in the stereotaxic instrument, should provide a basis for accurate stimulation or lesion work.

Lesions produce electrolytic or radio frequency damage to the particular structure, and will show degenerative effects which can be indicated by degenerative stains, gross behavioral maladjustment as in hypothalamic lesions, or glial cell infestation. Stimulation ordinarily produces electrical effects in connected parts of the nervous system which can be recorded on an oscilloscope or a paper-pen recorder. More recently these results of stimulation are being fed into automatic counters and put on tape which can be analyzed by high speed computers. In addition to the electrical lesion or stimulation techniques, recent at-

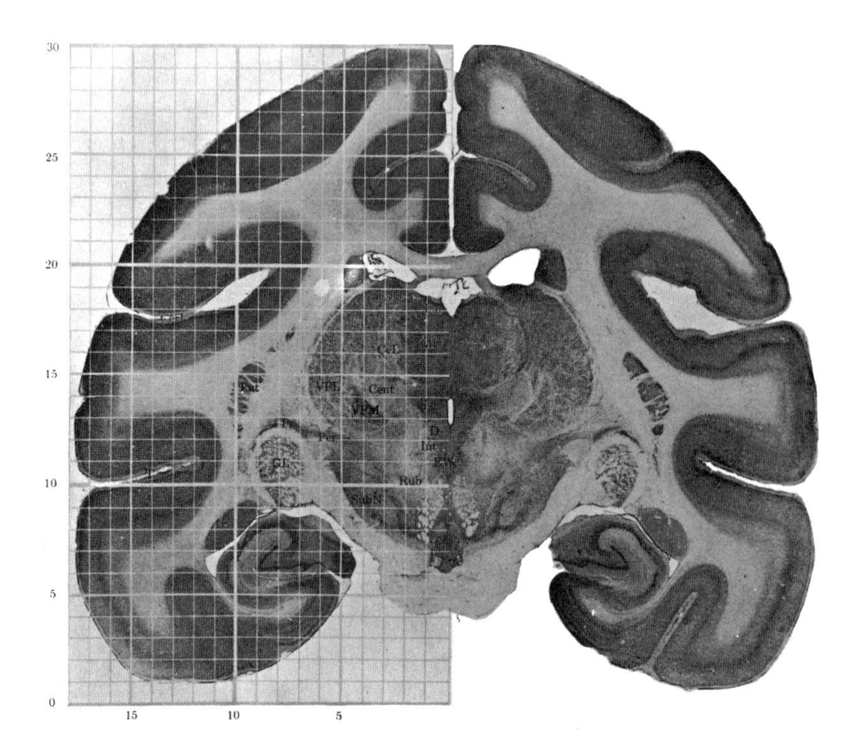

Source: John A. Gergen and Paul D. MacLean, *A Stereotaxic Atlas of the Squirrel Monkey's Brain (Saimiri sciureus)* (Health Service Publication No. 933 [Bethesda, Md.: U. S. Department of Health, Education, and Welfare, 1962]), p. 47.

Figure 3–2. Plate from Squirrel Monkey Atlas

tempts have been made at local chemical brain stimulation. Fine, hollow needles, serving as cannulae, are inserted in the brain by stereotaxic means. A chemical agent, such as atropine sulfate, acetylcholine, or epinephrine, is then injected through the cannulae into the particular nucleus or area. This method may have some advantages over electrical stimulation. Some of the chemicals used are the normal transmitter substances of parts of the nervous system. It is contended also that chemical stimulation affects other fibers passing through a nucleus much less than does electrical stimulation. The assessment of the results of chemical stimulation is the same as for electrical stimulation—either gross behavioral changes or electrical changes in connected brain centers, which can be recorded and analyzed.

CORTICAL ABLATIONS

One of the standard methods of studying the functions of different areas of the cerebral cortex or surface is by ablation. This involves removing a part of the cortex and noting the changes in the animal's behavior or in its response to stimulation. Use of the technique of cortical ablation depends on a knowledge of the cortical localization of function. The locations of visual, auditory, somatosensory, and motor cortex are vastly different in primates and man from their position in dog or cat. Nervous tissue generally, and particularly the cortical surface, is quite soft. It can be removed, therefore, by simple aspiration. Such suction, if carefully done, can remove the 1/8 to 3/16-inch thickness that comprises the cortical cell layers, with little damage to the underlying fiber bundles that interconnect one part of the cortex with another. Removal of the small area responsible for the tail movements on a monkey has clearly observable effects almost immediately.

DECEREBRATION

The separation of the cerebral cortex and the upper brain stem (thalamus, basal ganglia, etc.) from the lower centers of the brain stem by transection of the neural axis is known as decerebration. Decortication, by contrast, is the removal of the thin cortical surface, which amounts to less than 3/16 of an inch of thickness. In decortication all the subcortical centers are intact and, if all portions of the cortex are removed, it can be considered a total ablation. In decerebration the brain stem is transected, usually at the collicular level, above the level of pons and medulla. In operations for the decerebration of dogs or cats a thin spatula is inserted just rostral to the bony tentorium that separates the cerebellum from the occipital lobe of the cerebrum. If the spatula follows the forward slope of the tentorium the brain stem is transected so as to leave the inferior colliculi attached to the brain stem, they being just rostral to the cerebellum, and may spare the red nucleus from damage as well. The brain forward of the transection is scooped out with the spatula or aspirated by suction. Since this operation severs a number of blood vessels the brain case is packed with cotton to stop bleeding and hasten coagulation.

The decerebration operation leaves intact the visceral centers of the medulla, such as those controlling heart rate and respiration. The decerebrate animal can, therefore, live for some time if good care is given to its needs. Such preparations were essential in order to give us much of our present knowledge of reflex action. Accidental injury or gunshot wounds, such as may be caused by war, sometimes leave humans with similar damage.

Because the recovery of an animal in a decerebrate operation may depend on rapid recovery from the effects of anesthesia, it is customary to use inhalation of ether, which is blown off almost as soon as the pad is removed from an animal's nose.

CLINICAL STUDY

One of the oldest methods for studying the nervous system is by means of clinical cases. These are, perhaps, the major contact a medical man has with diseases or defects in the nervous system. The effect of a cerebral hemorrhage is a dramatic example of the relation between the integrity of the nervous system and normal behavior. Even more, however, it provides abundant confirmation of the extent to which the nervous system acts as a whole and not as a series of separable parts.

The other clinical manifestations comprise the study of neurology. In a fashion analogous to the cerebral hemorrhage, sensory deficit or numbness in the face or hands, motor deficit in trunk or limbs or neck, as well as partial paralysis of the face or eyelid provide clear evidence of neurological damage. Consequently, the study of clinical cases of neurological defect constitutes one of the important methods of study of the close relation between the nervous system and behavior.

Important knowledge about cortical function has been gained by stimulation of cortical areas in the course of human brain operations. It is often necessary to use local stimulation to identify the motor region of the brain, the location of which is not always evident due to limited exposure. In recent years, with the advent of stereotaxic instruments for humans, electrode probes are lowered through the cortex to the thalamus or corpus striatum. At these places it is possible to record and stimulate in order to identify a local region responsible for excruciating pain, or for abnormal involuntary movements as in dystonias or shaking palsy (Parkinsonism). Once identified as an offending area, mimicking the abnormal symptoms when stimulated, the area is inactivated by electrolytic or cryogenic (local freezing) lesions.

DRUG EFFECTS

The effect of certain drugs on the parts of the nervous system has been a standard technique of study. The application of strychnine, for instance, to a portion of the cerebral cortex results in electrical spikes in interconnected areas of the brain. This method, known as strychnine neuronography, has been used to identify interconnected parts of the cortex, such as the connection between the two hemispheres by way of the corpus callosum, or long fiber connections between anterior and posterior cortical regions.

Drugs have been used extensively also to study synaptic transmission, and particularly synaptic inhibition. Both strychnine and picrotoxin have been particularly prominent as indicators of the inhibitory transmitter substance.

FIXING, SECTIONING, AND STAINING

The conclusion of most of the careful lesion or stimulation or ablation studies is characterized by a microscopic study of the brain or spinal cord which has been subjected to experiment procedures. This microscopic study requires removing the brain or spinal cord from the animal, hardening it, usually in formalin, infusing and fixing it in a paraffin or celloidin black for sectioning, sectioning with a microtome into slices of 30-40 micra in thickness, fixing to slides, and staining. Only after these laborious steps have been taken can an investigator tell with absolute assurance that his lesion or point of stimulation was on target or was, unfortunately, too far off target to provide reliable evidence. The details of these several procedures can be found in a handbook of histological and staining techniques. Since they are not essential to the present volume, this reference must be sufficient.

SOURCES AND ADDITIONAL READING

Clarke, R. H., "Investigation of the Central Nervous System: Methods and Instruments," *Johns Hopkins Hospital Reports, Special Volume*. Baltimore, 1920.

Horsley, V. and R. H. Clarke, "The Structure and Function of the Cerebellum Examined by a New Method," *Brain*, 31 (1908), 45.

Ingram, W. R., S. W. Ranson, F. I. Hannett, F. R. Zeiss, and E. H. Terwilliger, "Results of Stimulation of the Tegmentum with the Horsley-Clarke Stereotaxic Instrument," *Archives of Neurology and Psychiatry*, 28 (1932), 513.

Penfield, W. and A. T. Rasmussen, *The Cerebral Cortex of Man*. New York: The Macmillan Company, 1950.

Four

THE NEURON AS A SPECIALIZED CELL

The complex animal organisms of recent geologic time would never have developed as they did without the two communicating systems which tie the parts together and make possible coordination of muscles or organs distant from each other. These two systems are the circulatory system and the nervous system. Transfer of information and transfer of nutrients were necessary before animal evolution could progress far beyond very simple animal forms. In this process of development the nervous system has demonstrated a gradual concentration of the controlling centers in the head end of the animal. Insects show this more than earthworms, vertebrates still more than insects.

As a conducting system the nervous system is made up of a connected series of separable units called neurons. These are highly specialized cells having the properties of irritability and conductivity. There are millions upon millions of these neurons in the nervous system, with about 10 billion in the most superficial layer of the brain, the cerebral cortex and, by contrast, between 50,000 and 75,000 in some of the small nuclei of the hypothalamus. The neuron is composed of a cell body with a nucleus and nucleolus surrounded by cytoplasm, and with protoplasmic processes extending outward from the surface. These are called dendrites and axon. There are ordinarily many dendrites and one axon, although the axon may be branched to allow multiple transmission to a number of other neurons. The sequence of dendrite→cell body→axon to dendrite or cell body of another neuron linked together through many units forms the conduction pathways. The nervous system always operates by these neuron chains. Figure 4–1 illustrates this point.

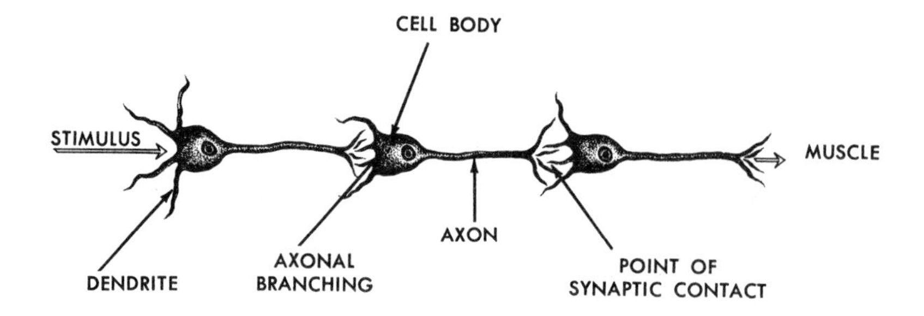

Drawing by Brenda Sutherland

Figure 4–1. Drawing of a Neuron Chain

The internal structure of the nerve cell is very distinctive. Outside the nucleus the cell body shows, upon staining, a large number of dark patches called Nissl substance. This Nissl substance extends into the dendrites but not into the typical axon. The base of the axon shows a clear space inside the cell body, aptly named the axon hillock. While there are many dendrites, with frequently a forest of branches, there is only one axon, although this may have several collaterals before reaching its termination on a muscle end plate, or in the terminal buttons at the synapse. These elements may be seen in Fig. 4–2. Careful studies show that, when the neuron is active and fires an impulse, oxygen is used up and carbon dioxide is given off. This metabolic activity is related to the amount of Nissl substance, for when a nerve cell is exhausted by repeated firings the Nissl substance is depleted.

Under normal conditions the dendrites conduct an impulse toward the cell, and the axon conducts away from the cell. But the direction of conduction is not determined by the structure of the dendrite or axon, for an impulse can travel back up the dendrite from the cell body; this is called antidromic conduction. The direction of conduction is deter-

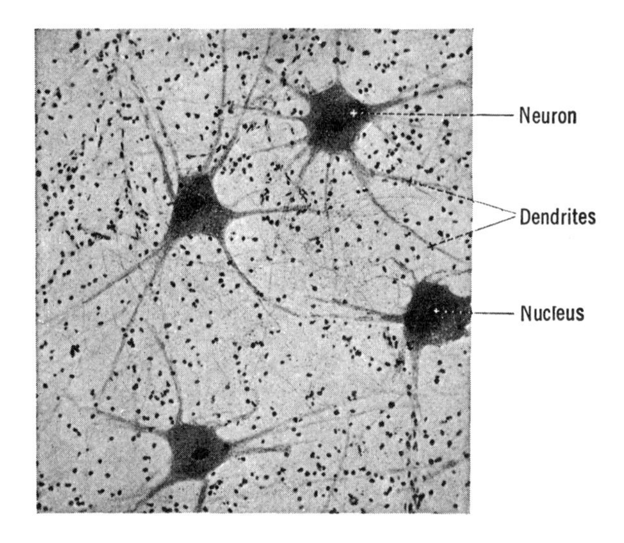

Source: Ernest Gardner, *Fundamentals of Neurology* (4th ed.; Philadelphia: W. B. Saunders Company, 1963), p. 66.

Figure 4–2. Typical Spinal Motor Neurons

mined by the polarity at the point of connection between the two neurons, that is, at the synapse. Neurons cannot function unless connected in chains, passing the impulse on from afferent dendrites to cell body to efferent axon, to dendrite to cell body to axon, and eventually to gland or muscle effectors. The simplest reflex chain (the knee-jerk) involves a neuron bringing an impulse from the patellar tendon, the axon of which makes connection with the dendrites of a motor neuron in the spinal cord or with an internuncial neuron. The axon of the motor neuron extends out to the extensor muscle of the leg. The processes bringing the impulse into the cord are afferent while those of the motor neuron are called efferent, as indicated in Fig. 4–3.

The neuron circuitry can be exceedingly complex. The extensive dendrite branches allow the accumulation of several subliminal impulses into one neuron and its resultant firing. The axon, by its collateral branching, may also stimulate simultaneously several diverse functional mechanisms. This is in large part how reciprocal inhibition (see p. 84) is made possible. See illustration of this reciprocal arrangement in Fig. 4–4. In any event, the mechanisms of correlation which depend on the characteristics of the neuron and the synapse are both varied and complex.

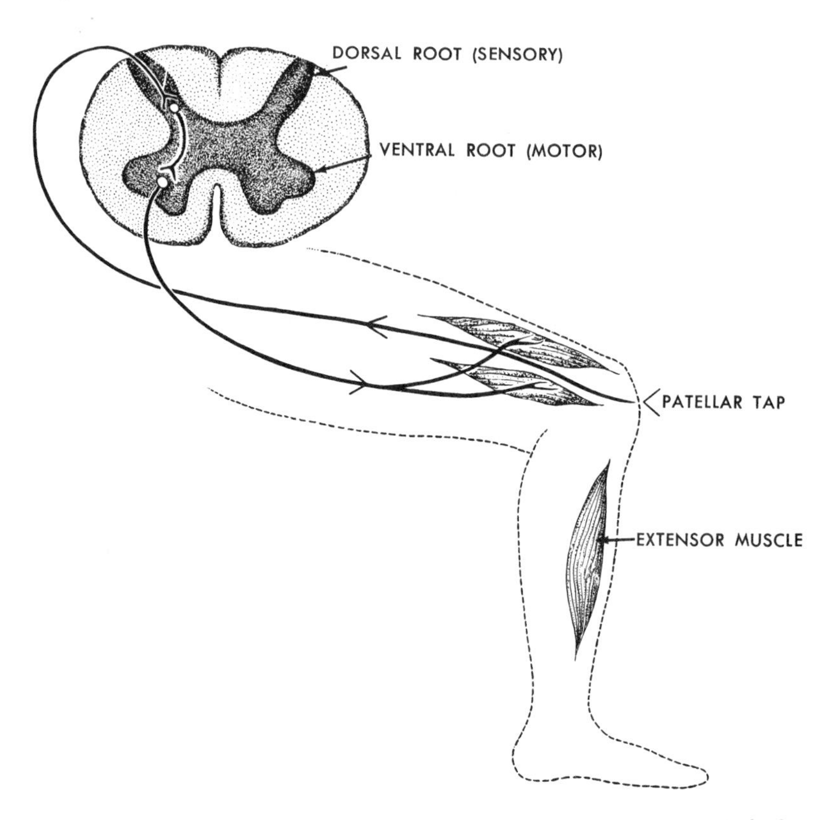

Drawing by Brenda Sutherland

Figure 4–3. Schematic Drawing of Reflex Response from Tap of Patellar Tendon

TYPES OF NEURONS

There are, within the classification of neuron, some half-dozen different shapes and functions. The most typical neuron (1) is one from the ventral gray of the spinal cord, the motor horn cell. This is roughly star shaped and is the final link in the innervation of muscle. (2) The pyramidal cell of the cerebral cortex (Golgi Type I) is like a small pyramid with a long apical dendrite reaching up from the apex toward the surface of the cortex and a longer axon running down through the internal capsule to the body. This pyramidal cell sends voluntary messages to striated muscles of arms and legs. (3) Another neuron with a

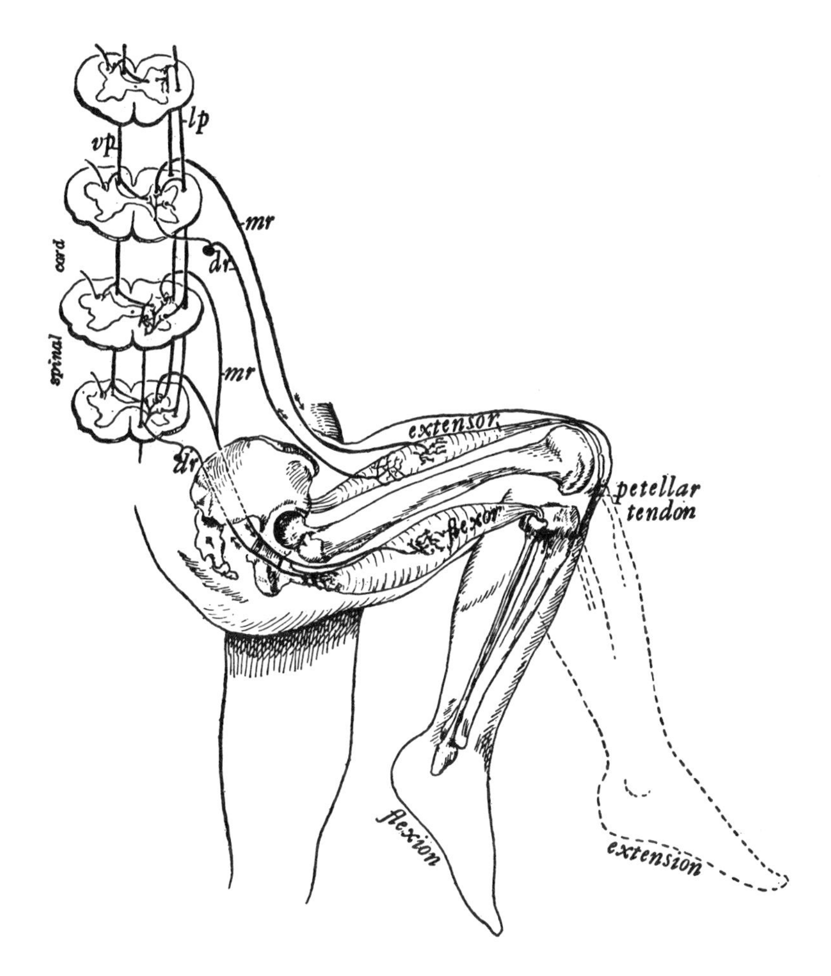

Source: James W. Papez, *Comparative Neurology* (New York: Hafner Publishing Company, 1964), p. 243.

Figure 4–4. Drawing of Reciprocal Innervation

pyramidal shape has a very short axon which branches near the cell body. This (Golgi Type II) assists diffusion and summation of information within a nerve center. (4) The "basket cells" of the cerebellum discharging through a number of axonal branches arranged in parallel can fire a number of Purkinje cells at one time. (5) The cell bodies of the spinal ganglia are unipolar, with both dendrite and axon issuing from the same spot on the body of the cell and dividing into afferent and efferent branches some distance from the cell body. (6) The round cell from the trapezoid body is invested over its whole surface by dendrites to form a sort of chrysalis around it. These six types are illustrated in Fig. 4–5.

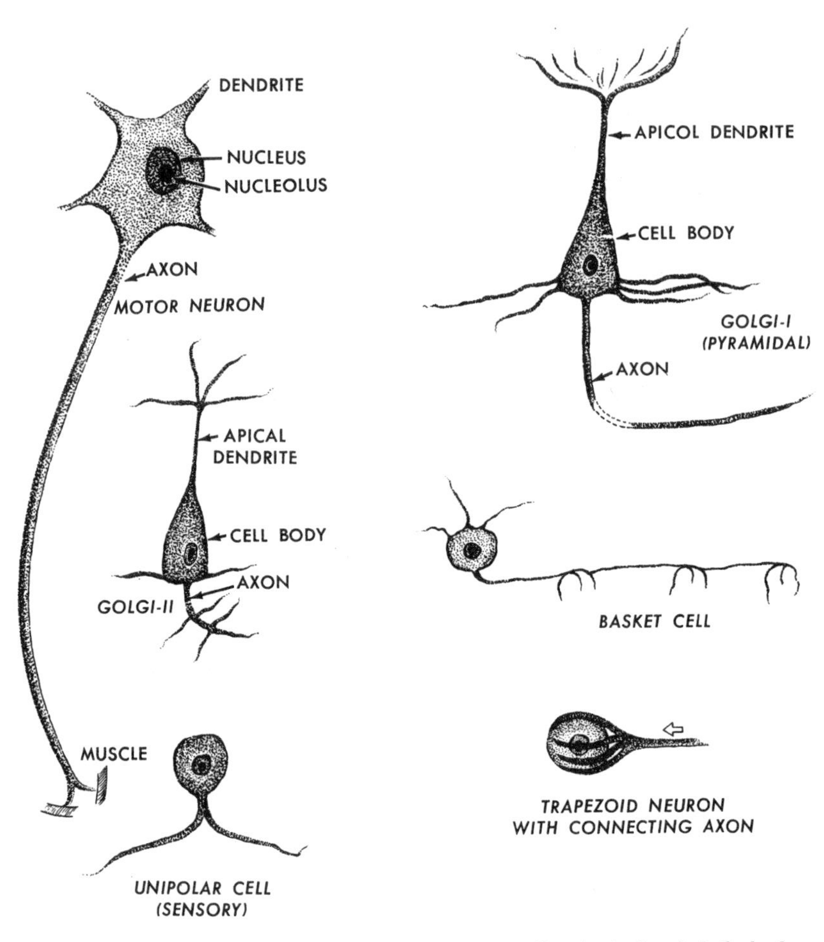

Figure 4–5. Six types of Neurons

If one studies the fine structure of a neuron which has been stained with silver he will see very fine, delicate strands which pass through all parts of the cell body except the nucleus. (See Fig. 4–6). These are neuro-

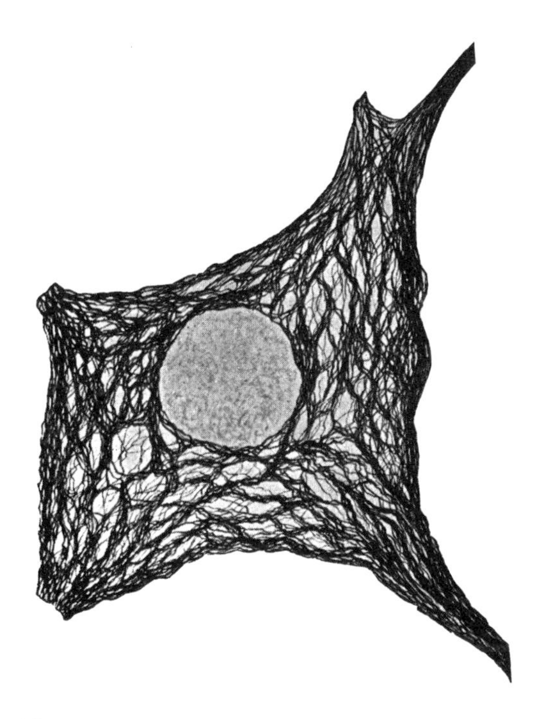

Source: William Bloom and Don W. Fawcett, *A Textbook of Histology* (8th ed.; Philadelphia: W. B. Saunders Company, 1962), p. 216.

Figure 4–6. Neurons with Neurofibrils

fibrils and were once thought to be the medium of conduction, but this now appears very doubtful.

As the axon, emerging from the axon hillock, leaves the cell body it is uncovered. Within a few microns the axon typically becomes covered by a whitish, fatty sheath known as myelin. This covers most of the larger and longer fibers and is protective, as well as having a special role in neural conduction which will be considered later. The myelinated processes of neurons comprise the white matter of the spinal cord and brain. The myelin in turn is covered by a neurilemma sheath, which is composed of flat translucent cells forming a thin layer around the myelin. The electron microscope shows only the flat Schwann cells and no separate neurilemma. The neurilemma and Schwann cell, then, are one and the same. The myelin covering is interrupted every few hundred micra so that the neurilemma directly invests the axis cylinder. These interruptions of myelin are the "nodes" of Ranvier which are

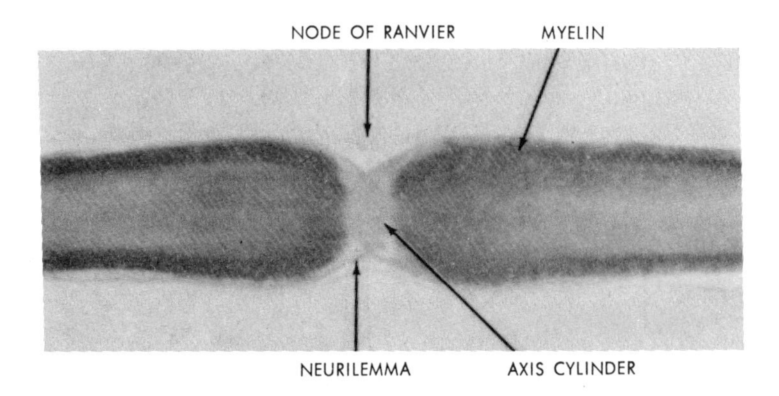

The myelin stains black and is interrupted at the node. The thin membrane external to the neurilemma represents endoneurium. The axis cylinder (stained grayish) continues through the node.

Source: Ernest Gardner, *Fundamentals of Neurology,* p. 73.

Figure 4–7. Photomicrograph of a Single Myelinated Fiber from Frog Sciatic Nerve, Stained with Osmic Acid.

important in nervous conduction. These features are illustrated in Fig. 4–7.

NEURILEMMA AND DEGENERATION

The neurilemma has a special function in degeneration or regeneration in the nervous system. When nerves are crushed, or cut by accident or in experimental studies, the axis cylinder and the myelin degenerate, breaking up into particles which are absorbed by phagocytosis carried out by the neurilemma. After the phagocytosis is completed, the neurilemma forms a hollow core, down which the axis cylinder can regrow to join the organ originally innervated or the neuron with which it was connected. In addition, when regeneration occurs, the neurilemma, with important assistance from the axis cylinder, reforms the myelin to surround the axis fiber. In injuries which have gone too far for regeneration the degeneration of both fiber tracts and nerve cells of origin gives the exact location, by blank spaces or glial cells, of fiber pathways and nuclei. This has been, in fact, with the aid of certain stains, one of the customary ways of tracing pathways of nerve fibers through the nervous system.

The nerve fibers of the brain and spinal cord which are without neurilemma sheaths are incapable of regeneration. The stump of the axon begins to grow but has no neurilemma conduit to guide its growth. Hence it may branch repeatedly into a forest of growing tips or be stopped in growth by the scar tissue at the site of the injury. Degenerating fibers which are followed by destruction of their cell bodies in the brain and cord are succeeded by a proliferation of glial cells which will occupy all the space of the nerve cells which have been destroyed. In experimental studies this method is used histologically to identify nuclei which have degenerated.

There are four kinds of nerve fibers classified by the presence or absence of sheaths which invest them. The four varieties are: (1) myelinated fibers with a neurilemma sheath, located principally in peripheral nerves; (2) myelinated fibers without a neurilemma, found within the brain and spinal cord; (3) unmyelinated fibers with a neurilemma sheath, found in the autonomic nervous system and fine afferent fibers of cerebrospinal nerves; and (4) unmyelinated fibers without neurilemma, found in the gray matter of the cord and brain and in some longer internal pathways.

Typically the neurilemma is found outside the brain and spinal cord, while glial cells, as supporting structures, are found in the brain and cord only. In addition, all axonal nerve fibers of whatever kind lose their sheaths at their terminal endings just before their synaptic or neuromuscular end plate attachments.

SYNAPSE

As we indicated already, the point of contact between two adjacent neurons is called the synapse. There is no real continuity of tissue at this point, but rather two thin membranes, separated by a cleft 0.02 micron wide, one forming the branching tips of the axon, and the other forming adjacent tips of the dendrites or cell body of the next neuron. This synaptic contact is illustrated in Fig. 4–8. Since the dendrite or axon will conduct in either direction, the synapse is the point at which the polarity or direction of conduction is determined. In essence the synapse is a membrane or pair of membranes selectively permeable to certain ions which are released when an impulse reaches the tips of the preceding axon. The transmission of an impulse of ions across a synapse takes a longer time interval than conduction over the same distance in a fiber.

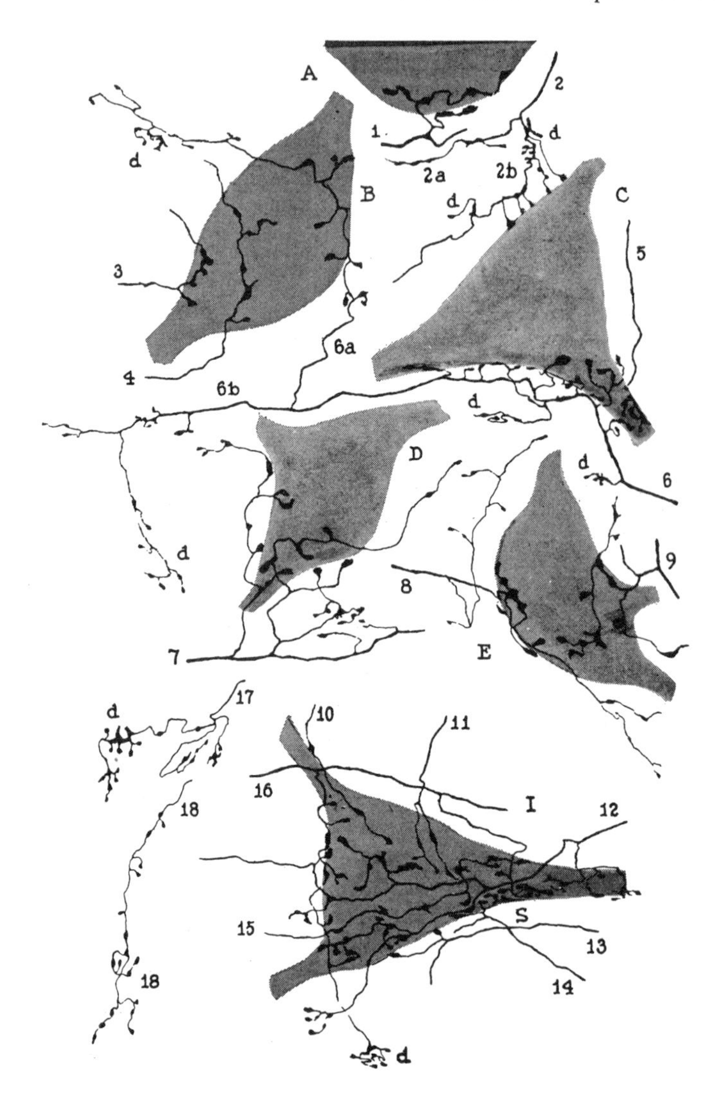

Source: Rafael Lorente de Nó in *Journal of Neurophysiology* (Springfield, Ill.: Charles C. Thomas), Vol. 1 (1938), p. 200.

Figure 4–8. Motor Neurons and Synaptic Connections

This delay in transmission is caused by the shift from one kind of energy transport to another kind. As we will see in more detail under the discussion of nervous conduction (Chap. 6), the conduction of an impulse in a fiber is essentially electrical, while across a synapse it is essentially chemical, being carried out by the ions referred to above. This shift from electrical to chemical and back to electrical transmission is then the reason for the delay. The tip of each axon branch is enlarged into an end button which has tiny vesicles within it as illustrated in Fig. 4–9. The

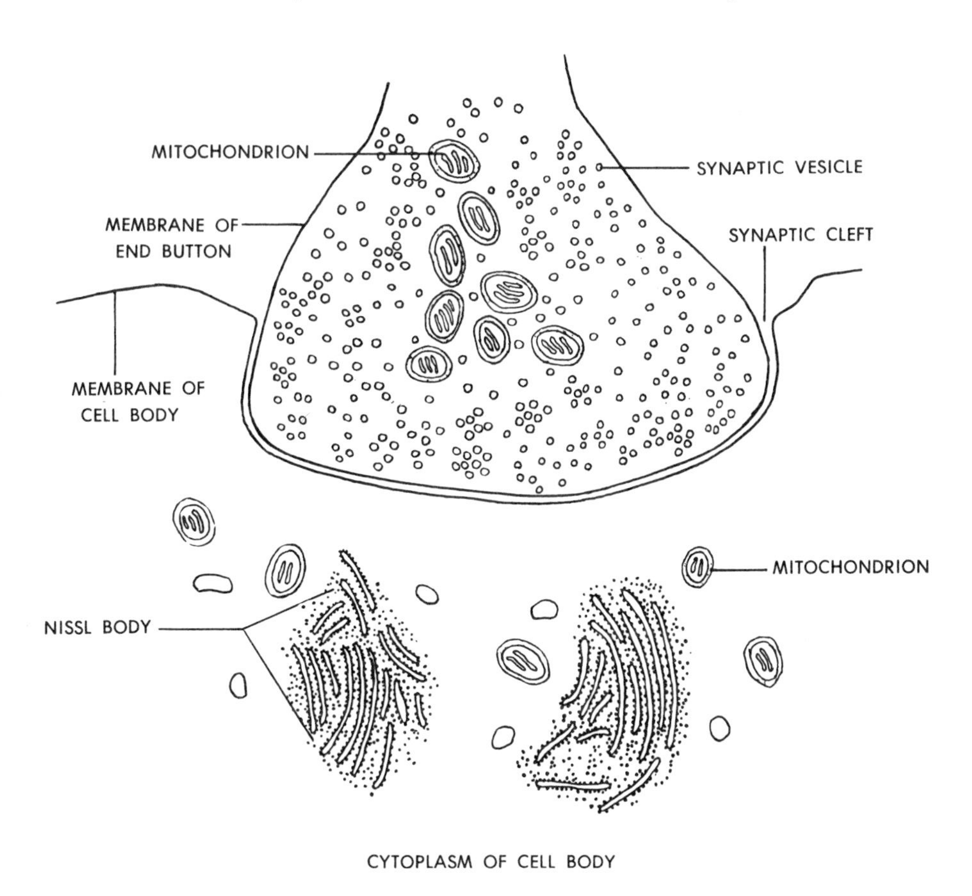

Source: Ernest Gardner, *Fundamentals of Neurology,* p. 78.

Figure 4–9. Drawing of Electron Microgram of Synaptic Gap, and Vesicles

tiny vesicles in the terminal buttons of the descending axon release a transmitter substance when an impulse reaches them, changing the permeability of the membrane of the next neuron and thus allowing ions to pass and set off another electrical impulse. The synapse is more susceptible to fatigue, nicotine, and anesthetic than the fibers or the cell body. It is also at this point that the so-called "nerve-gases" act by obstructing chemical transmission.

NEURON DOCTRINE

The *neuron doctrine* has been fully established only since the beginning of this century. It occupied some of the greatest neuroanatomists, histologists, and physiologists most of their lives. It is composed of four major propositions.

1. The neuron is genetically distinct, being derived from a neuroblast or single embryonic cell.
2. Within the nervous system no elements other than the neuron participate in nervous functions.
3. The neuron is anatomically separate and merely in contact with other neurons.
4. The neuron is the functional unit of the nervous system.

The neuron doctrine is still substantially subscribed to, although speculation (by Galambos and others) about a neural function for the glial cells raises questions about the immutability of some of the propositions outlined above.

SOURCES AND ADDITIONAL READING

Galambos, R., "A Glia-Neural Theory of Brain Function," *Proc. Natl. Acad. Sci.*, 47 (1961), 129-36.

Gardner, E., *Fundamentals of Neurology* (4th ed.), Chap. 6. Philadelphia: W. B. Saunders Co., 1963.

Ranson, S. W. and S. Clark, *The Anatomy of the Nervous System* (10th ed.), Chap. 5. Philadelphia: W. B. Saunders Co., 1959.

Five

SENSORY RECEPTORS

The way in which the human organism gets information from the outside world is one of the wonders of animal adaptation and specialization. As we advance from lower to higher evolutionary levels there appears an increasing dominance of the distance receptors of vision and hearing over the other sensory departments. Taken all together, however, our sense organs provide us with only an incomplete pattern of information about the external world. At a number of points, for instance, man has no receptors for certain levels of physical vibration. He has no sense organ and consequently gets no information from air vibrations below 20 per second or above 30,000 per second. In between, of course, is the whole range of hearing, both tone and noise. Below the level of hearing are the mechanical contacts of touch and pressure. Above the auditory level, we find radiant energy which gives us heat. Light rays are faster vibrations still, giving us light and color, but there are a number of emanations about which humans know nothing by means of special sense organs. Electrical waves do not transmit information to our consciousness unless a recording device is used. In addition, we have no special sense organ responsive to the frequencies of X-rays, ultraviolet rays, or gamma rays. It is for this reason, in part, that atomic radiation could be so deadly.

Animals are not all sensitive to the same levels, or limited to the same extent of sensitivity. One of the commonest examples of this is the dog's ability to hear and smell stimuli to which humans are not sensitive.

High pitches beyond the range of the human ear (20,000-50,000 cps) can be heard by the dog and can be responded to in terms of training.

The sense organs that we do possess, bringing to the nervous system various kinds of information on the basis of which we act, are divided into several groups. The first division, called *exteroceptors,* contains sense organs responsive to conditions outside the body. Included here are touch, pressure, temperature, pain, vision, hearing, smell, etc. The second division, known as *proprioceptors,* includes the semicircular canals and receptors in muscle, joint, and tendon; these keep us informed of our balance and of the flexion or muscular contraction of our joints and limbs. The third division, called *interoceptors,* brings sensation from internal organs. Smell and taste together are sometimes classified as the chemical senses; while smell, vision, and hearing bring us information from a distance, and are therefore known as distance receptors, or teloceptors.

EXTEROCEPTORS

Aside from the chemical and distance receptors most of the sense organs responsive to changes in the outside world are located in our skin. Here we find a series of receptors closely associated together just under the epidermis, and many of them nestled in the folds of the dermis. Touch is mediated by three different receptors; hair follicles, Merkel's disks, and Meissner's corpuscles. The bare nerve endings twine themselves around the bulbous base of the hair follicle at the level of the upper border of the sebaceous gland so that *any* deflection of the hair gives a touch sensation. On the parts of the body which have adequate hair covering, the other two touch receptors are nearly absent. But on the hairless parts of the body, such as palms of hands, soles of feet, and lips, the Meissner's corpuscles and Merkel's disks (in lower animals) are very thick. The disks look like a flat saucer in cross section, with the nerve fiber arising from the middle of the base; while the Meissner corpuscle is an intertwined central core of nerve fiber surrounded by a fairly thick connective tissue capsule. For an illustration of the different kinds of exteroceptors, see Fig. 5–1.

In addition to the receptors for touch the skin contains other receptors for pain, warmth, cold, and pressure. Pain is mediated by bare nerve endings close under the surface of the skin; this sensation has no specialized sensory ending.

Warmth and cold are believed to be mediated by the Ruffini organ and Krause's end bulb respectively, although this is not certain. The

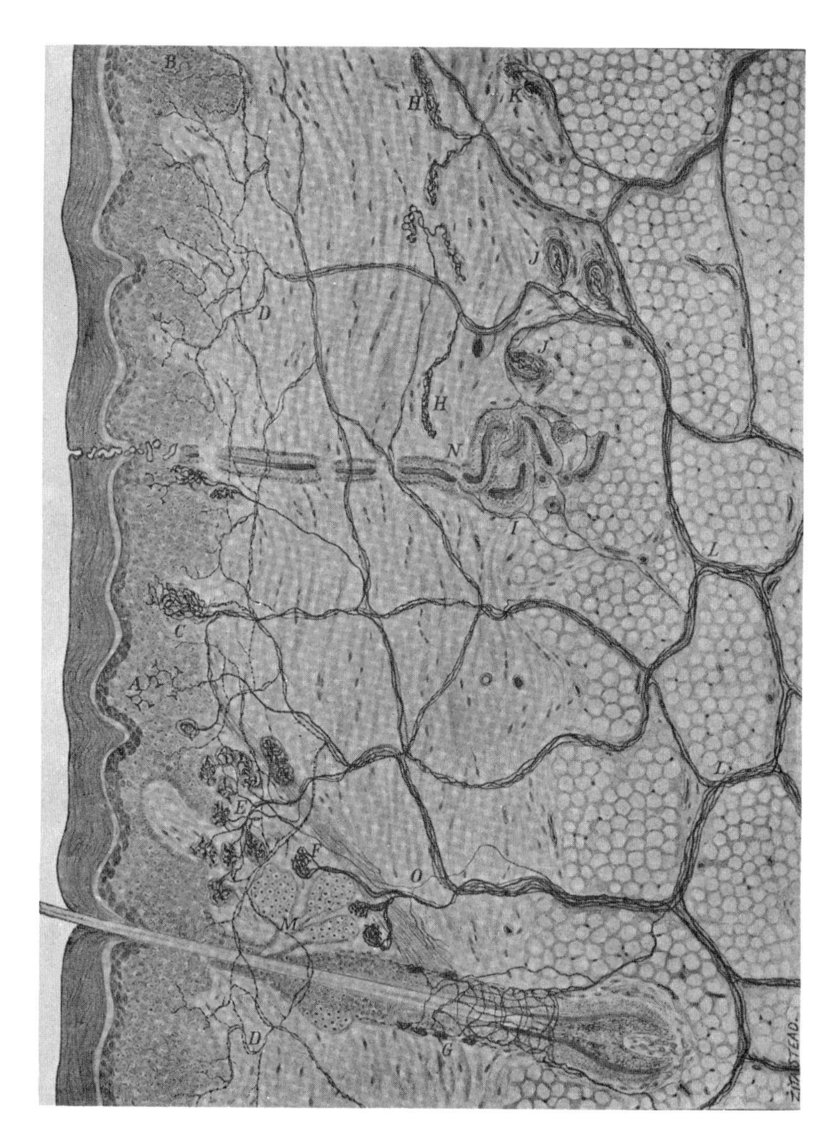

B—free nerve endings; C—Merkel's disks (tactile); E—Meissner corpuscle; F—Krause end bulb; G—nerve end coiled around hair; H—Ruffini ending; J—Pacinian corpuscle; M—sebaceous gland; N—sweat gland duct; O—piloerector muscle.

Source: H. H. Woolard et al. in *Journal of Anatomy* (Cambridge University Press), Vol. LXXIV (October 1939–July 1940), p. 427.

Figure 5–1. Exteroceptive Sensory Endings in the Skin

end bulb is a round capsule of connective tissue with intertwined nerve fibers occupying most of the interior except for a thin covering around the outside. The Ruffini organ looks like an elongated and irregular Meissner's corpuscle.

Lele reported that he could find no special ending but rather two plexuses of unencapsulated fibers, one close to the skin surface and one deeper near the blood vessels. But there has been shown to be good agreement between the warm and cold spots, experimentally determined, and the depth below the skin surface and the distribution of Krause and Ruffini organs as these were determined histologically. Lele also claimed that thermal endings respond to mechanical stimulation. This, however, is not possible since single temperature fibers either for cold or warmth cannot respond to mechanical or noxious stimuli in their respective fields.

The organ for the sense of pressure, the Pacinian Corpuscle, lies deeper under the skin than any of the other cutaneous receptors. It is very large relative to the others, being visible to the unaided eye. In actual size it is about a millimeter long, and is oval in shape. It is made up of an inner core of bare nerve filament surrounded by successive layers of tissue so that it looks somewhat like the layered or laminated cross section of an onion. Because of its size the Pacinian corpuscle has been studied extensively and is the sensory receptor used in an examination of the transducer function of sense organs to be considered later.

Each variety of cutaneous sensation is mediated by a separate set of nerve fibers. Both myelinated and unmyelinated fibers are present in cutaneous nerves. Light touch is mediated by large myelinated fibers and even if stimulated to maximum response they do not produce pain. Pain sensation is carried by fine fibers, both myelinated and unmyelinated. The channel for temperature is less clear, but it is likely that decrease in temperature stimulates larger myelinated fibers, while rise in temperature is carried by small unmyelinated fibers.

CHEMICAL SENSES

The organs of chemical sense are two only, taste and smell. The taste buds are located in the mucous membranes of the mouth and pharynx and on the tongue. The buds are somewhat tulip shaped and lie just under minute depressions in the surface, into which the sensitive cells project their receptor endings. The taste bud is made up of large supporting cells, with the cells of taste in between the supporting cells.

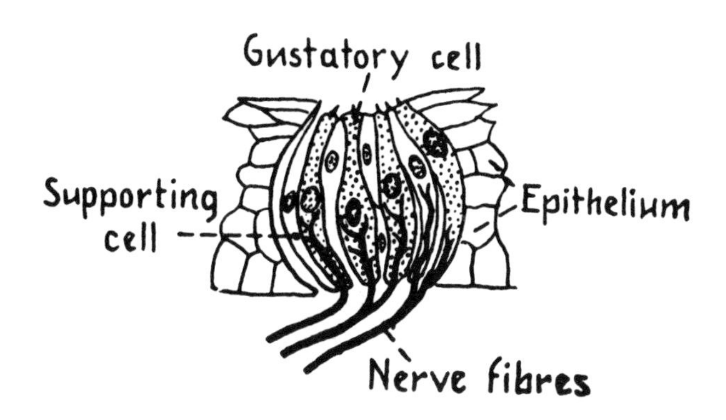

Source: Alf Brodal, *The Cranial Nerves* (Oxford: Blackwell Scientific Publications, Ltd., 1962), p. 71.

Figure 5–2. Taste Bud

From the top of each taste cell hair-like endings project into the depression mentioned above. (See Fig. 5–2.)

Compared to the other chemical modality, taste is a very crude one. There are only four clear taste sensations—sweet, sour, salt, and bitter. These are located in most concentrated form on different portions of the tongue: bitter on the back, sweet on the tip, sour on the sides, and salt on the tip and part of the sides.

The crudeness of taste as a modality is indicated by the small residue of taste sensation left when one has a heavy head cold. Most food in this circumstance tastes not much different from sawdust if the eyes are closed. Tests of monkeys' preference for water over bitter quinine show that the insular-opercular cortex, rather than amygdaloid and pyriform cortex, is concerned primarily with taste. Human studies indicate, in addition, that taste persists even after the destruction of the olfactory nerves, and hence is independent of the sense of smell.

All the fine sensitivity which we ordinarily attribute to taste is added to it by the other chemical sense of smell. Smell, for instance, can detect alcohol in a dilution 24,000 times greater than that required for taste sensations. This sensitivity is why the tea taster or wine taster does not smoke and must stop work if he catches a cold. The sense of smell will be considered in detail under the discussion of cranial nerves, as will vision, hearing, and equilibrium.

Aside from the cutaneous and chemical senses which give us information from the outside world there is a group of receptors which keeps us informed of the state of our body itself. This group is subdivided into proprioceptive and interoceptive modalities. The proprioceptive sense is primarily sensory information from muscles, tendons, skeletal joints, and vestibular apparatus. That called interoceptive is from visceral organs.

PROPRIOCEPTORS

Skeletal striated muscle fibers have four kinds of nervous innervation. There are two sorts of sensory innervation for proprioceptive information from muscle, and two types of motor nerve supply. Information about the state of stretch of the muscle is given either by annulospiral endings which are composed of nerve filaments which spiral around the intrafusal muscle fiber both ways from the point of entry, or by flower spray endings which are attached farther away from the waist of the intrafusal fiber than are the annulospirals. The annulospirals are denoted as the primary endings and the flower spray as the secondary endings, but this varies according to the species. In rabbits and man the primary endings are probably flower spray in type, not winding around the fiber. When the fiber is stretched these endings are activated and send impulses back to spinal cord and brain. For details of this innervation, see Fig. 5–3. The sensory endings for the detection of muscle contraction is called the Golgi tendon organ, and it is located in tendon near the ends of the muscle fibers. When the muscle fiber contracts there is a pull on the tendon and this activates the Golgi tendon organ. The motor innervation includes an alpha fiber for contraction of the main muscle fiber, and a gamma fiber for contraction of the smaller intrafusal fiber.

The main muscle fibers have associated with them smaller, more delicate intrafusal fibers or spindles to which the annulospiral and flower spray endings are attached. Since these endings are arranged "in parallel" to the main muscle movements, they fire as long as the main muscle is stretched. When, however, the muscle contracts the tension is taken off the spindle and the annulospiral endings are silent. In muscular contraction then the only sense organ which fires for the duration of the contraction is the Golgi tendon organ which is activated by the muscular contraction. For an illustration of annulo-spiral and Golgi tendon action, see Fig. 5–4. Thus one organ or the other fires, sending afferent impulses to the spinal cord when the muscle is either contracted or stretched. Frequently, it is essential to have information from the annulospiral ending during a prolonged contraction. A special mechanism has been developed for this known as the *gamma efferent* fiber. These

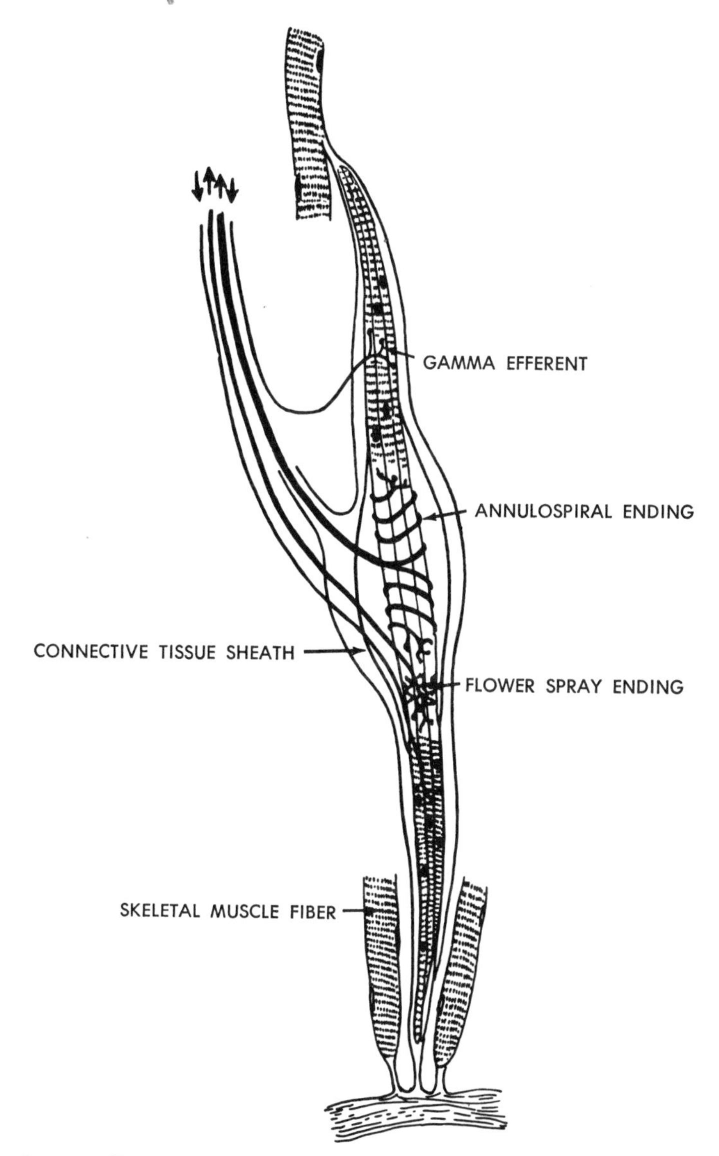

Gamma efferent discharge results in contraction of spindle muscle fibers at each end, thus stretching intervening non-contractile sensory segment of intrafusil fiber.

After Ernest Gardner, *Fundamentals of Neurology* (4th ed.; Philadelphia: W. B. Saunders Company, 1963), 123.

Figure 5–3. Muscle-spindle Showing the Motor Innervation

small nerve fibers innervate the intrafusal fibers and, if fired, "take up the slack" in the spindle, so that even during sustained muscle contraction the annulospiral or flower spray ending begins to fire again. In

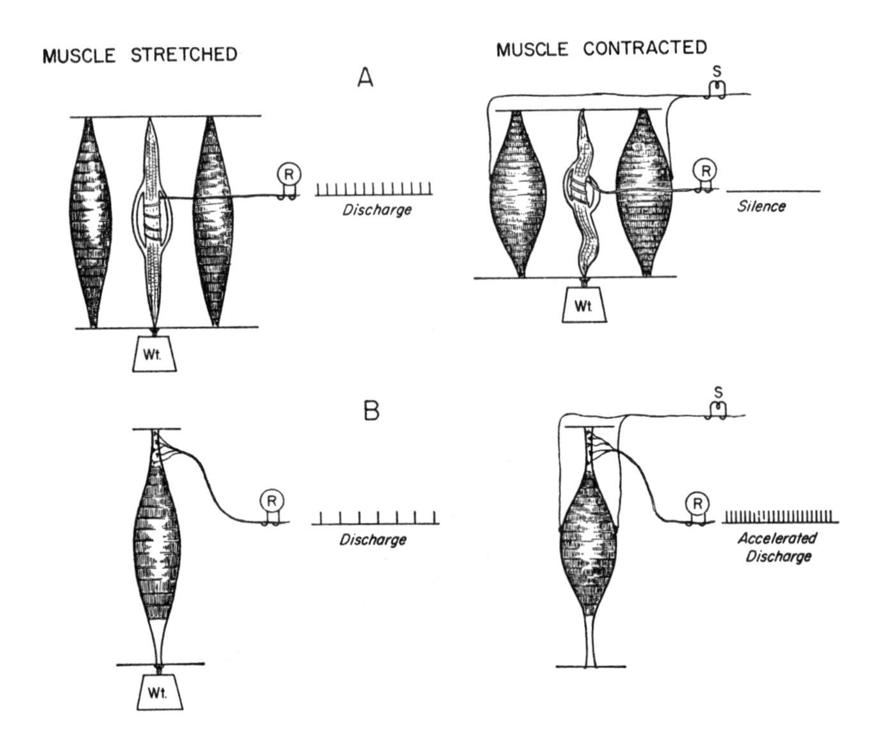

A, Spindle is arranged "in parallel" with muscle fibers so that muscle contraction slackens tension on spindle. *B,* Tendon organ is arranged "in series" with muscle fibers so that both passive and active contraction of muscle cause receptor to discharge.

After Theodore C. Ruch and John F. Fulton, *Medical Physiology and Biophysics* (18th ed. of Howell's *Textbook of Physiology;* Philadelphia, W. B. Saunders Company, 1960), p. 178 (altered slightly).

Figure 5–4. Relation of Muscle Spindles and Tendon Organs to Muscle Fibers

fact, in muscular contraction the "gamma" discharge always precedes the "alpha" impulse to the muscle fibers, allowing "reporting" on the state of stretch of the muscle before contraction occurs.

In addition to the sensory endings, separate motor nerves supply the impulse to muscle contraction. These end on motor end plates that are separated by a thin cleft from the muscle spindles themselves, as indicated in Fig. 5–5. The physiology of the motor end plate activity will be reserved until the discussion of the nerve impulse. The number of muscle fibers greatly exceeds the number of motor nerve fibers. So

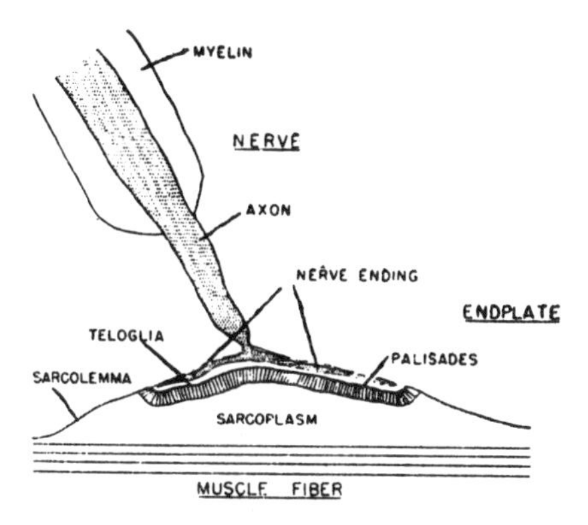

Source: George H. Acheson, "Physiology of Neuro-muscular Junctions: Chemical Aspects," *Federation Proceedings* (Baltimore: Federation of American Societies for Experimental Biology), Vol. 7 (1948), p. 447.

Figure 5–5. Diagram of Neuromuscular End Plate

each motor nerve supplies a number of associated muscle fibers which all contract together. This is the concept of a *motor unit.* (See Fig. 5–6.) For the large antigravity muscles of the legs and torso this ratio is several hundred muscle fibers to one nerve fiber. Since gross bodily movement is all that is needed, this ratio is adequate. But when fine, controlled adjustments of fingers and arms are necessary the ratio has

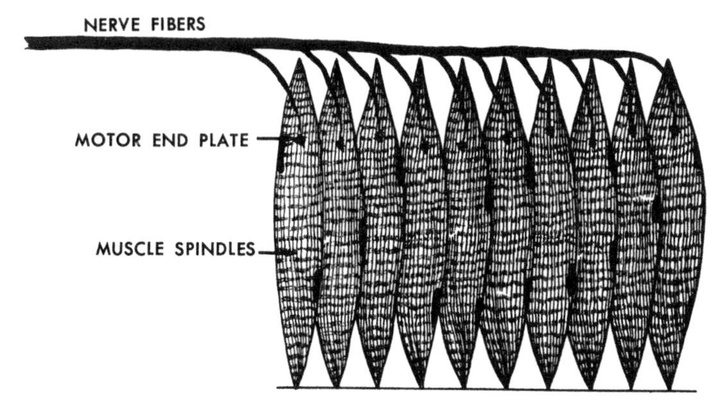

Drawing by Brenda Sutherland

Figure 5–6. Diagram of a Motor Unit—One Nerve Fiber Innervating Ten Muscle Spindles for Integrated Movement

to be much smaller. The muscle fibers that allow fine adjustment such as grasping and finger manipulation are innervated by separate nerve fibers in a ratio of 10:1, as indicated in Fig. 5–6.

Any bodily movement relies very heavily on this complex of nervous supply to muscles, for there is a continual bombardment of impulses from the sensory endings into the spinal cord and a corresponding return by way of motor nerves to muscle spindle. This in fact is the mechanism of maintaining muscle tone. In the normal waking state practically all bodily muscles are in a state of partial contraction or readiness to contract. This mechanism of muscle tone completes its circuit quite unconsciously. The information on the state of the muscle enters the spinal cord and triggers impulses for partial contraction without voluntary control or direction. The reverberating circuit goes on during all our waking hours, and continues to some degree even during sleep.

In addition to the muscle receptors, there are receptors which give

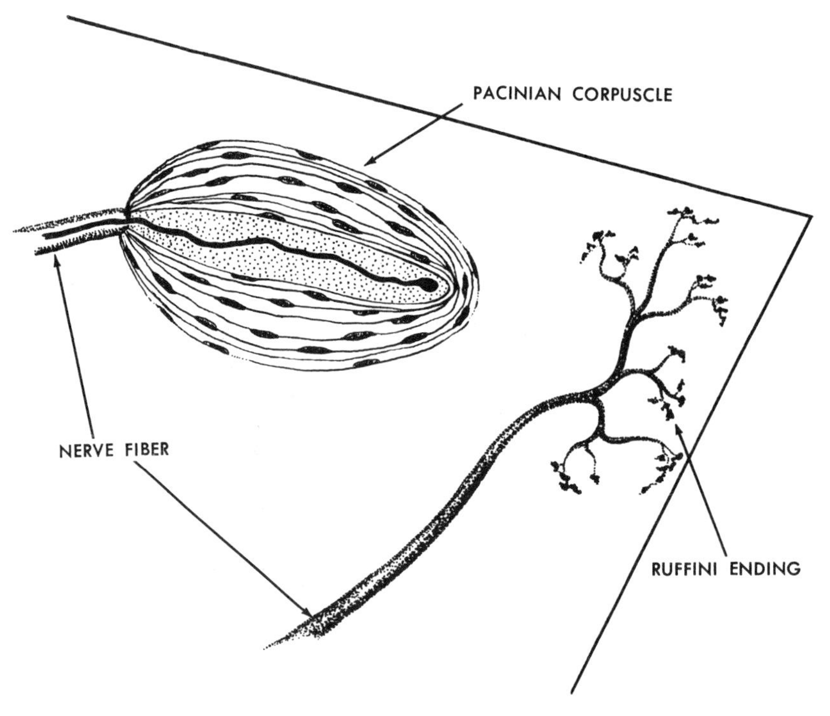

Drawing by Brenda Sutherland

Figure 5–7. Diagram of Pacinian Corpuscle and Ruffini Endings in a Joint

us knowledge of other moving parts of our body. In the tendons connecting muscles to bone there are Golgi tendon organs responsive to tension in the tendon by reason of muscle contraction. In the joints themselves are found Pacinian corpuscles and Ruffini organs which send back information about the closure of the joint. (See Fig. 5–7.) All of these then provide information of a proprioceptive nature which, when combined with equilibrium and organized—mainly by the cerebellum—provide the basis for the steady pulse for muscle tone and to antigravity muscles for upright bodily position.

INTEROCEPTORS

The two groups of receptors discussed thus far, exteroceptors and proprioceptors, do not exhaust the various types of sensory information we receive. There is one other main type of receptor in the viscera known as interoceptors. These are composed of either free nerve endings in smooth muscle of the viscera, Pacinian corpuscle in the linings of the visceral cavity, or encapsulated arborizations in or under the layers of mucous membranes. Most of these nerve endings subserve an uncomplicated type of sensory information. Throughout its entire length the gut is unresponsive to most methods of damage or destruction such as cutting with a knife, burning with a cautery, or strong acid. The only sensation which normally comes from the viscera is caused by distention so that the successive mucous layers are pulled against each other, thus stimulating these nerve endings. In addition to the three divisions described above there is the complex system of chemoreceptors and osmoreceptors which subserve water balance in the body, or hunger or temperature regulation. These will be discussed when we consider the hypothalamus.

SENSORY ADAPTATION

All of the receptors discussed thus far show different reactions to continuous stimulation or to fast repetition of stimuli. Some give no response after a few tenths of a second, while others continue to respond for longer than five seconds without much decline in the strength of the response. This adaptation to continued stimulation is nicely graded to our needs for continuous information. Continuous stimulation of the hair follicle gives only a brief pulse of activity, as indicated by the curve of firing against time. The curve for the touch receptors

(Meissner's corpuscles or Merkel's disks) is slower in its decline; while the Pacinian corpuscle and, even more, the muscle spindle receptors continue to fire for a considerable time interval. (See Fig. 5–8 for the

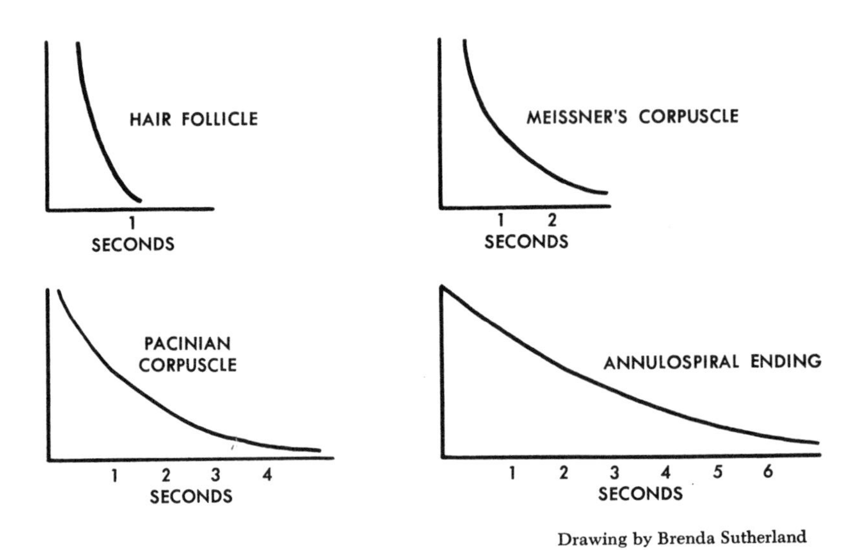

Figure 5–8. Adaptation of Sensory Receptors to Continuous Stimulation

curves of adaptation.) It is clear then that organs from which we need continuous information, Pacinian and muscle spindles, show the slowest adaptation, and the others respond more to change in stimulation than to stimulation itself. If the hair follicle and Meissner's corpuscle fired as long as the muscle spindles, and therefore did not adapt to continuous stimulation, it is likely that clothing and other skin contact would be intolerable.

TRANSDUCER FUNCTION OF SENSE ORGANS

Now that we have reviewed briefly the various kinds of sense organs the body possesses, with the exception of the equilibrium and distance receptors, it is time to examine by what means these sensory receptors transpose the form of energy to which they are sensitive into nervous impulse with a specific index of localization. For a long time this was ignored as a serious problem by the neurologists on one side and the physiological psychologists on the other. Recently, however, neurophysiologists in England and the United States have begun to learn substantially how this mechanism operates. Most sensory endings are too small for easy examination, with the exception of the Pacinian corpuscle. This pressure vesicle is visible to the naked eye, being 1 mm long and 0.5 mm wide, so that under a good dissecting scope its structure is sufficiently evident for experimentation. Much of the experimental work on the transducer function of sense organs has been carried out on either the Pacinian corpuscle or the muscle spindle, the organ of Corti of the ear, or the retina of the eye. Bernard Katz was able to show by 1950 that the normal stretching of a muscle spindle generates a local electric current. When this current reaches an adequate intensity it triggers an impulse in the nerve fiber which normally would lead to the spinal cord and the higher centers. The energy which gives rise to this "generated" current in the sense organ is the mechanical stretch normal to the muscle fiber. Here, then, we have a transformation of energy from mechanical into electrical that triggers the nerve impulse. This "transducer" function has recently been studied by Werner Loewenstein and his colleagues to try to find out how this transfer comes about and what its characteristics are. It is clear that the generator current follows the stimulus within 1/1000 second. In addition the intensity of the generator current varies directly with intensity of the stimulus—as contrasted with the amplitude of the nerve impulse, which does not alter with intensity of stimulus. In order to discover the site of the transducer element, a Pacinian corpuscle was dissected out and kept responsive in a Krebs solution. (See Fig. 5–9.) Under the dissecting microscope it was possible to tease off one layer after another of the onion-like wrapping around the inner core. After each layer was removed the corpuscle was stimulated again with a stylus of calibrated mechanical intensity. No change was found in the ability of the corpuscle to develop its generator current even when all layers were peeled away down to the core of nerve fiber covered only by a very thin sheath. The inner core without the large envelope was as good a transducer for punctiform stimulation as the entire capsule. This is illustrated in Fig. 5–10.

Next the investigators cut the nerve fiber inside the core of the capsule in a living animal and allowed it to degenerate. When this corpuscle was dissected out no generator current could be developed. The nerve ending in the inner core was established then as the transducer element.

The generator current developed in the nerve ending or dendrite by mechanical pressure does not become the nervous impulse, but triggers that impulse. Blocking the firing of the nerve impulse by the use of

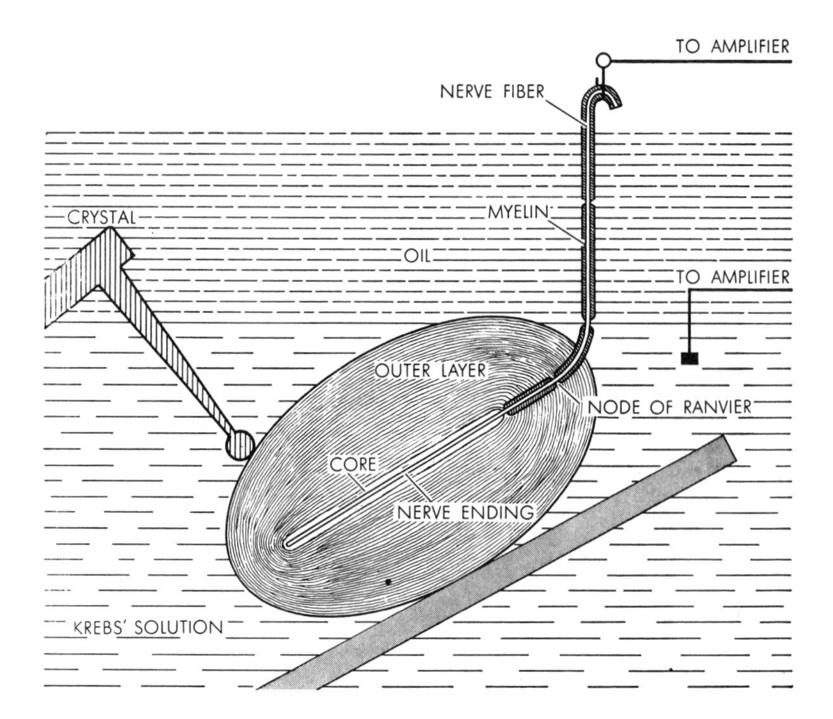

Source: W. Loewenstein in *Scientific American,* August 1960, p. 102.

Figure 5–9. Isolated Pacinian Corpuscle

procaine leaves only the generator potential, and this can be recorded by itself. Other experiments made it clear that the generator current has to reach the first node of Ranvier, still inside the corpuscle, to generate a nervous impulse. The nerve impulse proper then begins at the first node. If the generator current is blocked by inserting a tiny wisp of glass 0.004 mm in diameter into the first node of Ranvier, no nerve impulse is triggered. The initiation of the generator current at the transducer site seems to depend on the disturbance of a stable condition when the capsule is quiescent. This stable condition in its turn

Source: W. Loewenstein in *Scientific American,* August 1960, p. 103.

Figure 5–10. Core of Pacinian Corpuscle Peeled of Laminations

depends upon a potential difference across the membrane of the core, which is maintained by an unequal concentration of ions across that membrane. When mechanical deformation occurs there is a transfer of charged ions across the membrane, and this gives rise to the generator current.

The nervous impulse, triggered by the generator current, flows at an all-or-none amplitude and rate, but this is not related to the intensity of the generator current. Additional experimentation made it clear that the generator current is very different from the nervous impulse in at least one particular. This is that the generator current is proportional to the strength of the mechanical stimulus, while the nerve impulse is not. When the generator current varies in intensity, this change is translated into a varying frequency of firing in the nerve impulse. Because of its all-or-none character the nerve impulse cannot show intensity differences except by changes of frequency.

The inner core acts differently in another way. A stimulus applied to one small spot is not transmitted without decrement as is true of the nerve fiber. The strength of the generator current declines with distance away from the point of stimulation; because of this fact spatial summation of deformations at various points on the inner core is the principal means of showing increased intensity of stimulus. As the mechanical stimulus is increased in intensity, more and more spots on the membrane are excited, bringing about spatial summation. This activity will be clearer by reference to Fig. 5–11. It may well be that the function of the large onion-shaped capsule around the inner core is to provide for the addition of punctiform stimulation and to bring about

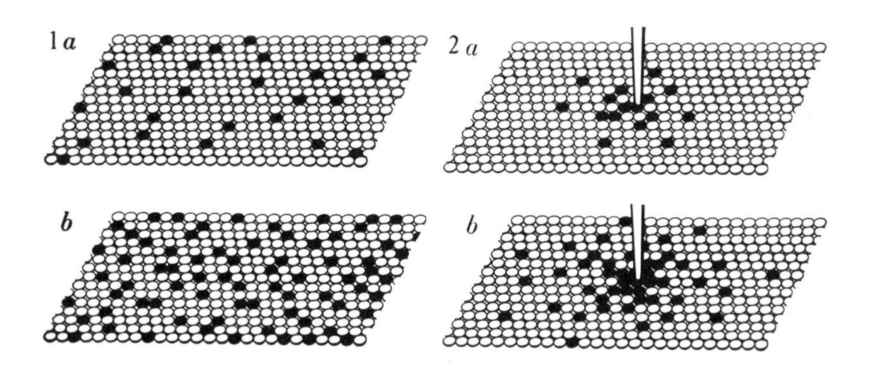

Source: W. Loewenstein in *Scientific American*, August 1960, p. 108.

Figure 5–11. Excited Regions, and Membrane Deformation

the spatial summation which we have seen determines the intensity of the generator current.

The Pacinian corpuscle and muscle spindles have been studied most extensively, while the hair cells of the organ of Corti in the ear and the rods and cones of the retina of the eye have had the most intensive recent study. It is assumed that the transducer function of the other sensory receptors operates in a fashion analogous to what has been described here. That is, the appropriate stimulus brings about ionic exchange in the sense organ; this ionic exchange gives rise to the generator current which triggers the nerve impulse.

SOURCES AND ADDITIONAL READING

The CIBA Collection of Medical Illustrations, Vol. I, *Nervous System.* CIBA Pharmaceutical Company, 1953.

J. Fulton, *Physiology of the Nervous System,* Chap. 1. New York: Oxford University Press, Inc., 1951.

Gardner, E., *Fundamentals of Neurology* (4th ed.), Chap. 9. Philadelphia: W. B. Saunders Company, 1963.

Handbook of Physiology, Sec. I, Vol. I, Chaps. 4, 17-20. Washington, D. C.: American Physiol. Soc., 1959.

Loewenstein, W., "Biological Transducers," *Sci. American,* Aug. 1960.

Ranson, S. W. and S. L. Clark, *The Anatomy of the Nervous System* (10th ed.) Chap. 6. Philadelphia: W. B. Saunders Company, 1959.

Walsh, G., *Physiology of the Nervous System,* Chap. 2. New York: Longmans Green & Co., Inc., 1959.

Six

NERVOUS CONDUCTION AND SYNAPTIC TRANSMISSION

In the consideration of the transducer function of sensory receptors it became clear that mechanical deformation of the membrane caused a change in ionic permeability of the membrane which allowed an exchange of ions, thus bringing about a shift in potential. This shift in potential became the generator current of the sensory ending. And when that generator current was sufficiently strong to reach the first node of Ranvier a nervous impulse was produced, which proceeded down the nerve to the spinal cord and higher centers. Before proceeding further with the structure of the central nervous system it is imperative to examine what happens when a nerve conducts an impulse, and whether anything different occurs at the synapse than in the nerve fiber.

FIBER TYPES

Before considering the biochemistry of nerve conduction, it is worthwhile to review the different kinds of fibers which are present in the nervous system. If we revert to our familiar sensory receptors we find three kinds of fibers represented. The fibers carrying proprioceptive information are heavily myelinated, those for touch and pressure are lightly myelinated, and those for pain and temperature are unmyelinated. In unmyelinated nerves of vertebrates the rate of conduction of the nerve impulse is from 0.2 to 8 meters (m) a second, depending on the size of the fiber. In a cold blooded animal such as the frog the conduction rate in the sciatic nerve (myelinated) is from 24-38 m per second. And in human myelinated nerves the rate of conduction may rise to 125 m per second. The rate of transmission is not solely a function of the myelinated or unmyelinated character of the fiber, but also of the fiber cross section diameter. The myelinated fibers of 20 micron diameter conduct at about 120 m per second. Smaller fibers, down to one micron, conduct at a slower rate. In large somatic axons of the A group (see below), which are myelinated, the rate of conduction in warm blooded animals has been shown to be in proportion to the fiber diameter. Fiber diameter in micra times 6 m per sec gives the rate of conduction for measurements outside the myelin sheath, or 8.7 m per sec for measurements of the axis cylinder alone. The presence of the myelin sheath speeds up the rate of conduction tremendously. For the same size of fibers the presence of myelin results in 10 times faster conduction than in unmyelinated fibers. The fiber types and their speeds of conduction are as follows:

1. $A = 1–22\mu$ diameter—myelinated, somatic afferent and efferent—speed = 5-120 m/sec.
2. $B = < 3\mu$ diameter—myelinated, efferent preganglionic autonomic—speed = 3-15 m/sec.
3. $C_{(s)} = 0.3–1.3\mu$ diameter—unmyelinated, efferent postganglionic autonomic (s = sympathetic)—speed = 0.7-2.3 m/sec.
4. $C_{(dr)} = 0.4–1.2\mu$ diameter—small, unmyelinated, afferent in peripheral nerves and dorsal root (dr)—speed = 0.6-2.0 m/sec.

Nerve supply is necessary for healthy, normal activity of parts of the body. Skeletal muscles wither and degenerate without motor nerves, while sensory afferents are needed for healthy skin. On the other hand, cardiac and some smooth muscle and glands can continue to function without nerve supply, although not in a normal manner.

NERVOUS CONDUCTION

When recording electrodes are attached to the outside and inside of an axis cylinder it is found that a potential difference exists across the membrane. There is then an electric polarity with opposite electrical charges across the membrane. The outside is (+) positive with respect to the inside and the inside is (−) negative with respect to the outside. A disturbance of this polarity resulting in depolarization causes a current to flow. The steps whereby this comes about need now to be examined in detail.

The polarity across the membrane of the nerve fiber is maintained by a differential balance of ions on the inside and outside of the membrane. There is ten times greater concentration of sodium (Na^+) outside the membrane than inside, and on the inside there is a concentration of 20–50 times more potassium (K^+) than outside, with chloride (Cl^-) conversely more concentrated outside than inside. The distribution of the potassium and chloride ions are roughly in equilibrium with the membrane voltage. The sodium ions are quite otherwise. The high external sodium and low internal sodium are out of balance with the membrane voltage. Since the membrane voltage is between −70 and −90 mV, there is a tremendous pressure for inward flow of sodium ions. The resting membrane is impermeable, however, to the sodium ions. But when the membrane becomes stimulated there is a sudden reversal, making the membrane highly permeable to sodium. With this increased permeability, the sodium ions flow in through the membrane at a rapid rate. In less than a millisecond the potential difference is not merely neutralized but relatively reversed. The external surface becomes negative in relation to the inside, and the membrane is depolarized as depicted in Fig. 6–1. This depolarization, as we will see, spreads along the fiber independently of the initial stimulus. At the peak of the potential shift there is a reduction of entry of sodium ions, and the potassium permeability of the membrane increases, allowing the potassium ions to flow out. After this exchange, there is an "active sodium transport" to the external side of the membrane and a slower diffusion of potassium back inside, restoring the membrane potential. The agent of this repolarization is a "hypothetical" sodium-potassium pump.

When the membrane becomes depolarized locally in this way, the ionic exchange sets up local electric currents (the source) which form a dipole, one loop going forward from the point of stimulation and one loop going back. The two portions of the dipole come back together at the point of stimulation, called the sink. Thus there is a source of origin and a sink to which the ionic flow returns. The leading edge of the forward dipole as it leaves the membrane becomes the adequate stimulus for the depolarization of the next segment of nerve fiber, and the permeability-depolarization-dipole sequence is repeated over again. The impulse moves down the nerve fiber as rapidly as the permeability-depolarization-dipole sequence can be repeated.

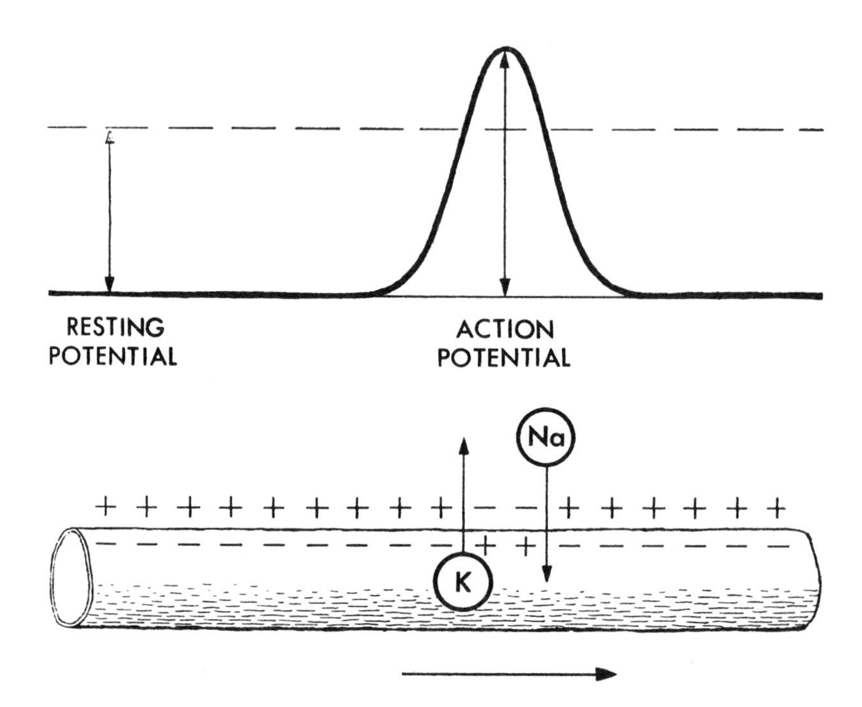

Source: B. Katz in *Scientific American,* November 1952, p. 61.

Figure 6–1. Action Potential Wave

REFRACTORY PERIOD

The portion of the dipole that goes back up the fiber to the sink is related to the recovery phase, and its duration is intimately related to the absolute and relative refractory periods. The *absolute refractory period* is that interval during which no added strength of stimulus can elicit an impulse; the *relative refractory period* is that interval during which an increased strength of stimulus would be required to fire a neuron or nerve fiber.

As we saw earlier, some nerve fibers are myelinated and some are not. It was evident from the rates of conduction that the unmyelinated fibers conduct more slowly than those which are myelinated, if the diameters are comparable. The function of the myelin has long been thought to be that of insulating the fiber. But recent findings assign it an even more important function in the speed of conduction. For the dipole currents cannot emerge from the fiber membrane when it is covered by myelin. The dipole currents in myelinated fibers can emerge only at the nodes of Ranvier. In this way the current dipole has to jump from one node to the next, increasing greatly the speed of conduction. This jump gives rise to the term *saltatory conduction.*

ALL-OR-NONE LAW

One of the clearest characteristics of nervous conduction comes out of this consideration of depolarization and saltatory conduction. This is that the nervous conduction is semiexplosive in that it conducts with its maximum energy or not at all. This is known as the "all-or-none" law. If the stimulus is sufficient to depolarize the membrane the rest of the sequence follows automatically. In view of the fact that nervous conduction uses up oxygen and gives off carbon dioxide, it is evident that the energy required for this conduction is the metabolism of the nerve cell. This is the source, too, of the energy for the local electric currents in the dipole. The nervous impulse flows along a fiber without decrement over distance because the energy needed for the dipole currents is renewed from the cell metabolism at each leading edge where stimulation occurs. This maintenance of strength of current flow without decrement is true even though there may be decrement within the tiny dipole currents. As we saw earlier, this "all-or-none" characteristic is important in understanding the relation between the sense organ and the nervous impulse. Because the nerve fiber reacts with its maximum energy, if at all, there can be no gradations of intensity in the nervous impulse. Changes in intensity of the sensory stimulus may be reflected, then, only in different frequencies of firing of nerve impulses in single fibers, the more intense the stimulus the greater frequency of the impulse. Greater intensity of stimulation can also bring more fibers into action.

SYNAPSE

An important part of ordinary nervous conduction occurs not in nerve fibers but in the point of connection between nerves—the synapse. This is the point of delay in nervous conduction. It is also absolutely necessary for any mechanism of choice to occur.[1] Far from being a

[1] According to cybernetic theory, two "bits" of information are needed for choice to occur. One "bit" or impulse cannot provide the basis of choice.

hindrance to nervous conduction the synapse makes possible selective excitation and inhibition. Without the synapse the mammalian nervous system would act like the nerve net in a jellyfish, where the impulse from outside is carried simultaneously to every part of the animal without any delay, interference, or choice. The synapse serves then as a selective routing mechanism and, as we will see, as an intermediate station where a power step-up can occur. A diagram of selective routing is presented in Fig. 6–2.

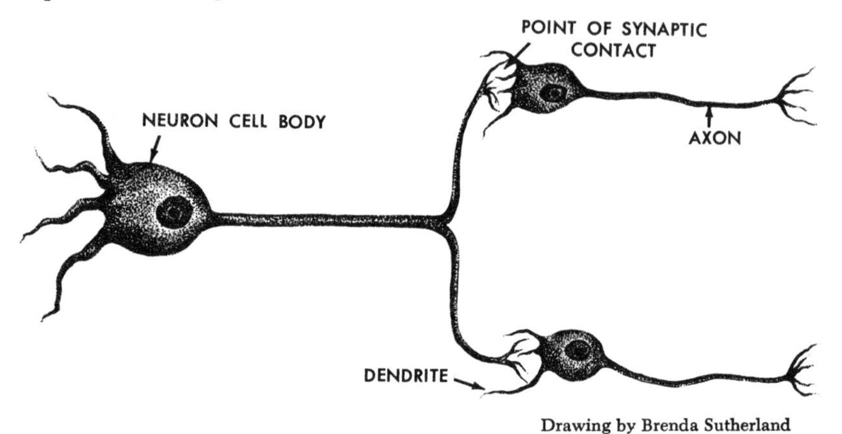

Figure 6–2. Three Connected Neurons (Diagrammatic) to Show Selective Routing Possibilities Dependent on Synaptic Connection

If we examine carefully the character of the synapse with the electron microscope, we find a clear cleft between the end of one neuron and its successor. The actual connection is achieved by microscopic feet on the tip of the branched ends of the preceding axon. These feet, or *boutons*—"buttons," are found in great profusion, particularly in connection with the dendrites and motor horn cells of the spinal cord. One careful estimate showed 400 such *boutons* on a single motor horn cell. (See Fig. 6–3.) It is clear, however, that such a large number of connecting *boutons* do not represent as many different axons. Each axon has a number of terminal buttons, or *boutons,* and the final branching ends are each supplied with a terminal button. When a number of these buttons transmit together, or two adjacent axons fire together, *spatial summation* occurs, making possible the addition of impulses which are each subthreshold for crossing the synapse. When such summation takes place we see the synapse crossed by the addition of impulses any one of which would have been unable to accomplish this alone. A similar additive effect of subthreshold impulses occurs when two impulses reach

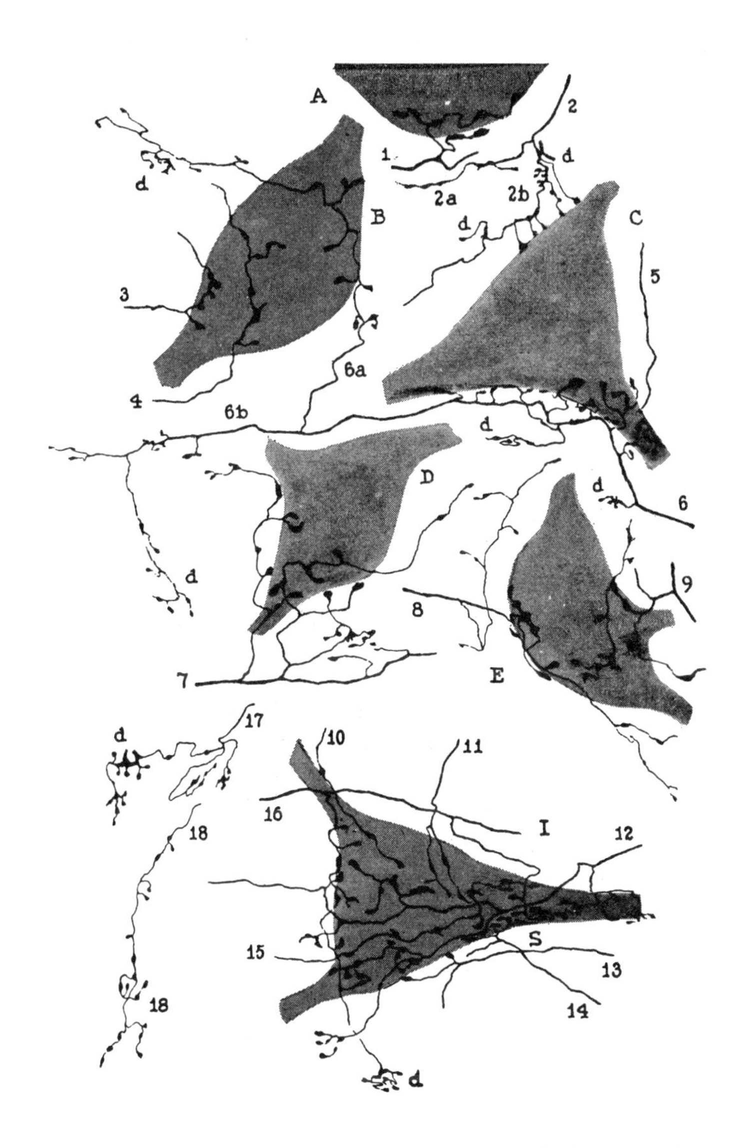

Source: Rafael Lorente de Nó in *Journal of Neurophysiology* (Springfield, Ill.: Charles C. Thomas), Vol. 1 (1938), p. 200.

Figure 6–3. Motor Neurons and Synaptic Connections

the *boutons* in rapid succession. The second impulse in this *temporal summation* must reach the synapse a few milliseconds after the first one and before the initial synaptic transmitter substance (to be explained below) is wiped out. We have, then, both spatial and temporal summation of impulses becoming effective at the point of synapse. But temporal or spatial summation does not occur by an electrical crossing of the synapses, but by an altogether different kind of mechanism. It is time to consider how synaptic transmission takes place.

The current flowing along an axon would, if unaided, find it an unsurmountable task to cross two membrane barriers of high resistance if it were to attempt to continue transmission by electrical means alone. The synapse is the place of greatest delay or latency in nervous conduction. As we will see, crossed or contralateral reflexes take an extraordinary length of time when compared to those on the same, or ipsilateral, side of the cord, even taking into account the differing lengths of nerve fiber. This lengthened time interval is caused almost entirely by transmission across two or more synapses, each of which requires 1 or 2 milliseconds. Synaptic transmission has some similarities to and many differences from nervous conduction.

TRANSMITTER SUBSTANCE

At the synapse, where the terminal *boutons* approximate the soma or dendrites of the next succeeding nerve cell by a cleft of 200Å[2] width, a marked change occurs in the kind of energy transfer that goes on. Refer to Fig. 6–4, on page 81, for an illustration of a synaptic cleft. The electrical current that characterizes the flow of impulse down a nerve fiber changes here to chemical activity. In each of the terminal buttons there are a considerable number of tiny synaptic vesicles of 200–600Å diameter. Closely related to these vesicles are a number of mitochondria which are always present when an unusual output of biological energy is required. The supposition is that the mitochondria form vesicles anew as these are used up by repeated synaptic transmission. The experimental data which is available seems to indicate that the synaptic vesicles are responsible for the release of the chemical transmitter which, flowing into the synaptic cleft, reduces the permeability of the postsynaptic membrane to the sodium ion and in this way leads to the depolarization of the postsynaptic membrane. The chemical transmitter substance is removed within a few milliseconds after it has changed the permeability by a hydrolizing enzyme, cholinesterase. Conduction in the next neuron of a chain is thus begun again by a depolarization process. This depolarization requires a definite minimal shift in permeability. Thus it is that two or more subthreshold impulses

---

[2] An angstrom (Å) = 1/100 millionth of a centimeter.

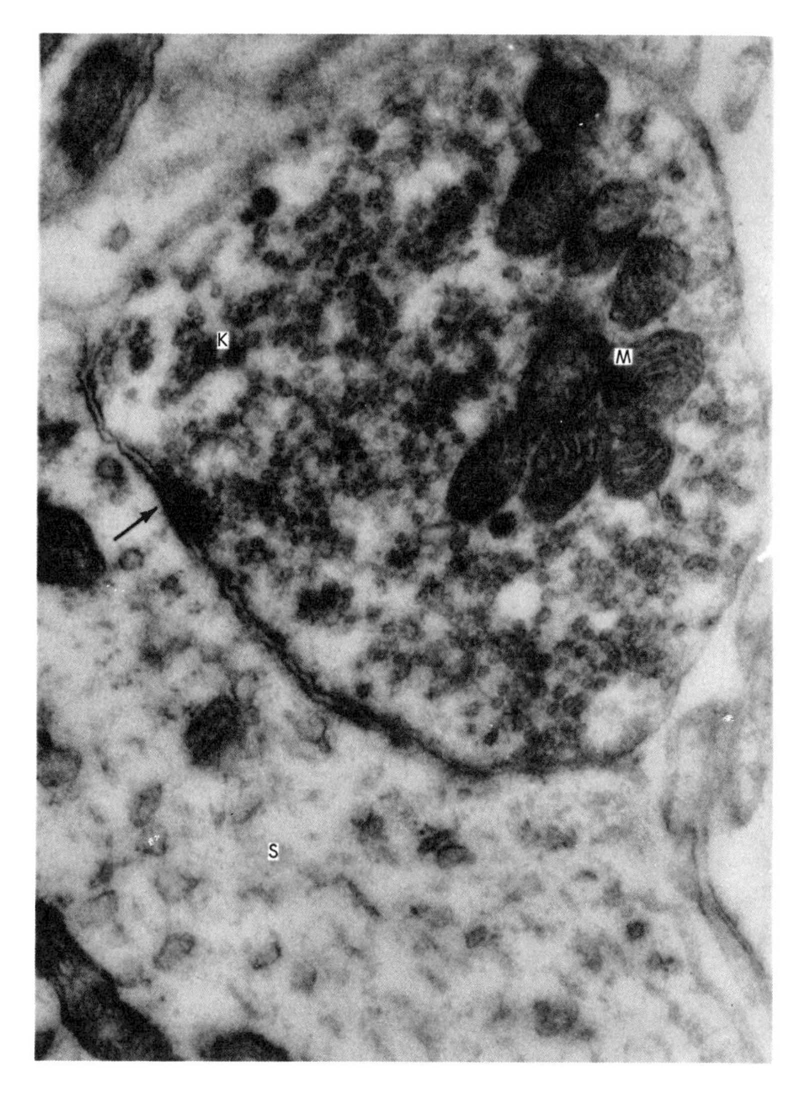

M = mitochondria; K = synaptic button with vesicles; S = adjacent cell; arrow = synaptic cleft.

Source: S. L. Palay "The Morphology of Synapses in the Central Nervous System," *The Submicroscopic Organization and Function of Nerve Cells* (Supplement 5, *Experimental Cell Research* [New York: Academic Press, Inc., 1958]), p. 276.

Figure 6–4. Electronmicrophoto of Synaptic Cleft

arriving at the presynaptic membrane at the same time or in rapid succession summate the chemical transmitter released and bring the postsynaptic potential to the threshold for depolarization, and a new impulse or spike is generated. The subthreshold transmitter substance leaks away quickly as a result of the action of hydrolizing enzymes, so that temporal summation requires very rapid succession in order for the potential to reach the impulse threshold. In the synapses of the sympathetic nervous system, which regulates the internal organs, of some parts of the cerebral cortex, and of the motor end plate or neuromuscular junction, the transmitter substance is acetylcholine (ACh); the hydrolizing enzyme is cholinesterase, which exists in substantial quantities at the end plate region and in the interstitial fluid. The transmitter substance in most other synaptic junctions is not known, as yet. The action of the nervous impulse at the neuromuscular junction is the same as at the synapse (see Fig. 6–5.)—release of transmitter substance and depolarization of the muscle fibers.

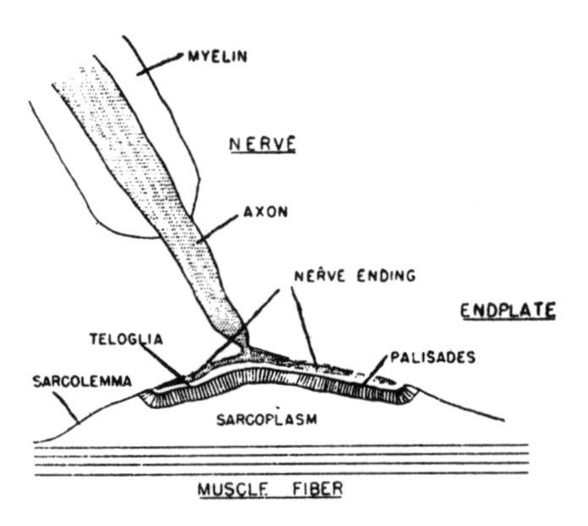

Source: George H. Acheson, "Physiology of Neuro-Muscular Junctions: Chemical Aspects," *Federation Proceedings* (Baltimore: Federation of American Societies for Experimental Biology), Vol. 7 (1948), p. 447.

Figure 6–5. Diagram of Neuromuscular End Plate Region

In normal excitatory synaptic transmission the injection of curare, syncurine, or other synthetic neuromuscular blocking agent of this nature stops the transmission of the chemical substance across the cleft in sufficient strength to depolarize the postsynaptic membrane. It acts in a peculiar way to accomplish this result. The muscle blocking agent (curare or equivalent) competes with acetylcholine for so-called "receptor" sites on the postsynaptic membrane. And unless curare leaves enough receptor sites to which acetylcholine can become attached, no depolarization can occur, the acetylcholine being hydrolized by cholinesterase without having had any effect on the postsynaptic membrane. Without effective transmission at the nerve-muscle junction the muscle cannot be excited to contraction, and paralysis results.

SYNAPTIC INHIBITION

One of the other important activities of the nervous system which occurs at the synapse and not in nerve fiber is inhibition of the nervous impulse. This is the type of action which occurs when the vagus nerve slows the heart rate, or when the contraction of one group of muscles requires that their antagonists be inactive. It has been shown in recent years that there exists in the gray matter of the spinal cord a special group of internuncial nerve cells, the Renshaw cells, whose function is to provide inhibitory impulses to motor neurons which innervate skeletal muscle. When impulses come into the gray matter of the cord calling for muscular contraction, collateral axon branchings of second-order neurons go to the soma and dendrites of the Renshaw cells, which act to inhibit the muscles antagonistic to those which are about to contract. This relationship is indicated in Fig. 6–6.

If we look for a moment at what happens at the inhibitory synapse, it is clear that the activity is vastly different from excitatory transmission. Excitatory transmission is begun, as we have seen, essentially by a change in membrane permeability allowing an inflow of sodium ions and an outflow of potassium ions, thus depolarizing the membrane and causing current flow. In terms of logic, the process of nervous inhibition must prevent these successive steps in excitatory transmission from occurring. The present state of experimental knowledge indicates that this is exactly what does occur. Certainly the action of the inhibitory synaptic knobs is to hyperpolarize the membrane of the nerve cell with which it has contact. This change in membrane potential in effect increases the charge on the membrane rather than taking the charge off, as would be true for excitatory transmission. On the basis of limited experimental data it seems evident that the action of the inhibitory synaptic knobs or buttons increases the postsynaptic membrane permeability to small ions, such as the chloride ion, thus increasing markedly the quantity of negatively charged anions. The action of the inhibitory transmitter substance is to open the pores in the subsynaptic membrane to a rigidly fixed size so that only small ions of less than 5 Å can pass through. Chloride is the only intracellular anion of this critical size present in a concentration sufficient to contribute to the potential, and movement of this ion down its concentration gradient

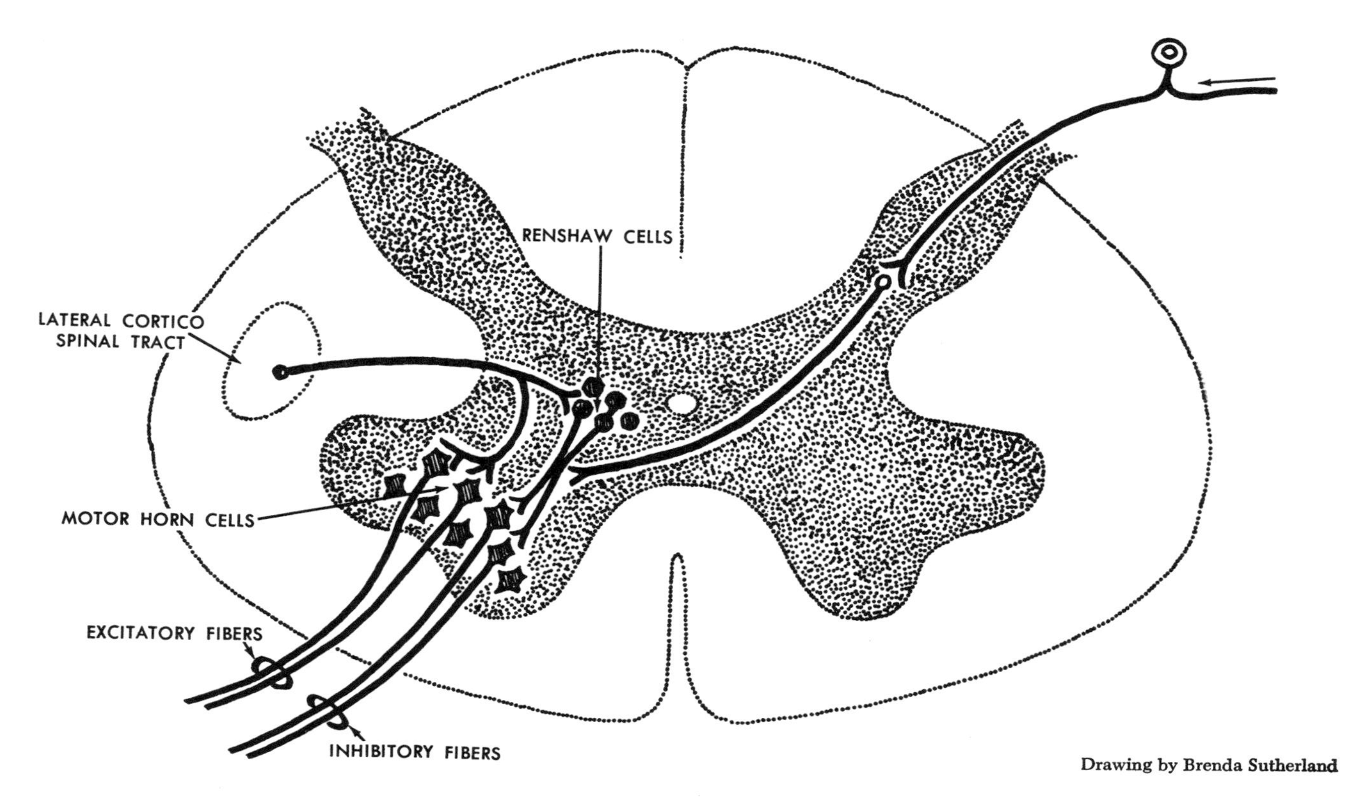

Drawing by Brenda Sutherland

Figure 6–6. Diagram of Cord Showing Motor Neurons and Renshaw Cells

would yield hyperpolarization. But the equilibrium potential of the chloride ion is only —70mV, whereas the inhibitory potential difference is at least —80mV to —90mV. There is some evidence therefore for a limited role of the potassium ions, which are small enough to pass the membrane; but the sodium ions are too large to pass through the membrane pores. In all probability, the inhibition of heart muscle is accomplished by potassium permeability only, inhibition of crustacean muscle by chloride flow only, and others by a combined movement of chloride and potassium. The presence of a large quantity of chloride and some potassium ions increases the negative charge on the inside of the postsynaptic membrane and effectively prevents the depolarization, which would require a reversal of charge across the membrane. Thus we see that the inhibitory knobs, by increasing permeability to chloride ions, raise the negative charge on the inside of the postsynaptic membrane above the resting potential. The resting potential is about —70mV, but when inhibitory knobs are active this membrane potential may go to —80mV or —90mV, which is the physical measure of this hyperpolarization. If impulses leading to excitatory transmission should occur, the membrane permeability would not allow the large sodium ions to pass through as long as the inhibitory transmitter substance was active.

PRESYNAPTIC INHIBITION

The experimental evidence seems to indicate that there are two ways in which inhibition can occur. The first is for the inhibitory postsynaptic potential (IPSP) to neutralize the excitatory process in the way we have just described. The second method is for the inhibitory process to reduce the excitatory transmitter substance, presynaptically, to an amount which would be below the threshold for the spike potential. The exact transmitter substances for inhibition have been only partially worked out. Acetylcholine seems to be one of the substances for the Renshaw cells, since strychnine and tetanus toxin block the action of the Renshaw inhibitory synapse. There is, however, another mechanism of transmission not touched by strychnine. The blocking of this second mechanism is produced by picrotoxin, and picrotoxin seems to work against the presynaptic inhibitory knobs which must reduce the excitatory transmitter below threshold. Recent experimental studies have shown that substances found only in inhibitory neurons, and absent from sensory and motor ones, may be the agent for reducing the transmitter substance below threshold. Florey has shown that gamma-aminobutyric acid (GABA) is found only in inhibitory neurons and is blocked by picrotoxin. Greater knowledge of these blocking agents will probably provide the key to the identity of the transmitter substance.

One other facet of inhibition is that there is a short delay of 0.8 milliseconds in its appearance. This is undoubtedly because there is one interneuron involved in the sequence. The incoming impulses in collateral branches from the dorsal roots go to Renshaw cells in the center gray matter of the cord, and thence, after one or more synapses, the impulses travel to motor cells of the ventral horn. In general, also, spatial summation is needed from several incoming channels in order to activate inhibitory cells.

SOURCES AND ADDITIONAL READING

Eccles, J. C., *Mechanism of Synaptic Transmission*. Berlin: Sonderdruck-Ergebnisse Physiol-Springer, 1961.

Florey, E., "Comparative Physiology—Transmitter Substances," *American Review Physiol.* 23 (1961), 501.

Handbook of Physiology, Sec. I, Vol. I, Chaps. 2, 3. Washington, D. C.: American Physiol. Soc., 1959.

Katz, B., "Nervous Impulse," *Sci. American*, Nov. 1952.

McLennan, H., *Synaptic Transmission*. Philadelphia: W. B. Saunders Company, 1963.

Nachmanson, D., *The Nerve Impulse* (5 vols.). New York: J. Macy Foundation, 1951.

Ruch, T. and J. Fulton, *Medical Physiology and Biophysics* (18th ed.), Chaps. 1–3. Philadelphia: W. B. Saunders Company, 1960. (See 19th ed., Chaps. 1–3, 6.)

Walsh, G., *Physiology of the Nervous System*, Chap. 1. New York: Longmans Green & Co., Inc., 1959.

Seven

THE SPINAL CORD AND PATHWAYS

If we consider the nervous system again as a mechanism for information input, coordination and processing, and output to effectors, we see that the spinal cord has a large place in both the input and output phases. It carries up to the brain all sensory information coming from the body and all motor commands coming down from the brain to skeletal muscles. It is, then, primarily a transmission pathway. In addition to the transmission function, there is also important reflex coordination at various levels in the spinal cord, as well as the inhibitory function mentioned in the last chapter.

The spinal cord is protected from injury by being encased inside the vertebral column. It extends, in continuity with the medulla oblongata, from the crossing of the pyramids at the level of the atlas, where the base of the skull articulates with the vertebral column, down to the lower border of the first lumbar vertebra. Although the cord does not extend into the lower lumbar and sacral vertebrae, its sensory and motor roots enter and exit there and thus serve the lower sections of the trunk and legs. During the evolutionary development of the human skeleton the vertebral column has become longer than the spinal cord. The result of this disjunction in growth was to force the spinal nerves, which leave the cord up in the lumbar region of the back, to travel down inside the vertebral column until they reach the foramen at the correct level for exit. This group of spinal nerves filling the lower vertebral column is known as the "cauda equina," or horse's tail.

As was implied above, the spinal cord has both afferent (sensory) roots for information input and efferent (motor) roots for innervation of muscles and glands. The sensory input and the motor outflow occur at each vertebral segment, there being 31 pairs of spinal nerves. Between each two adjacent vertebrae there are laterally paired foramina for the exit and entry of nerves serving that particular segment of the body. These arrangements are illustrated in Fig. 7–1.

SEGMENTATION IN CORD

There is in the spinal cord, and nowhere else in the central nervous system, a segmental organization of the nerves to the body. This dermatomal segmentation is known precisely and has much clinical importance. The cervical nerves serve the shoulders, arms, neck, and lower jaw and chin; the thoracic nerves serve the dermal segments of most of the torso; the lumbar nerves serve the small of the back and the front of the legs; and the sacral nerves serve the back of legs and buttocks as well as the sex organs. Since the area served by each spinal nerve has been mapped, a loss of sensation in a particular segment points to the possibility of the involvement of the corresponding spinal nerve or its upward projection to the brain. The final terminations of each spinal nerve are not limited strictly to the segment where it originates. There is overlapping between the terminal arborizations of adjacent spinal nerves. Sensation from one spot on the body wall may be mediated by three spinal nerves, the central one carrying the largest portion of sensory input, but assisted to a lesser extent by the two nerves adjacent to it.

A somewhat similar, but not identical, arrangement holds true for the motor nerves. This overlap, providing as it does alternate, if incomplete, channels of communication, assures against loss of sensation or motor control if only one segmental nerve is injured or destroyed.

The internal structure of the spinal cord superficially looks simple, but in reality is very complex. The sensory information from the periphery of the body, from skeletal muscles, joints, tendons, and from viscera is carried over the (afferent) dendrites of the unipolar ganglion cell (p. 45) in the dorsal root ganglion, and thence, by its axon, enters the dorsal or posterior horn of the gray matter of the cord. This central gray matter is arranged in a rough H shape and is surrounded by white myelin-covered bundles of fibers carrying messages up and down.

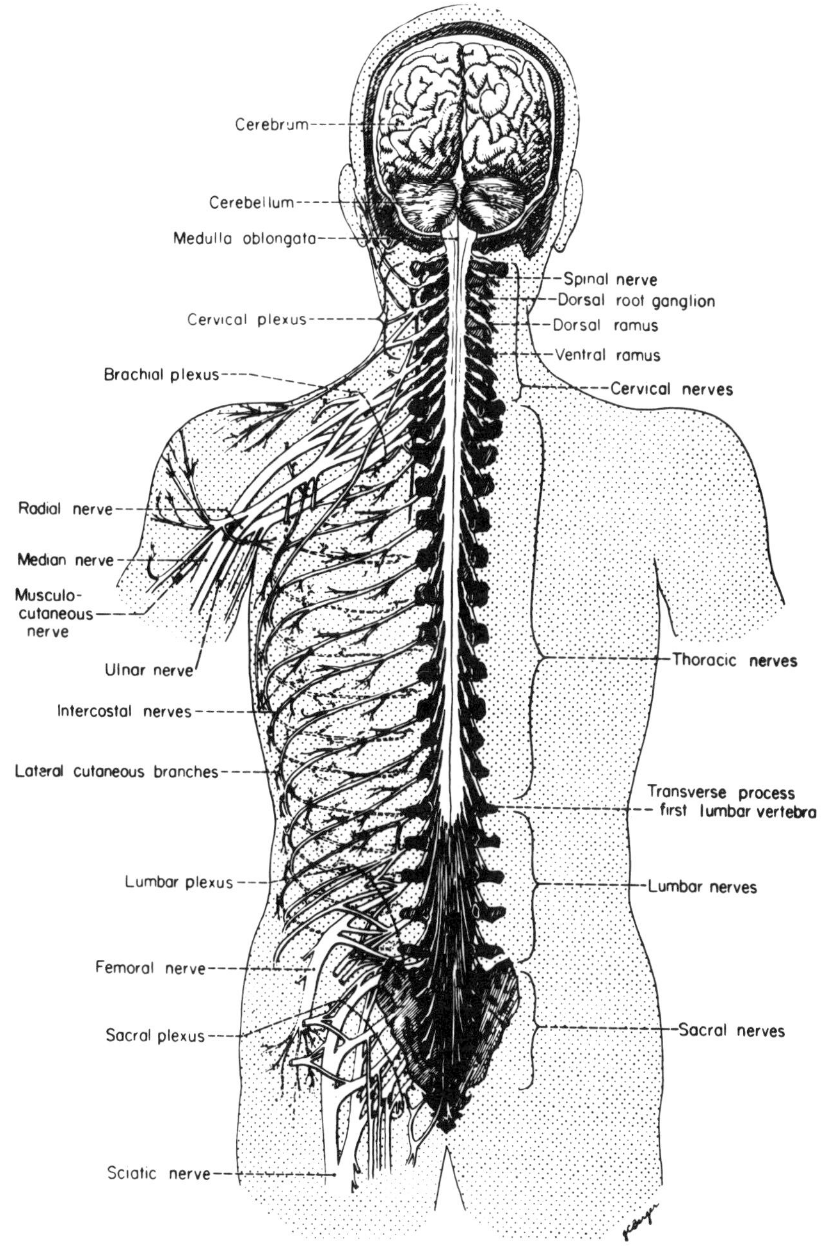

Source: *Essentials of Human Anatomy* by Russell T. Woodburne, 3d edition, 1965. Copyright 1957, 1961, 1965 by Oxford University Press, Inc. Reprinted by permission.

Figure 7–1. Spinal Cord and Segmentation of Spinal Nerves

After synapsing with appropriate nerve cells in the gray matter the nervous impulse may pass out through the ventral or anterior horn to the segmental muscles or glands. The gray matter is made up of nerve cells and their processes. The cells are grouped into functional nuclei with discrete and different functions to be considered below.

The spinal cord has a central canal containing cerebrospinal fluid. Just ventral to this canal lies a bundle of fibers connecting one side of the cord with the other, and known as the ventral, or anterior, commissure. There is also a much smaller dorsal, or posterior, commissure just dorsal to the central canal. By means of these commissures contralateral connections are made possible.

The physiological unit of the white matter of the cord is a tract of fibers having a similar function, origin, and type of termination. Cross sections of the cord at different levels are of different shapes. The lower sacral cord is almost round, with narrow fiber tracts surrounding the central gray matter. This is understandable because the only information going to higher levels and the brain proper is from the buttocks, the genitals, and the tail of lower animals. The same is true of motor impulses coming down; all impulses destined for arms and trunk and legs exit at higher levels. Because of this fact the spinal cord increases in size as it proceeds up to the neck region. The difference in cord levels

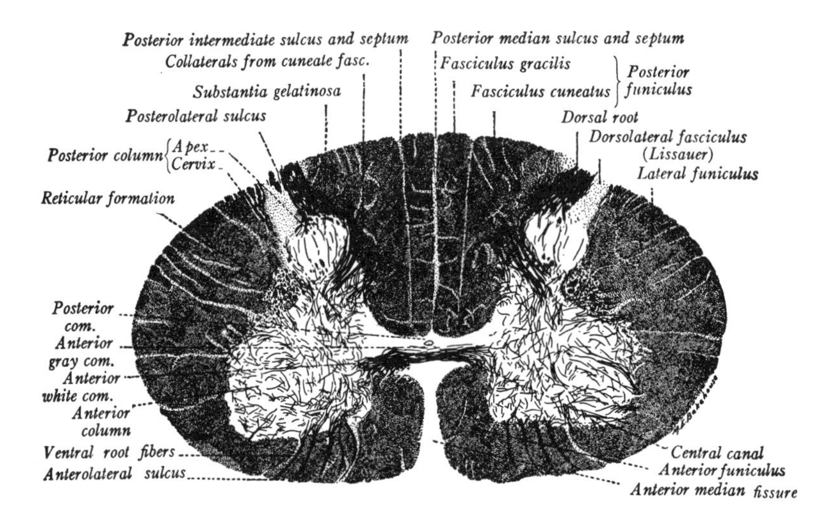

Source: S. W. Ranson and S. L. Clark, *The Anatomy of the Nervous System: Its Development and Function* (10th ed.; Philadelphia: W. B. Saunders Company, 1959), p. 167.

Figure 7–2A. Cross Section of Cervical Cord

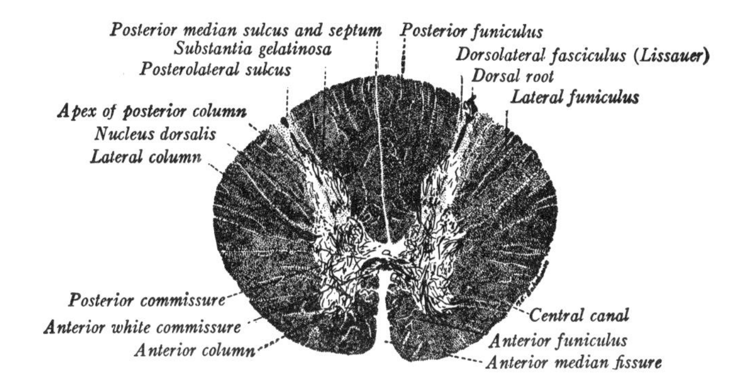

Source: S. W. Ranson and S. L. Clark, *The Anatomy of the Nervous System*, p. 167.

Figure 7–2B. Cross Section of Thoracic Cord

is exemplified in Figs. 7–2A through 7–2D. Each segment of the body, as well as arms and legs, sends in sensory fibers and receives motor fibers. This segmental accretion is the cause for the increase in size. The white fiber tracts carry information from the back of the legs and buttocks the whole length of the cord, but information from arm and shoulder only a fraction of that distance. The concentration of infor-

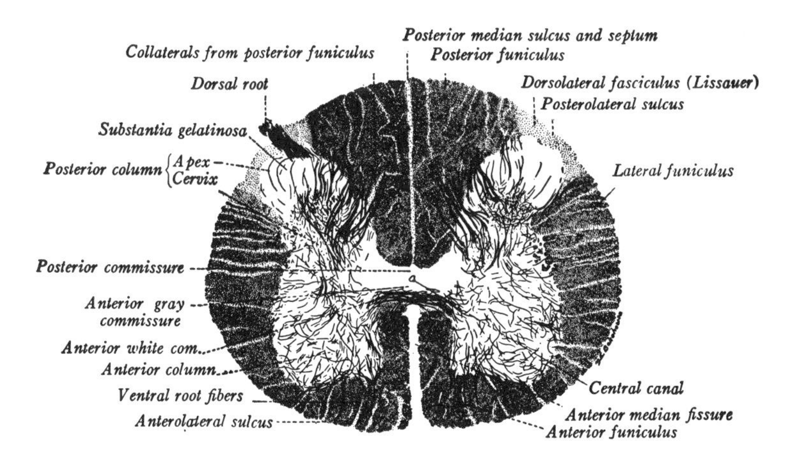

Source: S. W. Ranson and S. L. Clark, *The Anatomy of the Nervous System*, p. 168.

Figure 7–2C. Cross Section of Lumbar Cord

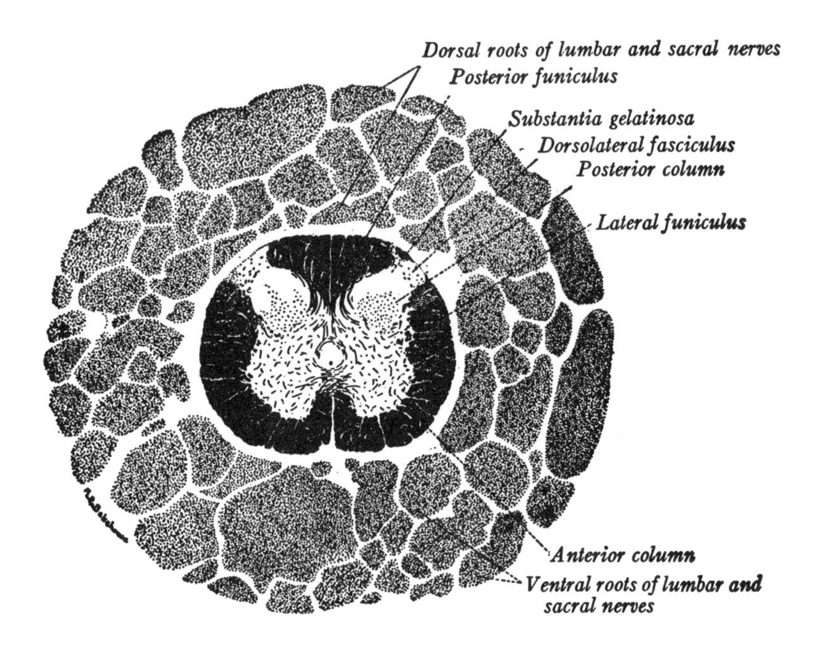

Source: S. W. Ranson and S. L. Clark, *The Anatomy of the Nervous System*, p. 169.

Figure 7–2D. Cross Section of Sacral Cord

mation needed for and from arms and legs causes two enlargements in the cord, one for the arms in the cervical region, and the other in the lumbosacral region for the legs. In comparison with lower animals the conduction pathways between the cord and cerebral hemispheres are larger in man. This represents the increased cerebral dominance which characterizes the higher primates.

ASCENDING FIBER PATHWAYS

Proprioception

As has been indicated already, the fiber pathways run both up and down the cord. In general, the ascending pathways lie lateral to the descending pathways. The cross section of the cord shows two wedge shaped areas between the dorsal horns of the cord. These are made up, for the largest part, of two columns, *fasciculus gracilis* and *fasciculus cuneatus.* The fibers in *gracilis* arise from sensory (dorsal) roots of the sacral, lumbar, and lower thoracic regions. The fibers in *cuneatus* come from the sensory (dorsal) roots in the upper thoracic and cervical regions and lie lateral to gracilis. Gracilis then is the only one of these two fascicles found below the midthoracic level. Both of these columns carry proprioceptive impulses from skeletal muscles, tendons, and joints, giving information essential to control of posture. They also transmit tactile information from the skin which is needed for spatial localization and coordination of movements of precision such as two-point discrimination. The fibers in these bundles are the axons of dorsal root sensory cells which ascend the length of the cord without synapse and without crossing to the other side. The first synapse in this pathway, of proprioception and fine touch to thalamus and cortex, is at the caudal end of the medulla in the *nuclei gracilis* and *cuneatus.* From this point the second-order neurons transmit to the thalamus and cerebral cortex. These second-order connections will be described in a following section.

The incoming dorsal root fibers of fine touch and proprioception have descending axon branches as well, which make connections with neurons at other levels of the cord. These travel by way of two small tracts in the posterior, or dorsal, funiculus. These are (1) *fasciculus interfascicularis,* which lies between *gracilis* and *cuneatus;* and (2) *fasciculus septomarginalis,* which lies on both sides of the midline septum.

The cortical pathway for proprioception does not provide for other uses of this same information. The large-stretch afferent fibers originating in the annulospiral endings on intrafusal fibers of muscle spindles do not project upward in the dorsal columns of gracilis and cuneatus, but relay in *nucleus dorsalis* of Clarke, and pass to the *dorsal spinocerebellar*[1] pathway. The fibers from tendon organs for impulses of muscle contraction project upon cells which are *lateral to Clarke's nucleus,* and which are the point of origin of the *ventral spinocerebellar* path. Joint receptors, Ruffini endings and Pacinian corpuscles, are very important for data on bodily position. The transmission pathway for joint information is uncertain. There are, therefore, two other major pathways for proprioceptive information, the *dorsal* and *ventral spinocerebellar fascicles.* These lie on the periphery of the lateral funiculus of the cord just ventral to the entering dorsal root fibers. As the name implies, the fiber bundles travel up the cord to end in the cere-

---

[1] The first term of the complex titles for transmission pathways gives the origin of the fibers, while the second term indicates their termination.

bellum. Automatic adjustments of posture and equilibrium depend on this source of information. The incoming sensory fibers in the dorsal roots enter the gray matter of the cord and make synaptic connections in the *dorsal nucleus* (nucleus dorsalis) of the same side of the cord. The *dorsal spinocerebellar* arising in this nucleus transmits information relative to muscle stretch from annulospiral endings. It runs from the upper lumbar through the thoracic and cervical segments. The ascending fibers in this bundle arise largely from the *dorsal (Clarke) nucleus* of the same side, but perhaps slightly from the opposite side as well. For details of this relationship, see Fig. 7–3. As we will see, the bundle

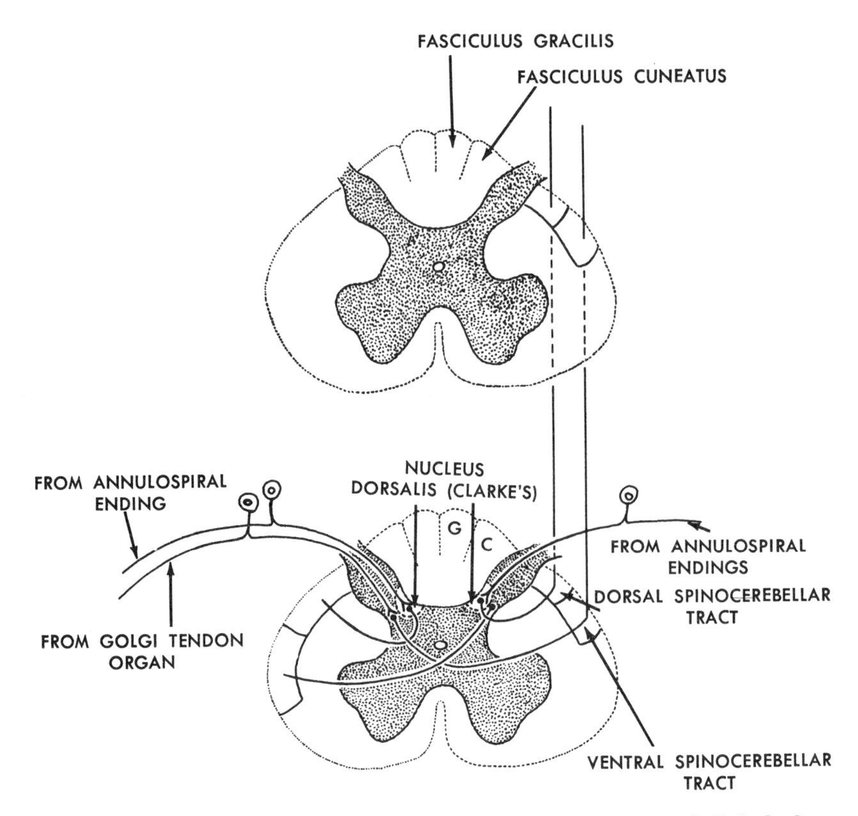

Figure 7–3. Proprioceptive Path from Spinal Cord to Cerebellum

enters the cerebellum by the *inferior cerebellar peduncle.* There are, then, only two neurons in this chain of connection from skeletal muscle or tendon to cerebellar cortex. The *ventral spinocerebellar* path is made up of fibers carrying information about muscle contraction from the tendon organs and ascends farther cephalad to enter the cerebellum alongside the *superior cerebellar peduncle.* The *ventral spinocerebellar* fibers arise from cells in the dorsal gray matter lateral to Clarke's column. The axons from these cells, almost all of which cross at their level of entry by way of the ventral commissure, then turn forward just ventral to the position of the *dorsal spinocerebellar* pathway. These four major pathways *(gracilis, cuneatus, dorsal spinocerebellar,* and *ventral spinocerebellar)* provide then for both cortical and cerebellar reception of proprioceptive information.

Skin Senses

The sensations of touch, temperature, pressure, and pain from the periphery of the body occupy a most important part in many of the adjustments of both animals and man to changes in environmental conditions. Tactile fibers from the face go to the chief sensory nucleus of the trigeminal (V) cranial nerve, while pain and temperature from the face go down to the spinal nucleus of V. The cranial nerves will be considered in Chapter 9. The pathways carrying sensory information of this kind from the body are called *spinothalamic* bundles, *lateral* and *ventral.* The dorsal root fibers for crude touch and pressure are large and myelinated, while those for pain and temperature are small and only slightly myelinated or unmyelinated. When they enter the cord these two types of fibers remain separate. They synapse with neurons in the *nucleus of the dorsal gray* of the same side. The axons of these second neurons cross the cord by way of the ventral commissure within one or two segments after entry and then proceed upstream as the *lateral* or *ventral spinothalamic* pathway to the thalamic nuclei. (See Fig. 7–4.) The separation of function is represented by the smaller, lightly myelinated fibers carrying temperature and pain, traveling by way of the *lateral spinothalamic* tract. This is situated just medial to the ventral portion of the *ventral spinocerebellar* path.

The sensations of crude touch and pressure are carried by the larger and more heavily myelinated fibers which constitute the *ventral spinothalamic* tract in the anterior funiculus midway between the ventral gray and the anterior edge of the cord. The separation of these four sensory channels into two bundles is important clinically in that injury can sever the *lateral spinothalamic* tract, causing loss of pain and temperature sense from the opposite side of the body without disturbing the sense of touch and pressure. The reverse, of course, is also true.

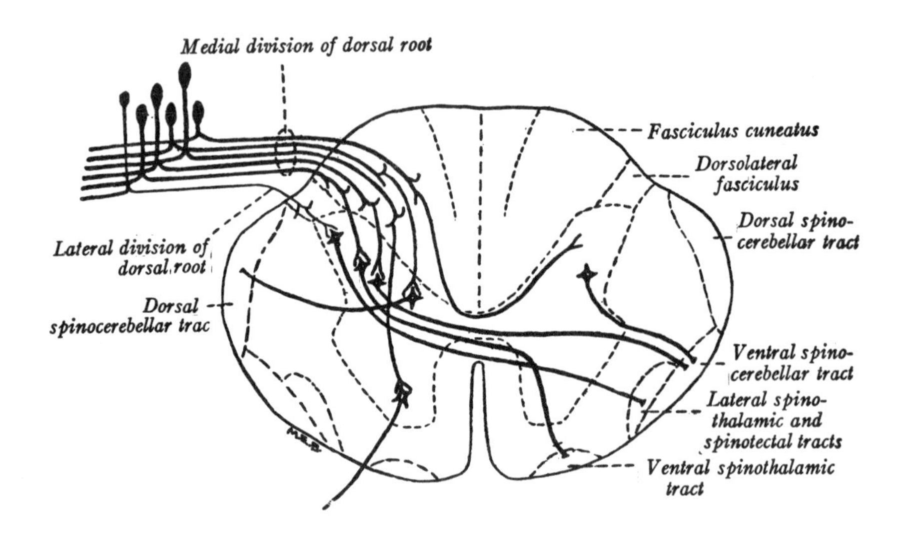

Source: S. W. Ranson and S. L. Clark, *The Anatomy of the Nervous System*, p. 186.

Figure 7–4. Spinal Cord and Spino-thalamic Bundles

The two spinothalamic pathways carrying sensory information to the *ventrolateral nucleus* of the thalamus together constitute the *spinal lemniscus*. Traveling along with the lateral spinothalamic bundle is the *spinotectal* path which, in the cord, is just ventral to the lateral spino-thalamic tract. This tract brings sensory information into contact with the nuclei of the midbrain roof, or tectum. Since the tectum is largely a reflex center for audition and vision, the spinotectal pathway presumably provides for coordination of these motor reflexes with sensory information from the body. The other important ascending pathway is the *spino-olivary*. This pathway arises in the upper thoracic and cervical cord and passes upward to the inferior olive. Since the fibers from the olive end in the same cerebellar zones as do the dorsal spinocerebellars, it is likely that the *spino-olivary* carries proprioceptive information from the neck and shoulder girdle. The spino-olivary and spino-reticular pathways subserve proprioceptive reflexes. These ascending tracts are illustrated in Fig. 7–5.

With the exception then of the *spinoreticular* fibers, perhaps some *spinopontine*, and also interoceptive fibers, these eight tracts (see Table 7–I, at the end of the chapter) account for all ascending information which passes from the body upward to the brain.

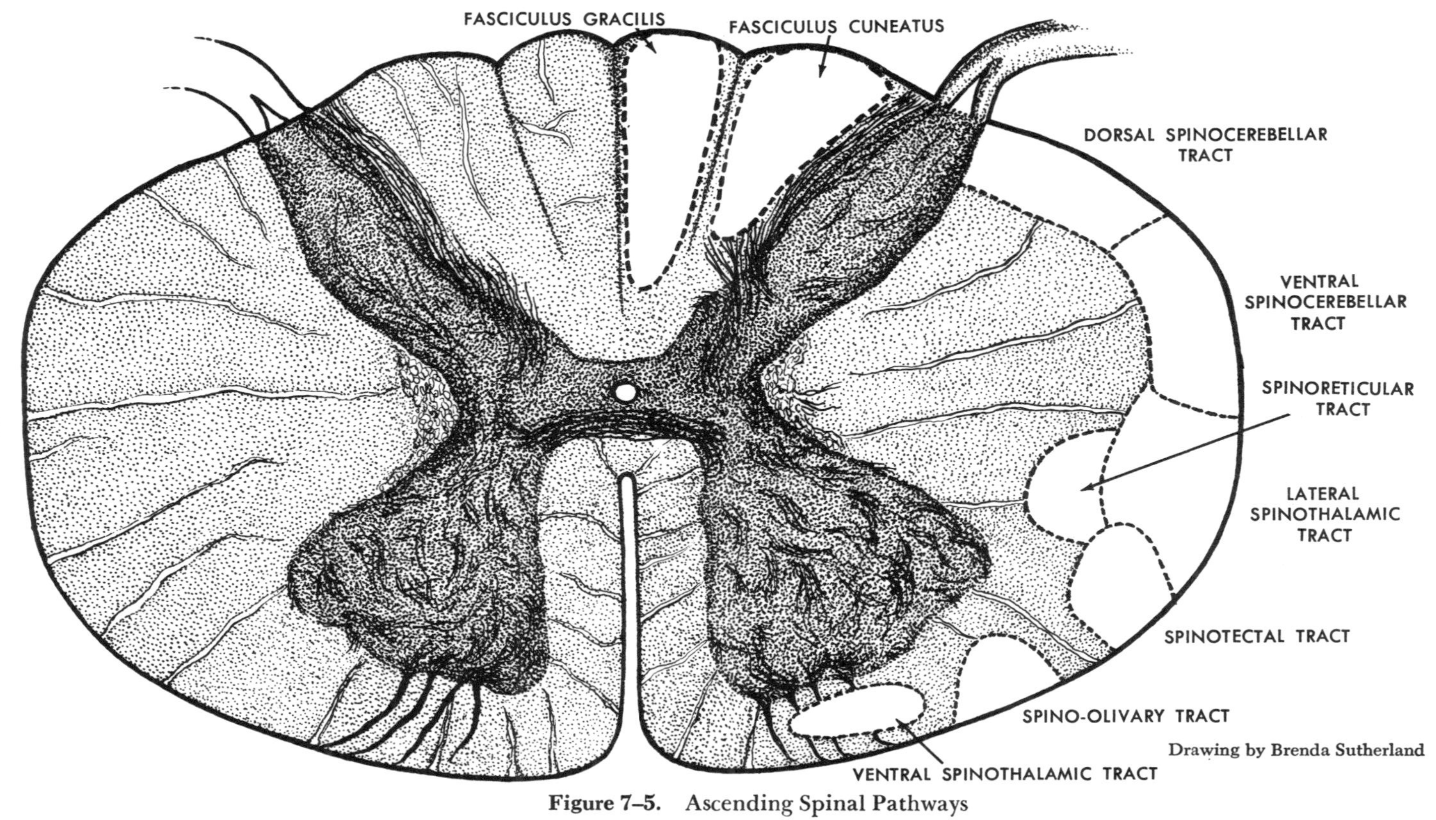

Figure 7–5. Ascending Spinal Pathways

DESCENDING PATHWAYS

The other pathways in the cord are either descending fibers from the higher centers or interconnecting fibers between different levels of the cord. The descending pathways pass down the cord medial to the peripheral ascending sensory bundles. The most prominent bundles of descending fibers are the *corticospinal* tracts. These fibers are axons of pyramidal cells in the precentral motor cortex and in other areas of the brain. They then pass without synapse by way of the internal capsule and the cerebral peduncle and the pons down to the caudal border of the medulla oblongata, where the majority of them cross in the pyramidal decussation.[2] Those that cross to the other side (the *lateral corticospinal tract*) take up a position in the lateral funiculus just medial to the *spinocerebellar tracts.* The fibers continue to descend in this location, ending successively in synaptic contact with motor cells in the cervical, thoracic, and lumbar regions. Approximately half the pyramidal fibers serve cervical segments, while one-third of the fibers make synapse with motor neurons in the lumbar area. As will be seen later, these fibers make possible fine control of muscle movement such as foot, leg, arm, finger, and wrist manipulation.

The *ventral corticospinal* (direct corticospinal) pathway is an uncrossed bundle which continues down on the same side below the pyramidal decussation of the lateral fibers. It is located in the cord just lateral to the anterior median fissure. The fibers in this tract cross at the different levels of the cord by way of the anterior (ventral) commissure and make synapse with motor neurons of the opposite side, usually after an intercalary neuron. They terminate in the cervical and upper thoracic region. Their function is similar to that of the *lateral corticospinal* fibers.

The other descending pathways mediate coordinated automatic or reflex control over body musculature. The extrapyramidal motor system has a number of avenues of control, as do the cerebellar mechanisms of balance and posture. These other descending pathways are five: *rubrospinal, olivospinal, tectospinal, reticulospinal* and *vestibulospinal.* The rubrospinal, which is the largest of the five in lower animals, lies adjacent and ventral to the lateral *corticospinal* tracts. Since this path from nucleus ruber, a relay nucleus between the cortex and cerebellum,

---

[2] The name "pyramidal" comes from the vague pyramidal shape of the bundle on the ventral surface of the medulla.

is already crossed above the cord level, it makes synaptic connection with the motor cells in the anterior horn of the same side. The *olivospinal* pathway is located just lateral to the *spino-olivary*, with which it forms a circuit between the inferior olive and the spinal cord. The *tectospinal* bundle arises from cells in the roof of the midbrain and crosses at that level to descend in the ventral funiculus of the cord. Here it is wedged between the *ventral corticospinal* tract and the *vestibulospinal*. This *tectospinal* bundle mediates mainly optic and auditory reflexes as these affect bodily movement. The *vestibulospinal* tract arises in the cells of the *lateral vestibular nucleus* in the medulla and descends in the most peripheral portion of the ventral or anterior funiculus close to the median fissure and located between the *tectospinal* and the *olivospinal* paths. The descending paths are illustrated in Fig. 7–6. This pathway is very important for reflex movements involved in the maintenance of equilibrium. It is, therefore, largely under the control of the cerebellar mechanisms. The *reticulospinal* pathway is between the *spino-olivary* bundle and the anterior gray horn, at the edge of the lateral funiculus. It carries impulses from reticular nuclei in the medulla and pons to the spinal levels. These reticular centers are, in part, a way station in the extrapyramidal and cerebellar systems of muscular control. The reticular nuclei have other functions as well. (See Chap. 18.)

The area of the cord closest to the anterior and posterior gray matter of the cord is occupied by *fasciculi proprii*, groups of short fibers. These short bundles provide interconnections between different levels of the cord. They are essential for the spread of reflex response to cooperating muscle groups in adjacent segmental levels and are, therefore, of basic importance in many reflex activities. As we will see in the next section, few reflexes are strictly limited to one or even two adjacent segmental levels of muscular activity.

NERVE CELL GROUPS IN CORD

Motor

In addition to these ascending and descending conduction pathways (white matter) the spinal cord has, in the gray matter, a large number of nerve cell groups with which most of these conduction pathways make connection. All of the descending fibers make synapse with the motor neurons in the anterior gray horn of the same or the opposite side. In addition, many of the ascending pathways, particularly the

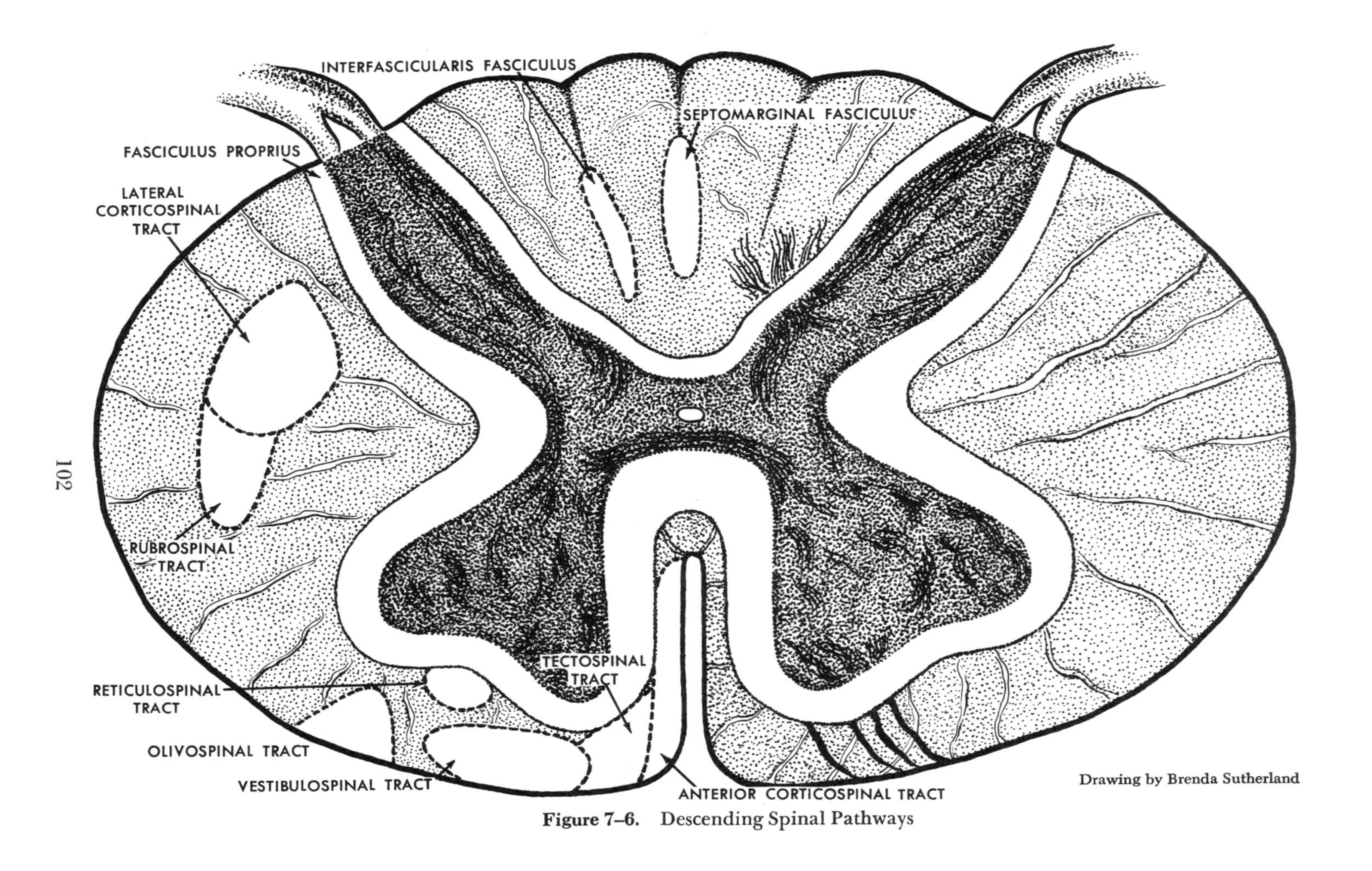

Figure 7–6. Descending Spinal Pathways

cerebellar and thalamic fibers, are the axons of neurons in the cord, where synapse is made with incoming sensory fibers. Two groups of neurons mediate impulses to skeletal muscles. Both are in the anterior horn of the gray of both sides. The *ventromedial* group innervates the somatic muscles of the trunk, and these cells are found throughout the length of the cord. The *ventrolateral* group, or nucleus, innervates the muscles of the limbs, and these cells, as a consequence, are found only in the regions of the cervical and lumbosacral enlargements. It is these two groups of cells with which the crossed and uncrossed corticospinal tracts make connection in order to exercise cortical control over the body musculature. A number of other pathways also make synaptic connection with these ventral nuclei. This allows for muscular adjustments which are not cortically directed, as for instance in maintenance of equilibrium or posture.

While there are a number of descending pathways in the cord, they all, in so far as they are concerned with bodily movement, make synaptic connection with the motor horn cells. And since there is a group of neurons for each muscle group, the descending pathways compete with each other at times for the exclusive control of a particular group of motor neurons. Because all of these tracts impinge upon the motor horn cells, we find a heavy concentration of synaptic buttons congregated on the dendrites or the soma of these cells.

In addition to excitatory synaptic action, the axons from the inhibitory Renshaw cells in the cord also must impinge on the motor neurons in order to inhibit antagonistic muscle groups when voluntary or involuntary action is undertaken. This is indicated in Fig. 7–7.

On the lateral border of the middle of the cord gray matter lies a group of neurons of importance in automatic visceral adjustments. They are called the *intermediolateral* (IML) column of cells. It extends from the upper thoracic only through the upper two lumbar segments. This cell column in the cord is present only in those segments, then, which have white connecting rami with the sympathetic ganglion chain. These (IML column) are visceral efferent cells of the sympathetic division of the autonomic nervous system and constitute, with their dendrites and axons, the preganglionic neuron in the two-neuron chain of sympathetic innervation. The neurons in this cell group can be further divided into medial and lateral groups. The IML *medial* cells provide sympathetic innervation to visceral organs such as the heart and gastrointestinal tube. The IML *lateral* division provides innervation for the superficial blood vessels and the glands of the body wall. All the fiber pathways and cell groups of the spinal cord can be seen in Fig. 7–9 at the end of Table 7–I.

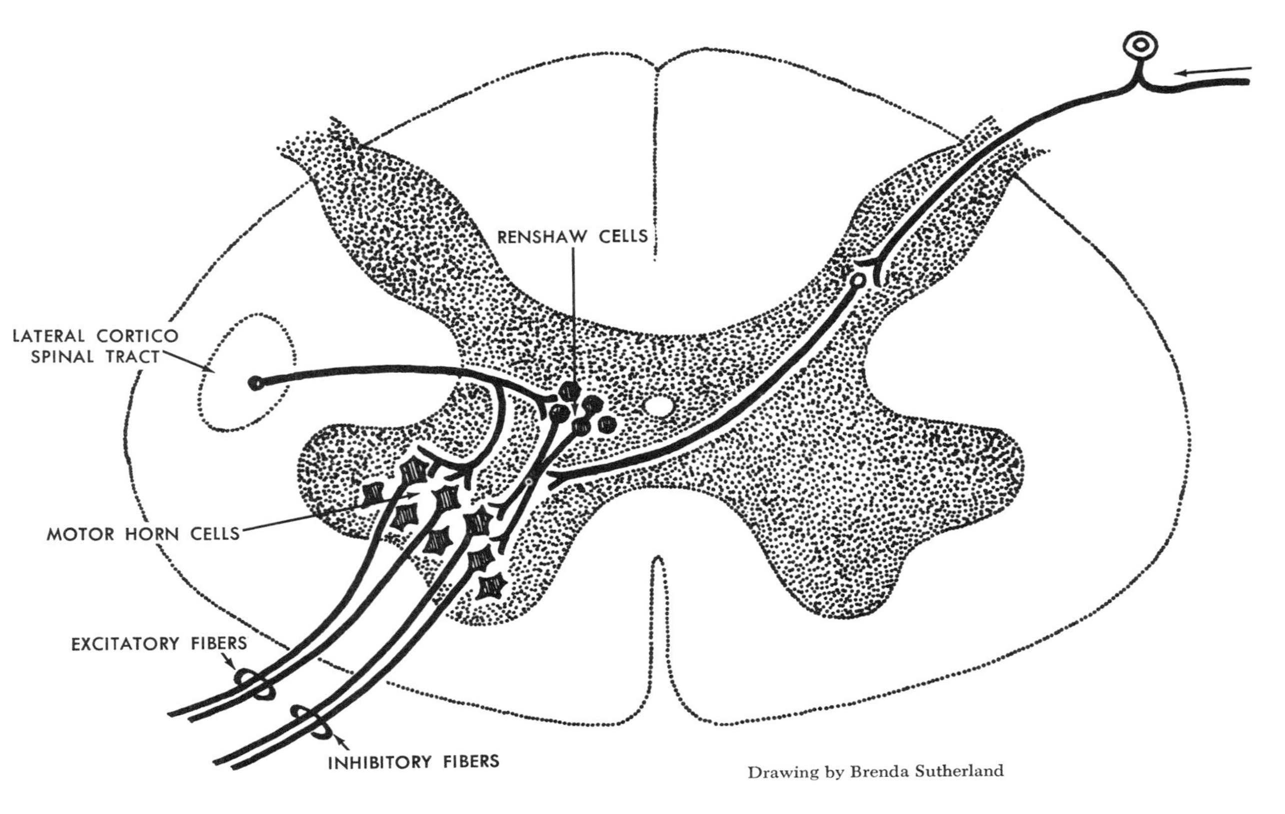

Drawing by Brenda Sutherland

Figure 7–7. Relationship of Ventral Horn Cells and Renshaw Cells

Sensory

In the dorsal-most section of the posterior horn of the cord is a group of smaller dorsal funicular cells which receive exteroceptive information from the sense organs for touch, pressure, temperature, and pain. The axons from this *nucleus of the dorsal horn gray* cross to the other side through the ventral commissure to become components of the *lateral* and *ventral spinothalamic* bundles. This is the pathway, then, of skin sense to the thalamus and cortex. The cells involved are shown in Fig. 7–8.

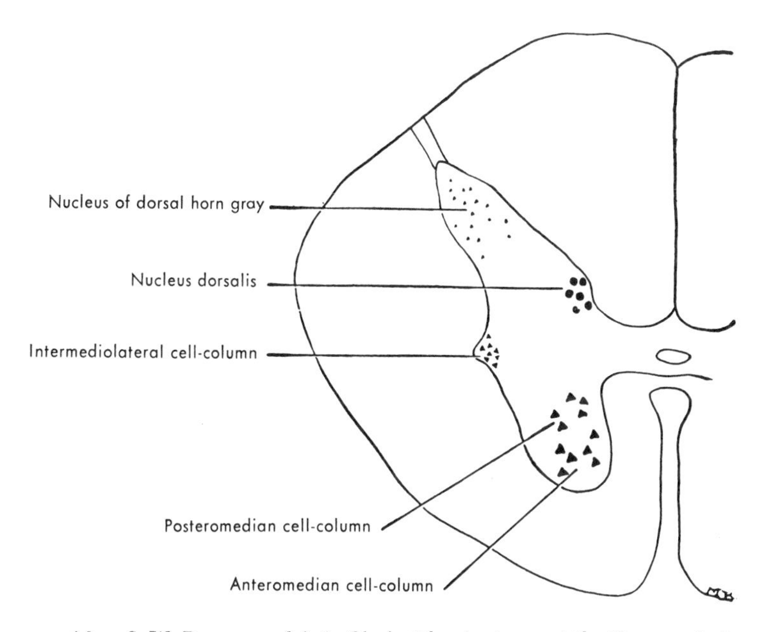

After S. W. Ranson and S. L. Clark, *The Anatomy of the Nervous System*, p. 176.

Figure 7–8. Diagram of Cell Groupings Nucleus Dorsalis, Dorsal Horn Grey, and Intermedio-lateral Column

Below and medial to the nucleus of the *dorsal horn gray* is another group of cells called the *nucleus dorsalis* or *Clarke's column*. This nuclear group receives impulses from the annulospiral or flower spray endings of muscle spindles by way of the dorsal roots. These cells are relatively large and send their axons laterally to the outer edge of the cord on the same or opposite side to form the *dorsal spinocerebellar* bundles. This is the proprioceptive pathway to assist in cerebellar adjustment of equilibrium and posture. Clarke's nucleus does not continue above the level of the eighth cervical segment. A nucleus found in the first and second cervical levels, the lateral cervical nucleus (of Stilling), lies in the same dorsoventral position as the nucleus dorsalis and may be involved in the touch and proprioceptive channel for the foot placing reaction. Its axons feed into the inferior olive and thence to the cerebellum.

Just ventral to *Clarke's column,* in the medial part of the cord and midway between Clarke's nucleus and the *ventromedial* motor group, is a group of cells with a specialized function, that of inhibition. These are called *Renshaw cells* for their discoverer. This group is designated as the *intermediate nucleus.* These cells also send their axons to impinge on the motor neurons in the ventral horn. They receive collateral branches from many of the incoming fibers of the descending pathways, and their function is essential to the proper synergy of opposing muscle groups. When a reflex or cortical stimulation of one group of muscles is triggered, the *Renshaw cells,* by releasing a different transmitter substance, inhibit the opposing muscles. This seeming antagonism is a requisite for smoothly graded muscular action and manipulation.

These, then—ventromedial, ventrolateral, intermediolateral, dorsal horn gray, dorsal nucleus (Clarke), gamma efferent, Renshaw (intermediate), lateral of nucleus dorsalis—are the eight major cell groups in the cord. In addition there are other, smaller cell groupings which serve secondary purposes. In the ventral horn are small neurons which innervate the *gamma efferent* fibers to the intrafusal fibers of muscle spindles. The gamma efferents constitute one-third of the axons composing the ventral motor nerves. Also in the sacral region (S-2-4) are visceral efferent cells, like the intermediolateral column at higher levels, whose axons form the preganglionic portion of the sacral section of the parasympathetic division of the autonomic nervous system (p.275).

Table 7–I

Fiber Tracts and Nuclear Groups in Spinal Cord

	Name	*Location*	*Level of Termination*	*Function*
Ascending	1. F. Gracilis	Medial dorsal columns	Lower medulla	Proprioception, 2-pt. discrimination from lower cord to thalamus
	2. F. Cuneatus	Lateral dorsal columns	Lower medulla	Proprioception, 2-pt. discrimination from upper cord to thalamus
	3. Interfascularis	Between Gracilis and cuneatus	Several segments down and upstream	Intersegmental connections in cord
	4. Septomarginalis	Both sides of midline	Several segments down and upstream	Intersegmental connections in cord
	5. Dorsal Spinocerebellar	Lateral funiculus just ventral to dorsal root	Posterior lobe cerebellum	Annulospiral endings for muscle stretch (involuntary)
	6. Ventral Spinocerebellar	Ventral to d.s-c.	Anterior lobe cerebellum	Golgi tendon endings for muscle contraction (involuntary)
	7. Lateral Spino-thalamic	Ventromedial border of v. s-c.	Ventrolateral thalamic n.	Pain and temperature from opposite body
	8. Ventral Spino-thalamic	Between vestibulospinal and ventral motor neurons	Ventrolateral thalamic n.	Crude touch and pressure from opposite body
	9. Spinotectal	Ventromedial border of lat. sp. thal.	Midbrain roof (Tectum)	Proprioception from neck and shoulder girdle
	10. Spino-olivary	Ventrolateral border of cord	Inferior olive	Proprioception from neck and shoulder girdle
	11. Spinoreticular	Between sp-oliv. and ventrolateral gray horn	Reticular nuclei	Proprioceptive reflexes

Table 7–I *(continued)*

	Name	*Location*	*Level of Termination*	*Function*
Descending	12. Lateral Corticospinal	Medial to junction of dor. sp.-cereb. and ventr. s. c.	Motor horn cells cervical enlargement = ½; Motor horn cells lumbar = ⅓	Voluntary control of arms and legs
	13. Ventral Corticospinal	Adjacent to ant. median fissure	Motor horn cells = trunk	Voluntary movements of torso
	14. Rubrospinal	On ventromedial border of lat. cort-spin.	Motor horn cells, entire cord	Extrapyramidal pathway for motor control
	15. Tectospinal	Lateral of ventr. cort-spin.	Motor horn cells, entire cord	Visual and auditory reflexes from midbrain roof
	16. Olivospinal	Just lateral to spino-olivary	Cervical cord	Reflex movements of neck and shoulder girdle
	17. Reticulospinal	Between rubrosp. and ventr. gray horn	Motor horn cells, entire cord	Postural reflexes from cerebellum and extra-pyramidal path from subst. nigra and ruber
	18. Vestibulospinal	Most ventral path in cord	Motor horn cells, entire cord	Reflexes of adjust. of equilibrium
Nuclear Cell Groups	19. Ventromedial	Medial portion of ventral gray horn	Thoracic level	Innervation of muscle of trunk
	20. Ventrolateral	Lateral portion of ventral gray horn	Cervical and lumbar enlargement	Innervation of arm and leg muscles
	21. Intermediolateral (a) Medial Div.	Most lateral extension of middle gray	Thoracic and upper lumbar cord only	Visceral organs—heart and gastrointestinal
	(b) Lateral Div.			Superficial blood vessels and glands of body wall
	22. Dorsal Horn Gray	Most dorsolateral nucleus after entry of dors. horn	All levels of spinal cord	Skin senses of pain, temp., touch, pressure (spinothalamic)

Table 7–I *(continued)*

	Name	*Location*	*Level of Termination*	*Function*
Nuclear Cell Groups	23. Nuc. Dorsalis (Clarke's)	Medial portion of mid-dorsal horn	All levels of cord up to 8th cervical	Point of origin of dorsal spinocerebellar tract
	24. Lat. of Nuc. Dorsalis	Lat to nuc. dorsalis	All levels of spinal cord	Point of origin of ventrospinocerebellar tract
	25. Intermediate Nucleus (Renshaw) (Cells)	Between nuc. dorsalis and central canal	All levels of cord	Inhibitory column affecting antagonistic muscles
	26. Gamma Efferent	Ventral horn intermixed and dorsal to motor cells	All levels of cord	Innervate intrafusil muscle spindles

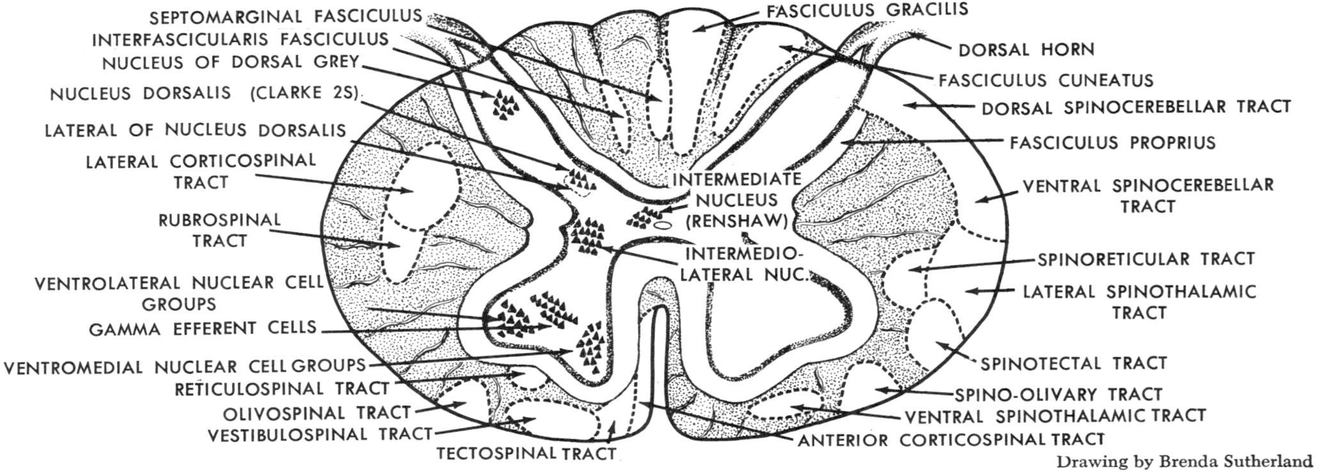

SEPTOMARGINAL FASCICULUS
INTERFASCICULARIS FASCICULUS
NUCLEUS OF DORSAL GREY
NUCLEUS DORSALIS (CLARKE 2S)
LATERAL OF NUCLEUS DORSALIS
LATERAL CORTICOSPINAL TRACT
RUBROSPINAL TRACT
VENTROLATERAL NUCLEAR CELL GROUPS
GAMMA EFFERENT CELLS
VENTROMEDIAL NUCLEAR CELL GROUPS
RETICULOSPINAL TRACT
OLIVOSPINAL TRACT
VESTIBULOSPINAL TRACT
TECTOSPINAL TRACT
FASCICULUS GRACILIS
DORSAL HORN
FASCICULUS CUNEATUS
DORSAL SPINOCEREBELLAR TRACT
FASCICULUS PROPRIUS
INTERMEDIATE NUCLEUS (RENSHAW)
INTERMEDIO-LATERAL NUC.
VENTRAL SPINOCEREBELLAR TRACT
SPINORETICULAR TRACT
LATERAL SPINOTHALAMIC TRACT
SPINOTECTAL TRACT
SPINO-OLIVARY TRACT
VENTRAL SPINOTHALAMIC TRACT
ANTERIOR CORTICOSPINAL TRACT

Drawing by Brenda Sutherland

Figure 7–9. Fiber Pathways and Cell Groupings of Spinal Cord

SOURCES AND ADDITIONAL READING

The CIBA Collection of Medical Illustrations, Vol. I, *Nervous System.* CIBA Pharmaceutical Company, 1953

Crosby, E. C., T. Humphrey, and E. W. Lauer, *Correlative Anatomy of the Nervous System.* New York: The Macmillan Company, 1962.

Ranson, S. W. and S. L. Clark, *The Anatomy of the Nervous System.* (10th ed.), Chaps. 6, 8, 9. Philadelphia: W. B. Saunders Company, 1959.

Riley, H. A., *An Atlas of the Basal Ganglia, Brain Stem, and Spinal Cord.* New York: Hafner Publishing Company, 1960.

Eight

REFLEX ARCS

Having outlined the symmetry of the cord topography, it is important to put the various pathways into functional relationship by a consideration of reflex activity. This has been studied extensively on decerebrate animals whose nervous systems have been severed just above the centers for respiration and blood supply. Such an experimental animal will still show much reflex activity. A frog, for instance, whose spinal cord has been separated from the brain will attempt to brush off a drop of acid on his skin with a hind foot. If one foot is held the other hind foot will attempt to perform the same function. The fibers of the various dorsal root elements, exteroceptive and proprioceptive, in addition to synapses with neurons of ascending pathways, make connection with secondary association and commissural neurons in the cord which are involved in spinal reflexes. Reflexes are the simplest functional unit of nervous activity. This functional unit must include: (1) a peripheral or visceral sensory ending such as for pain; (2) an afferent neuron with its axon terminating in the gray matter of the spinal cord; (3) a synaptic connection, at least in the anterior horn gray of the cord; (4) an efferent neuron with cell body in the anterior horn gray, and sending its axon out through the spinal nerve to effector mechanisms; (5) an effector mechanism, such as muscle or gland, which is triggered by the efferent impulse; (6) a collateral connection, in most instances with the Renshaw cells, to inhibit antagonistic muscles.

One of the intersegmental reflexes studied extensively by Sherrington was the scratch reflex in the dog. After a dog's spinal cord had been severed at the upper cervical level, a pull on its shoulder hairs would be followed by rhythmic movements, characteristic of scratching, of the hind leg on the same side. These connections are sketched in Fig. 8–1.

Similarly, if a cat has been decerebrated it can stand if prevented from falling to the side. In addition, simultaneous stimulation of nerves on both sides of the animal results alternately in flexion and extension, which are normal components of rhythmic stepping.

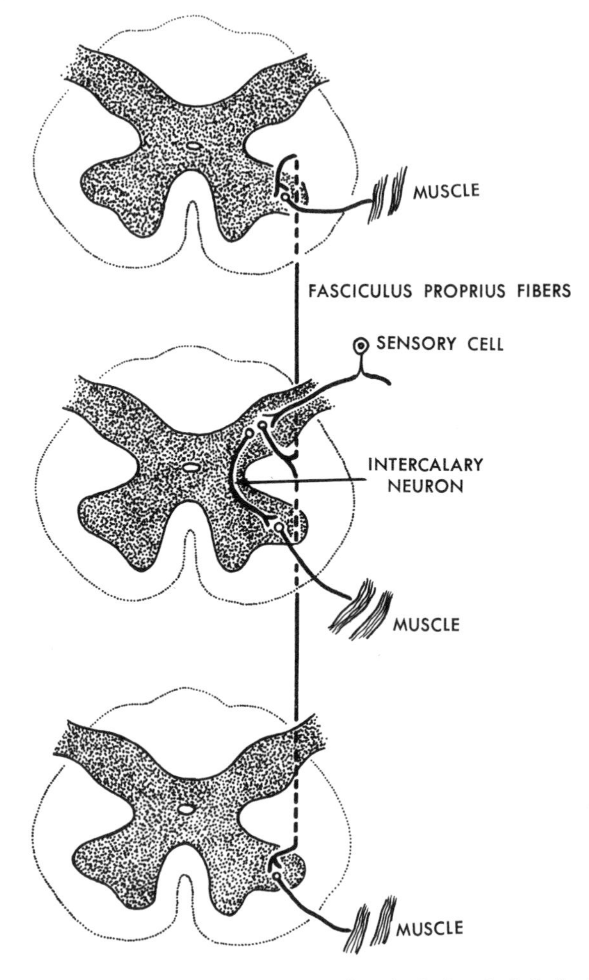

Drawing by Brenda Sutherland

Figure 8–1. Simple Intersegmental Reflex

In spinal animals, generally, the characteristic squatting or leg elevation seen in urination and defecation can still be seen unimpaired. It should be evident how complex the reflex circuitry must be to carry out these intersegmental reflexes.

The flexion reflex is the most primitive pattern of response of vertebrates, for it is effective in withdrawing a hand or foot from injury. This then is *nociceptive* reflex action and ordinarily takes precedence over other reflexes. Extensor reflexes are opposed to those of flexion and resist the effect of gravity. Hence they are essential in upright posture. Intersegmental reflexes such as stepping or scratching have been mentioned above.

A few reflexes are contained within one spinal segment, and of these few, several are called *monosynaptic* reflexes. This means that the reflex response can be evoked with only one synapse in the cord being involved. The most common reflex of this kind is the patellar or knee-jerk reflex, which occurs with such a short latent period that the response is recorded in man in about 18-20 milliseconds. Since the main factor slowing down nervous conduction is the delay at the synapse, the short latency is one of the main items of evidence for its monosynaptic character.

For the most part, however, spinal reflexes are seldom of this simple kind, but involve more than one synapse, and frequently many segments of the cord and consequently many muscle groups. Illustrations of several reflex circuits can be seen in Fig. 8–2. Some of the most significant of these more complex reflexes are involved in the maintenance of posture. Here the stretch reflex is of particular significance. During standing the stretch reflex is evoked by the continuous tendency of the force of gravity to bend the knee joint. The quadriceps muscle, which straightens the leg, is activated by afferent impulses coming from individual receptors with different thresholds. There is, therefore, a continuous and asynchronous bombardment of impulses which calls forth a smooth and sustained contraction of the muscle. This mechanism of reflex response is repeated thousands of times in a coordinated temporal pattern in order to maintain upright posture. The annulospiral or flower spray sensory ending described in considering sensory receptors is certainly the proprioceptive receptor for this stretch reflex.

In addition to the main muscle contraction in the stretch reflex, or flexion reflex, other neural circuits are active in these activities. There is in fact a separate series of small fibers which supplies not the main muscle spindle, but the intrafusal fibers of the muscle. These nerve fibers are called *gamma efferents,* and run from the ventral gray of the cord to these intrafusal fibers. The effect of the activity of these gamma

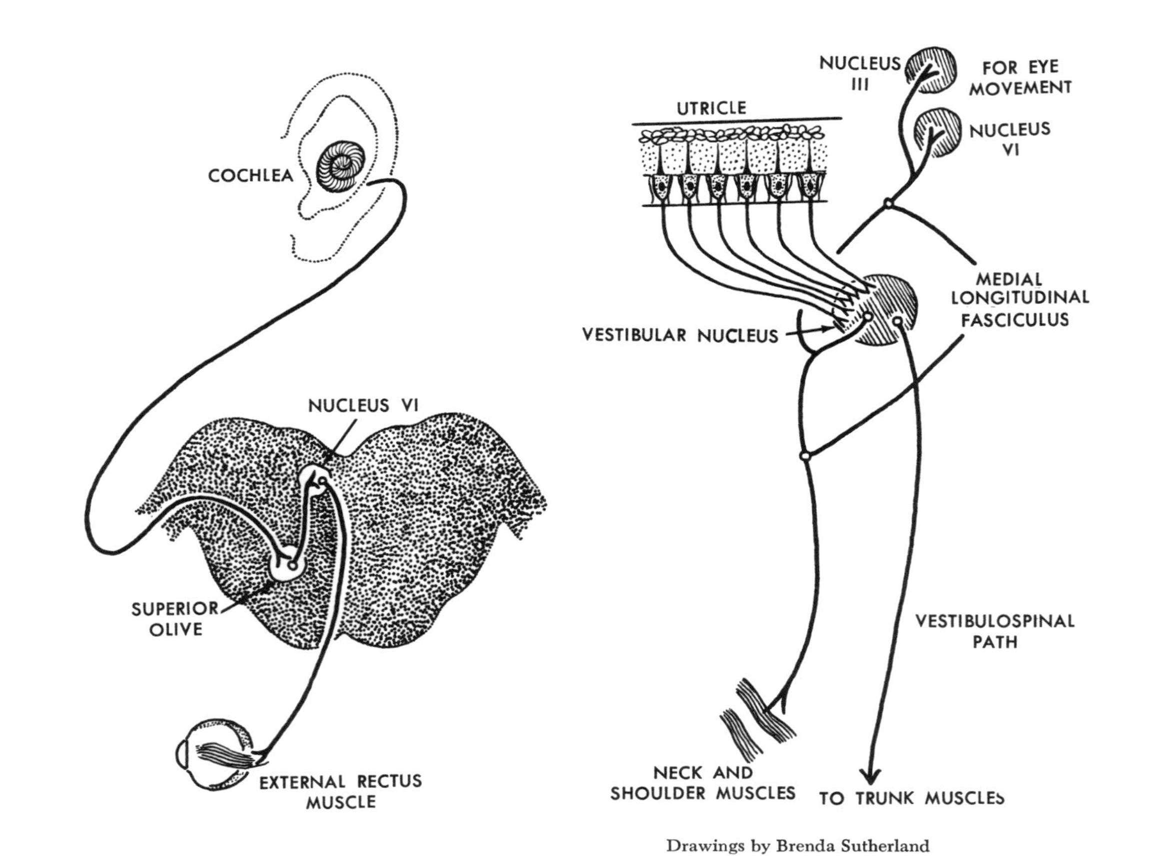

Drawings by Brenda Sutherland

Figure 8–2. Auditory-Eye Movement and Vestibular Righting Reflexes

efferents is to alter the tension on the intrafusal fibers, which are otherwise slack during contraction, so as to allow the annulospinal endings to fire again, thus influencing the state of the reporting activity of the stretch endings. This is particularly important in muscle tone, and the main impulses from the ventral motor neuron are always preceded by gamma efferent impulses.

Reflexes of the segmental body structure have considerable clinical importance. One form of poliomyelitis results in the deterioration and degeneration of the motor neurons of the anterior gray horn of the cord. When this occurs in the lumbosacral region the customary paralysis of the legs is seen. This disease condition is, then, on the motor side; others affect the sensory input through the dorsal roots. In "tabes dorsalis," sequel to syphilis (p.344), for instance, the site of infection and degeneration is in the dorsal roots; this interrupts the sensory information input on which any synergic muscular activity depends.

SOURCES AND ADDITIONAL READING

Fulton, J., *Physiology of the Nervous System,* Chaps. 4, 6–8. New York: Oxford University Press, Inc., 1951.
Ranson, S. W. and S. L. Clark, *The Anatomy of the Nervous System* (10th ed.), Chap. 20. Philadelphia: W. B. Saunders Company, 1959.
Ruch, T. and J. Fulton, *Medical Physiology and Biophysics* (18th ed.), Chaps. 5, 6. Philadelphia: W. B. Saunders Company, 1961. (See 19th ed., Chaps. 6, 7.)
Sherrington, C. S., *Integrative Action of Nervous System.* New Haven, Conn.: Yale University Press, 1961.

Nine

THE MEDULLA OBLONGATA AND CRANIAL NERVES

As we have seen, the spinal cord white matter is largely bundles of myelinated tracts which constitute a transmission system for information of touch, pressure, temperature, pain, and muscle sense traveling upstream to centers of coordination, and for fibers of muscular control traveling caudal or downstream for control of trunk, arms, legs, and neck and shoulders. As the sensory information moves rostral or upstream, the first suprasegmental center of coordination above the cord is the *medulla oblongata*. This is a short segment beginning just above the first cervical level and ending at the lower border of the pons. In this segment several separate pathways converge into common functional systems and go forward to higher centers. There is also a rearrangement of motor pathways as in the pyramidal decussation, and a heavy visceral input and output including the centers controlling respiration. In addition, many of the cranial nerves have nuclei of origin or termination located in the medulla.

CHANGE FROM CORD TO MEDULLA

At the point of transition from the cord to the medulla there occurs a sharp change in cross-sectional topography. The H shape of the gray matter of the cord breaks up, and the nuclei move dorsally and flatten out horizontally until all the nuclei are arranged near the dorsal border of the medulla. Moving from the lateral surface to the midline, these nuclei are arranged in the following order: somatic afferent, visceral afferent, visceral efferent, somatic efferent. Thus the nucleus of the vagus (X)[1] is lateral to the nucleus of the hypoglossal nerve (XII), while the sensory nucleus of the trigeminal (V) is more lateral still. Just below and medial to these nuclei are others which represent this same stratification or topographic order. The progression from cord to medulla can be seen in Fig. 9–1.

There are three major reasons for the change in shape from cord to medulla. First, the dorsal funiculi, composed mainly of the gracilis and cuneatus bundles, end in the nuclei of the same name in the lower part of the medulla. The axons of cells in the *gracile and cuneate nuclei* sweep ventrally and medially in a broad curve crossing the midline under the central canal and gather themselves together into a compact bundle, just above the pyramids, to become the *medial lemniscus.* This is the channel by which proprioceptive and other information reaches the thalamus and cerebral cortex. The *medial leminscus* carrying fibers for proprioception, two-point discrimination, localization, and vibratory sense is arranged in the medulla as follows:

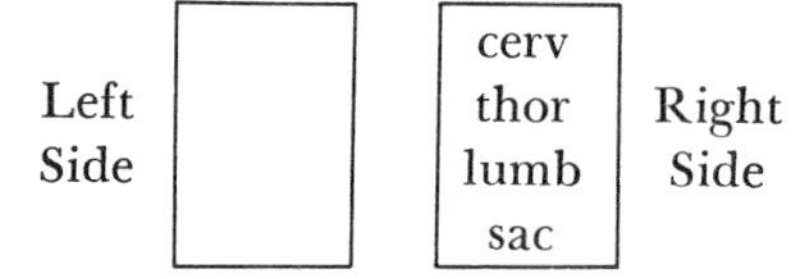

These fibers maintain the topographic relations of the spinal cord, with the cervical-cuneate fibers being more dorsal, the lumbar-sacral gracilis fibers more ventral. When the two nuclei have sent all the axons ventrally and medially as components of the medial lemniscus, the nuclear groups disappear. The stage of nuclei gracilis and decussation of the pyramids can be seen in Fig. 9–2. Second, this process, together with the accumulation of the pyramids and medial lemniscus in the ventral portion of the medulla, pushes the somatic and visceral cell groups up to the dorsal border at about the point that the central canal opens out into the fourth ventricle.

INFERIOR OLIVE

The other major source of topographic change in the medulla from the structures in the cord is the appearance of the large *inferior olivary*

---

[1] For cranial nerves, see pp. 124–131.

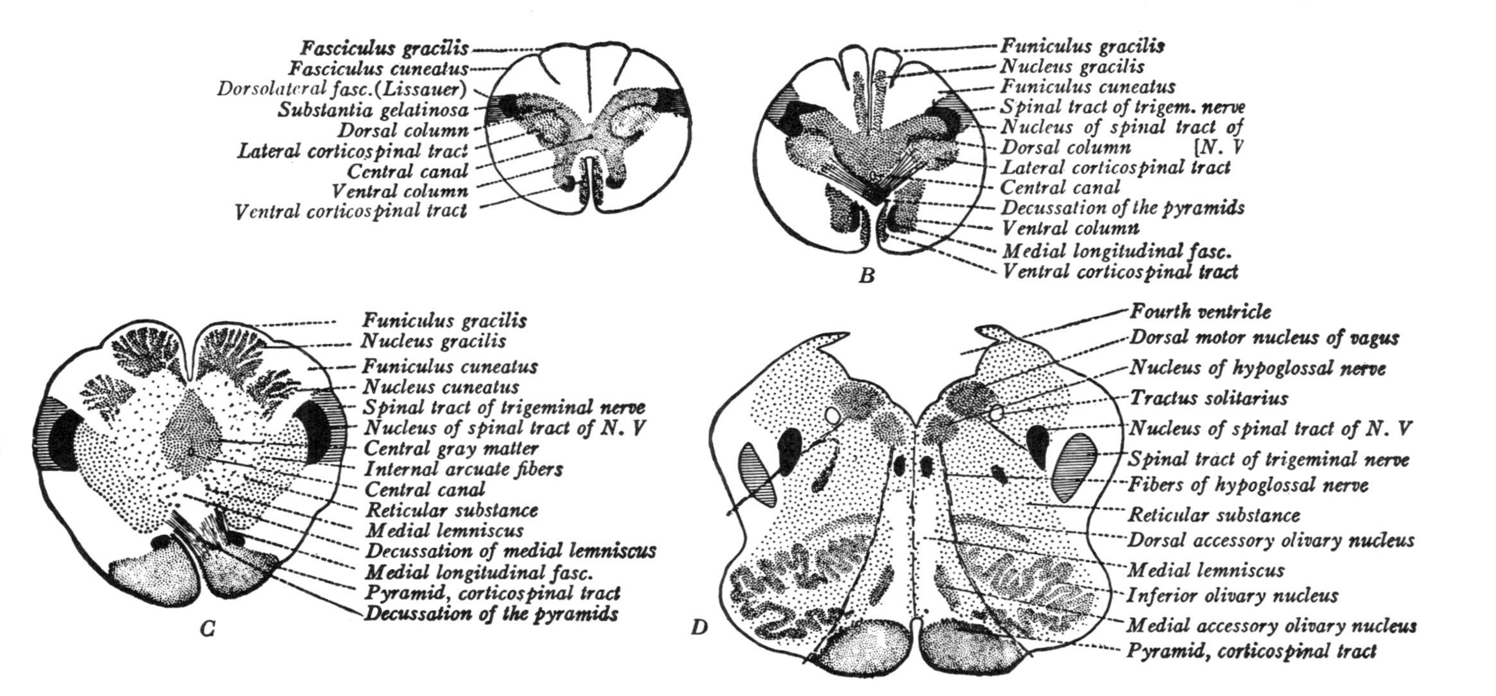

Source: S. W. Ranson and S. L. Clark, *The Anatomy of the Nervous System: Its Development and Function* (10th ed.; Philadelphia: W. B. Saunders Company, 1959), p. 205.

Figure 9–1. Diagrammatic Cross Sections to Show the Relation of the Structures in the Medulla Oblongata to those in the Spinal Cord. *A,* First Cervical Segment of Spinal Cord; *B,* Medulla Oblongata, Level of Decussation of Pyramids; *C,* Medulla Oblongata, Level of Decussation of Medial Lemniscus; *D,* Medulla Oblongata, Level of Olive

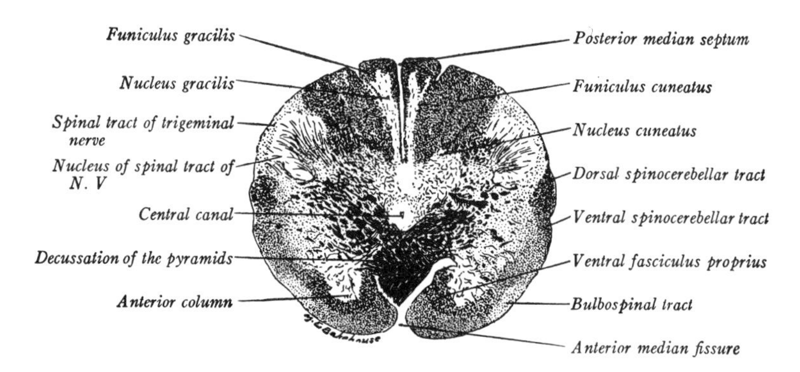

Source: S. W. Ranson and S. L. Clark, *The Anatomy of the Nervous System*, p. 207.

Figure 9–2. Section through the Medulla Oblongata of a Child at the Level of the Decussation of the Pyramids.

nucleus and its connections with the cerebellum through the *inferior cerebellar peduncle*. The inferior olive is a major switching center for pathways from spinal cord and thalamus to reach the cerebellum. The olive is a highly convoluted group of cells lying just dorsal to the pyramids and lateral to them and the medial lemniscus. It is open only at the medial edge. Its neurons send their axons across the midline and upward in a slow curve to enter the *inferior cerebellar peduncle*. These medullary relationships can be seen in Fig. 9–3. In this sweep the fibers cross part of the contralateral olive, several nuclei in the lateral segment of the medulla, and may separate strands of cranial nerves such as the glossopharyngeal (IX) or the vagus nerves (X). (These will be reviewed in a later section.) The progressive development of the main *inferior olive* in mammals is accompanied by the hemispheric development of the lateral cerebellum. The inferior olive must be considered, therefore, as a dependency of the cerebellum in carrying to the cerebellum proprioceptive impulses from at least the upper regions of the body (shoulder girdle and neck) by the spino-olivary and olivo-cerebellar bundles. By contrast the *medial accessory olive* is particularly well developed in strong swimming animals. This accessory olive is associated with great development of trunk and tail muscles to mediate the reflex mechanisms involved in swimming.

Lateral to the *medial lemniscus* and dorsal to the *inferior olive* there appears an undifferentiated mass of *reticular gray* composed of small

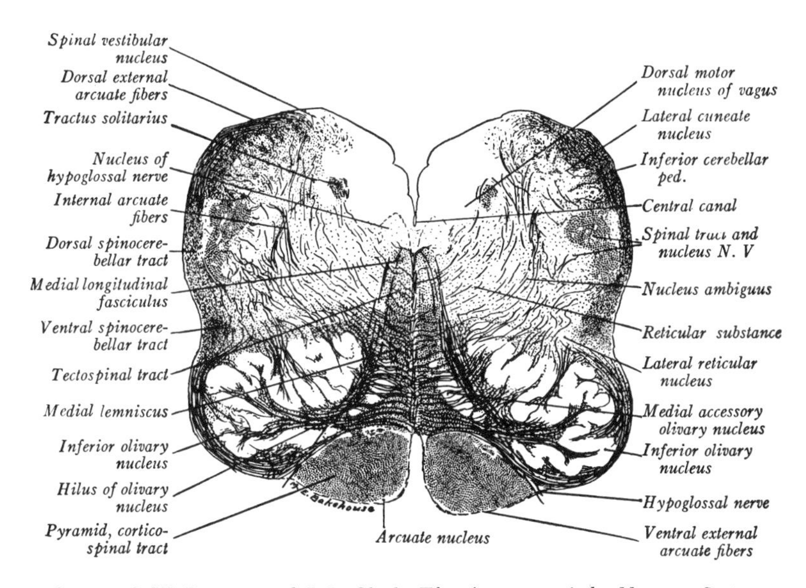

Source: S. W. Ranson and S. L. Clark, *The Anatomy of the Nervous System*, p. 210.

Figure 9–3. Medulla Oblongata (Cross Section at Level of Inferior Olive)

nuclei concerned with visceral reflexes or having connections with the spinal cord. Here we find the respiratory centers of expiration and inspiration, with the expiratory center dorsal to the inspiratory center.

ASCENDING AND DESCENDING TRACTS

The sensory fiber pathways, moving upstream, have all moved laterally to the lateral border of the medulla, except for the medial lemniscus. The dorsal *spinocerebellar* tract has begun to move dorsally to become a component of the *inferior cerebellar peduncle,* the most caudal of three pathways to and from the cerebellum. The *ventral spinocerebellar,* just ventral to the dorsal spinocerebellar tract, will continue forward, without change in its dorsoventral position, to turn sharply back and enter the cerebellum by way of the *superior cerebellar peduncle.* The *lateral and ventral* spinothalamic tracts for crude touch, pressure, temperature, and pain have joined and lie just medial to the *ventral spinocerebellar.* Here they constitute the *spinal lemniscus,* which will join the *medial lemniscus* in the pons. On each side of the midline are three sets of pathways which form two narrow columns of fibers lying medial to the olive. The uppermost is the *medial longitudinal fasciculus* which connects the eye muscle nerves (p. 130) and vestibular and auditory input. The middle one is the *tectospinal* path, whose fibers run down to the cord to make possible neck, shoulder, and trunk reflexes to visual and auditory stimuli. The *medial lemniscus* already referred to is most ventral, medial to the inferior olive, and next dorsal to the pyramids. These fiber paths can be seen in Fig. 9–4.

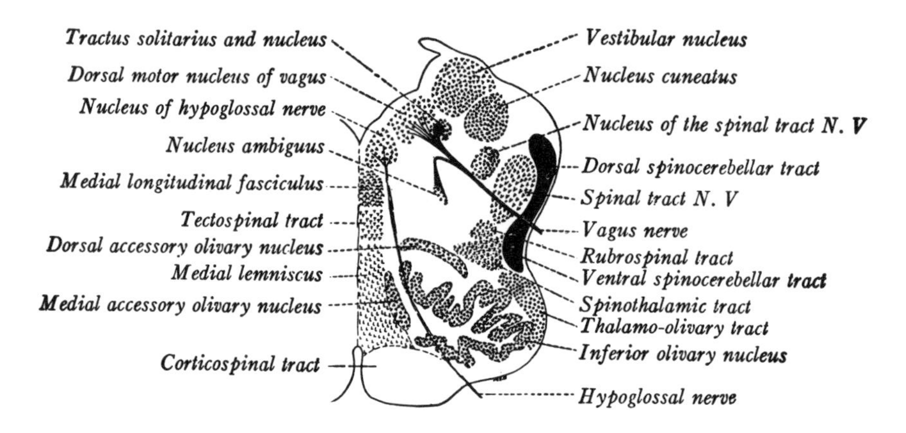

Source: S. W. Ranson and S. L. Clark, *The Anatomy of the Nervous System*, p. 214.

Figure 9–4. Nuclei and Fiber Tracts of the Medulla at Level of Olive

The major ascending pathways, then, send proprioceptive information to the cerebellum (spinocerebellar), proprioceptive to the thalamus (medial lemniscus), and somatic sensation to the thalamus (spinal lemniscus). Thus all of the information available from the body feeds into centers of automatic muscular adjustment or to centers allowing choice of the appropriate reaction pattern.

The major descending pathways in the medulla are: (1) the *corticospinal* fibers which form the pyramids and lie in the most ventral portion of the medulla. The *lateral* and *ventral corticospinal* tracts are here united in the pyramids, and only more caudally in the decussation does the lateral corticospinal cross over to the lateral funiculus of the spinal cord for innervation of arms and legs, leaving the ventral corticospinal to course downward without change in its original location. (2) The second descending system is represented in the extrapyramidal pathway from the *globus pallidus* of the corpus striatum to the *nucleus ruber* (red nucleus) and the reticular nuclei. These pathways may eventually reach the cord by way of the *rubrospinal* or *reticulospinal* tract. (3) In addition to these mainly voluntary control pathways, the medulla contains at all levels the *tectospinal* bundle and, caudal to their nuclei, the *olivospinal* and *vestibulospinal* tracts.

The lower part of the medulla is dominated by the visceral connections of some of the cranial nerves, specifically *glossopharyngeal* (IX), *vagus* (X), and *accessory* (XI). In this region and a bit rostral we find the centers for respiration. They lie just lateral to the medial longitudinal fasciculus and tectospinal tract, with the expiratory center dorsal to the inspiratory center. These are the centers which may be knocked out by an overdose of barbiturates, to which they are especially sensitive. This is also the location of the visceral connections of the vagus nerve (dorsal motor nucleus) which, among its many functions, slows the heart rate. By connections running down the medial longitudinal fasciculus from the medial vestibular nucleus to the dorsal nucleus of the vagus, the internal organs are made responsive to seasickness or airsickness by the excessive stimulation to which the vestibular apparatus is at times subjected. This is the circuit which brings on the normal results of seasickness—nausea and vomiting.

DECUSSATION OF PYRAMIDS

At the caudal end of the medulla, just rostral to the first cervical level in the cord, one sees an interlacing of fibers on the ventral surface that is known as the decussation of the pyramids. Here the corticospinal fibers which have been coursing downstream to synapse with cord motor neurons split into (1) the *ventral corticospinal* path that continues down the cord with no marked change in location and (2) the *lateral corticospinal* path, which here crosses the midline and moves from the ventral position into the lateral funiculus of the cord medial to *spinocerebellar* tracts. The decussation marks the caudal end of the medulla and is found in the same coronal[2] sections as the *nuclei gracilis* and *cuneatus*. In the decussation the fibers which provide for control of arm muscles cross more rostrally and the fibers controlling leg muscles more caudally.

---

2 Coronal sections are sections at right angles to the anterior-posterior axis of the brain and spinal cord.

CRANIAL NERVES

Feeding into the medulla, and to the pons and midbrain rostral to it, are a series of cranial nerves which, aside from the dorsal root nerves of the spinal cord, provide most of the sensory information upon which our nervous system acts and to which it reacts. These cranial nerves are not segmental, as in the cord, but each subserves mainly one type of sensory or motor information. They are functional units rather than segmental ones. There are considered to be twelve cranial nerves.

Beginning at the caudal end of the medulla the *12th nerve,* the *hypoglossal,* makes its appearance as a number of separate filaments emerging medial to the olivary eminence and the filaments join outside the medulla to form one nerve strand. The hypoglossal nerve is motor, or efferent in function, and provides innervation to the muscles of the tongue. The nucleus of the hypoglossal nerve lies ventral to the central canal and, more rostrally, ventral to the IV ventricle. It is both medial and ventral to the dorsal nucleus of the vagus and extends rostrocaudally[3] to about the same extent as that nucleus.

The *11th nerve* is called the *accessory.* This nerve has two branches, the "spinal" branch issuing as rootlets from the upper cervical cord and innervating the trapezius and sternocleidomastoid muscles of the shoulder girdle. This, incidentally, is the only cranial nerve not possessed by all vertebrates. The fish, having no shoulder girdle, lack it. The other branch of the accessory is the bulbar division, which joins the vagus branches and becomes indistinguishable from the vagal motor innervation of abdomen, pharynx, larynx, palate, and uvula. The nuclei of origin of the accessory nerve are three: (1) *dorsal nucleus of vagus,* from which fibers join the vagus to thoracic and abdominal viscera; (2) *nucleus ambiguus,* lying both ventral and lateral to the dorsal nucleus of the vagus, from which fibers join the vagus and go to the muscles of pharynx and larynx; (3) cells in the anterior gray column of upper cervical segments, from which fibers ascend, and on exit run to the trapezius and sternocleidomastoid muscles.

The *10th cranial nerve,* the *vagus,* is very complex. (See Fig. 9–5 and Table 9–I, Cranial Nerves, p. 134.) One tiny branch brings sensation from the skin of the external ear and this is called, therefore, the auricular branch. For the most part the vagus carries visceral sensory fibers from lungs, heart, pharynx, stomach, and abdominal viscera, and vis-

---

[3] Rostral is toward the head end; caudal is toward the tail end.

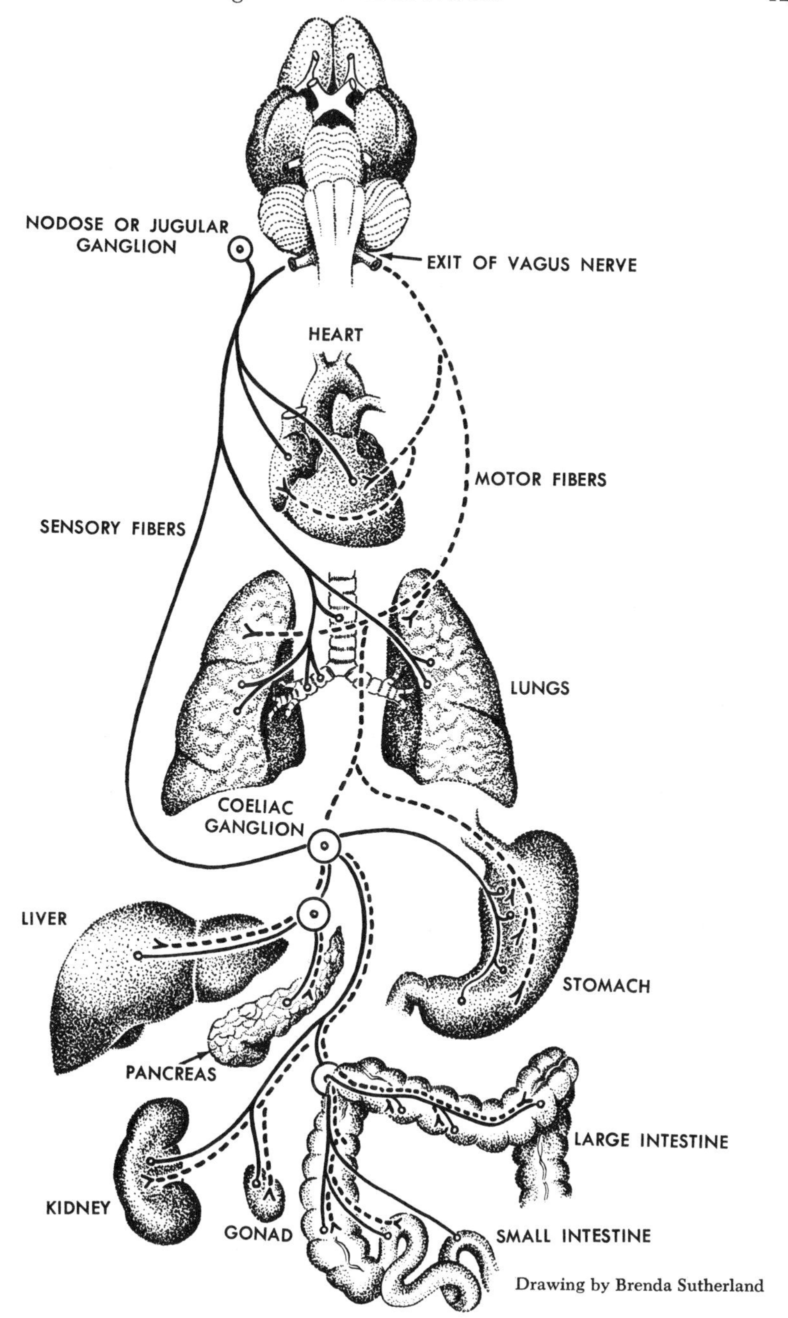

Figure 9–5. Diagram of Sensory and Motor Components of the Vagus Nerve

ceral efferent fibers to these same structures as well as to the arteries. Its efferent fibers arise in the *dorsal nucleus of the vagus* in the medulla and run to the parasympathetic ganglia which are on or near the particular visceral organs. It functions then as a nucleus in the preganglionic part of the parasympathetic-autonomic division. Nuclei which are the source of efferent fibers of the vagus are *dorsal (motor) nucleus of vagus* and *nucleus ambiguus*. The dorsal nucleus extends most of the length of the medulla, lateral to the central canal and just below the 4th ventricle. The *nucleus ambiguus*, composed of cell bodies of neurons which innervate the muscles of larynx and pharynx, lies both ventral and lateral to the dorsal nucleus and also extends the length of the medulla.

The *9th cranial nerve* is named *glossopharyngeal*. It is largely but not entirely sensory, providing sensory information from the soft palate, tonsils, and pharynx and taste sensation from the taste buds of the posterior one-third of the tongue. The efferent components go to innervate the pharynx and the parotid and salivary glands. The nuclei of origin of the *glossopharyngeal* are (1) the *inferior salivatory nucleus*, lying at the border of the pons and medulla and just medial to the glossopharyngeal nerve as it runs ventrolaterally to exit from the medulla; and (2) *nucleus ambiguus*.

The *8th cranial nerve* is the *vestibulocochlear*, having two divisions, the cochlear and the vestibular. These are both almost entirely sensory, bringing auditory and equilibratory information to the brain. These two senses will be examined later; for the present, mention of their nuclei will be sufficient. The auditory (cochlear) nerve ends in two nuclei, a dorsal and a ventral cochlear nucleus, located one above the other at the lateral border and at the point of transition from the medulla to the pons. They are separated from each other in part by the inferior cerebellar peduncle. The vestibular nerve feeds into four nuclei just inside the lateral border of the medulla and caudal to the inferior cerebellar peduncle. These nuclei, which extend into the pons, are the superior, lateral, medial, and spinal vestibular nuclei. The connections of these nuclei will be dealt with later (144–145).

The *7th cranial nerve* is called the *facial* because it supplies innervation to the muscles of facial expression. It arises as axons of cells in the motor nucleus of the facial nerve. This nucleus is, in part, one of the special somatic efferent group. It lies just rostral to the *nucleus ambiguus*, and just caudal to the *superior olivary* nucleus. After going around the VI nucleus in the genu the 7th nerve travels ventrally, laterally, and caudally from the motor nucleus to emerge at the lower border of the pons. It passes out of the skull to reach the muscles of the face.

In addition to the motor fibers to facial muscles, the 7th nerve also includes, in part, special visceral afferent fibers. Thus, it carries taste fibers from the anterior two-thirds of the tongue to the nucleus of the solitary tract (nucleus solitarius) in the rostral part of the medulla. These fibers pass by way of the lingual nerve to the geniculate ganglion and thence by the intermediate nerve to the *nucleus of the solitary tract.* After synapse in this nucleus, the taste information passes rostrally, in close conjunction with the medial lemniscus, until the fibers end in the ventral nucleus of the thalamus, specifically the nucleus *ventralis posteromedialis,* sometimes known as the arcuate nucleus (pp. 240–241). From the ventroposteromedial nucleus the neurons pass directly to the "face area" of the postcentral gyrus and to the taste receptive area in the insula. It is clear from both clinical and experimental studies that unilateral ablations or tumors of this area destroy taste sensation from the contralateral side of the tongue. The details of this innervation can be seen in Fig. 9–6.

In addition to the fibers that move upstream, the nucleus solitarius gives rise to fibers which pass to the hypothalamus and to other cranial nerve nuclei for visceral and emotional responses, reflex or learned, to taste information. The other cranial nerves connected to solitarius are the glossopharyngeal (IX) innervating salivary glands, and the vagus (X) for stomach reaction. A visceral efferent group of fibers forms a part of the facial (VII) nerve. They arise as axons of cell bodies in the superior salivatory nucleus and pass out to the sphenopalatine ganglion or by the lingual nerve to the submandibular ganglion for innervation of lacrimal and salivary glands.

In addition to the facial muscle movement and the taste sensation from the anterior part of the tongue, the 7th nerve includes fibers serving the skin of the concha of the ear. But this is of lesser importance than the sensory information of taste, and the motor control of muscles used in closing of the eyes, frowning, smiling, whistling, etc. In certain clinical cases an asymmetry in facial expression due to imbalance of the muscle movements involved in these simple actions may indicate the site of tumors or lesions.

The *5th cranial nerve,* the trigeminal (V), is also concerned with facial function. It is the largest cranial nerve and carries sensory information from the face and its cavities, including the teeth, to the central nervous system. The nerve branches very extensively to supply sensory fibers to face, head, and jaws. For this purpose there are divisions of the nerve to supply the ophthalmic region, the maxillary area, and the mandibular area. Since it feeds sensory information from such a large and highly innervated skin surface, the sensory branch of the trigeminal is

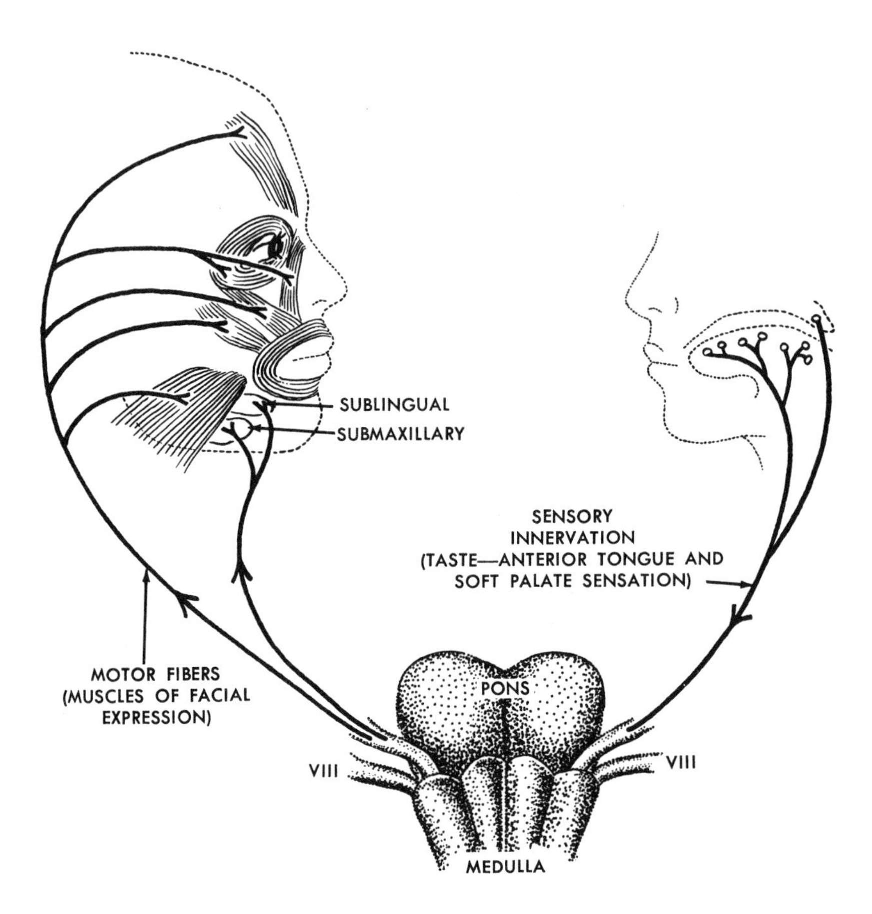

Figure 9–6. Components of the VII (Facial) Nerve

the largest part of the entire nerve. The three major divisions of the trigeminal (ophthalmic, maxillary, and mandibular) meet at the semilunar ganglion (Gasserian), which lies adjacent to the pons. The cells of the semilunar ganglion are not completely unipolar and are therefore called *pseudounipolar cells.*

The motor segment of the trigeminal nerve is considerably smaller than the afferent branch. On leaving the *motor nucleus of V,* it follows the course of the sensory mandibular branch of the 5th nerve. This branch is somatic efferent, serving the muscles of mastication. Details of this sensory and motor innervation can be seen in Fig. 9–7.

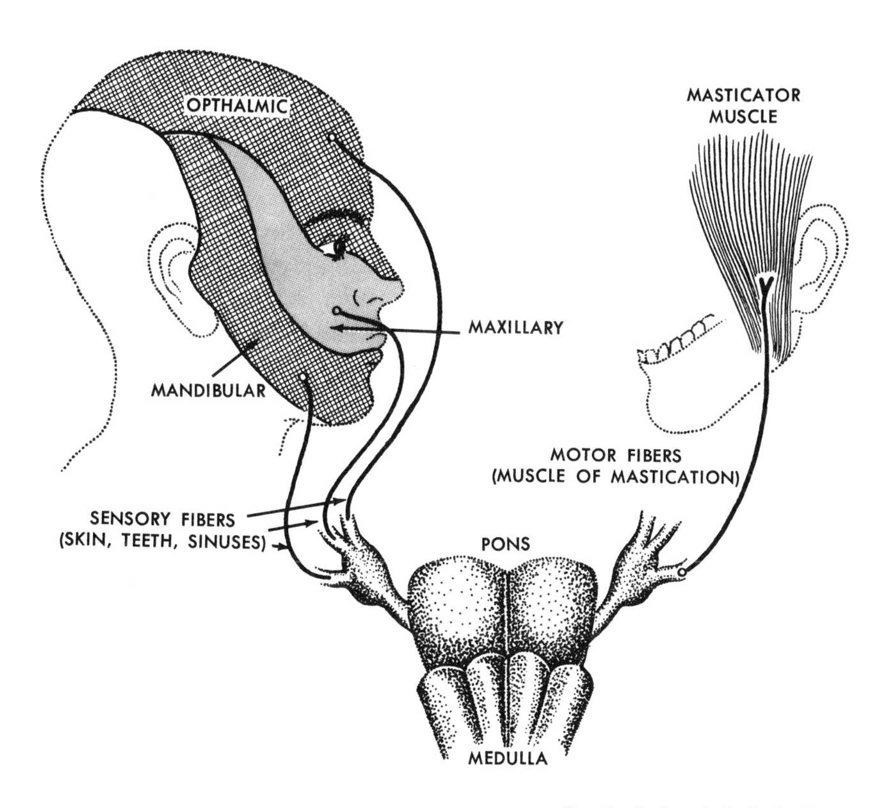

Drawing by Brenda Sutherland

Figure 9–7. Components of the V (Trigeminal) Nerve

The nuclei of the trigeminal nerve are spread widely over the medulla and pons. The sensory nuclei extend from the lower medulla, where the *nucleus of the spinal tract of V* has continuity with dorsal horn gray of the spinal cord, up through the pons, where the *principal sensory nucleus* is located, and still farther rostrally into the midbrain where, naturally, the *mesencephalic nucleus of V* is located.

The three divisions of the trigeminal sensory nucleus serve different functions. The spinal portion receives sensations of pain and temperature, the principal nucleus receives sensations of touch and pressure, and the mesencephalic nucleus receives proprioceptive information. The fibers carrying pain information end in the lower portion of the spinal tract nucleus. This fact has been used in relieving excruciating facial pain by making, in the caudal part of the medulla, an incision which blocks the pain fibers from transmitting the sensation to consciousness. Since the trigeminal nerve is sensory for the face, the second-order fibers travel upstream to the thalamus alongside the medial lemniscus, and from the ventral thalamic nucleus (after synapse) go to the face area in the postcentral gyrus.

The *motor nucleus of the trigeminal V* is undivided and lies just medial to the principal sensory nucleus. It is just rostral of the motor nucleus of VII, and a bit lateral and rostral of the motor nucleus of VI. Its fibers go to the muscles of mastication, and it is therefore somatic efferent.

The abducens (VI), trochlear (IV), and oculomotor (III) cranial nerves are all concerned with eye movement. The *6th cranial nerve, the abducens,* leaves the brain at the lower border of the pons. It ends in the orbit, in the lateral rectus muscle of the eye. In the midbrain, the fibers of the abducens nerve arise as axons of the nucleus of the 6th nerve situated dorsally rather close to the midline and between VII and V nuclei. The nucleus of the 6th nerve is just underneath the floor of the IV ventricle at the lowest level of the pons. It is connected directly with the medial longitudinal fasciculus and through this fiber bundle with the other eye muscle nuclei, as well as the vestibular and cochlear centers.

The *4th cranial nerve* is called the trochlear. It leaves the dorsal aspect of the brain and after winding ventralward around the midbrain travels to the orbit, where it rotates the eyeball inward and downward. There it ends on the motor end plate of the superior oblique muscle. Centrally the trochlear, like the abducens, arises as axons of the cells in the 4th cranial nerve nuclei. The nucleus of the trochlear nerve is at the level of inferior colliculus, just below the aqueduct of Sylvius and just ventral of the periaqueductal gray. It is also connected with the other eye muscle nuclei and vestibular and cochlear centers by means of the medial longitudinal fasciculus.

The *3rd cranial nerve, the oculomotor,* consists of neurons providing for the movement of the remaining five muscles of eye movement in the nasal, upward, and downward directions. The oculomotor is then the largest of the nerves for eye muscle innervation. In addition to the fibers for muscle innervation (somatic efferent), the oculomotor also carries visceral efferent fibers for the pupillary light reflex and for accommodation of the lens. The oculomotor nucleus lies at the level of the superior colliculus and just ventral to the periaqueductal gray. It is a larger nucleus than IV and VI, and its cells are arranged in groups according to the muscles and muscle spindles which they supply. Experimental studies of eye muscle injury have been followed rapidly by chromatolysis of corresponding cell groups in this nucleus. The fibers from the 3rd nucleus also connect with the medial longitudinal fasciculus for eye movement coordination and for other connections.

The reflex adjustments of the eye, both pupillary and accommodative to change the shape of the lens, are carried out by visceral efferent fibers of the autonomic nervous system. The cells of origin of the parasympathetic visceral efferents are found in a special nucleus, the Edinger-Westphal, situated dorsal and a bit medial of the oculomotor. The fibers travel via the 3rd nerve and end in a synapse in the ciliary ganglion, from which postganglionic fibers go to the ciliary muscle and the pupillary sphincter. Dilation of the pupil is initiated by sympathetic preganglionic fibers that arise in the intermediolateral cells of the upper thoracic cord, from which they emerge to enter the superior cervical sympathetic ganglion. From this ganglion postganglionic fibers go out to the dilator pupillae muscles. The pupillary muscles in the iris receive two kinds of autonomic innervation: that from the ciliary ganglion, which constricts the pupil; and that from the superior cervical ganglion, which dilates it. Pupillary constriction also accompanies accommodation of the lens to close vision. The ciliary muscle of the lens receives only one set of fibers, the parasympathetic.

Since vision, together with audition and olfaction, form the only distance receptors of the cranial nerves, they are considered separately in Chapters 13, 14, and 15. The *optic nerve* (II) is the *2nd cranial nerve* and provides the visual sensory input on which humans and primates are most dependent for information about the outside world. The optic nerve is not a true nerve but a brain tract, as the development from the optic cup indicates. The *1st cranial nerve* is *olfactory* (I); olfaction and taste constitute the chemical senses. The extent of cranial nerve nuclei can be seen in Fig. 9–8.

MEDIAL LONGITUDINAL FASCICULUS

The three cranial nerves which are concerned with eye movements—oculomotor (III), trochlear (IV), and abducens (VI)—originate in corresponding nuclei in the pons and midbrain where they lie close to the midline. The nuclei of the oculomotor and trochlear are located just ventral and lateral to the cerebral aqueduct, while the abducens is in the lower pons, medial to the four vestibular nuclei. The connections between these eye muscle nuclei, and between them and the vestibular nuclei or cervical cord, comprise two bundles of fibers on either side of the midline called the *medial longitudinal fasciculi.* (See Fig. 9–9.)

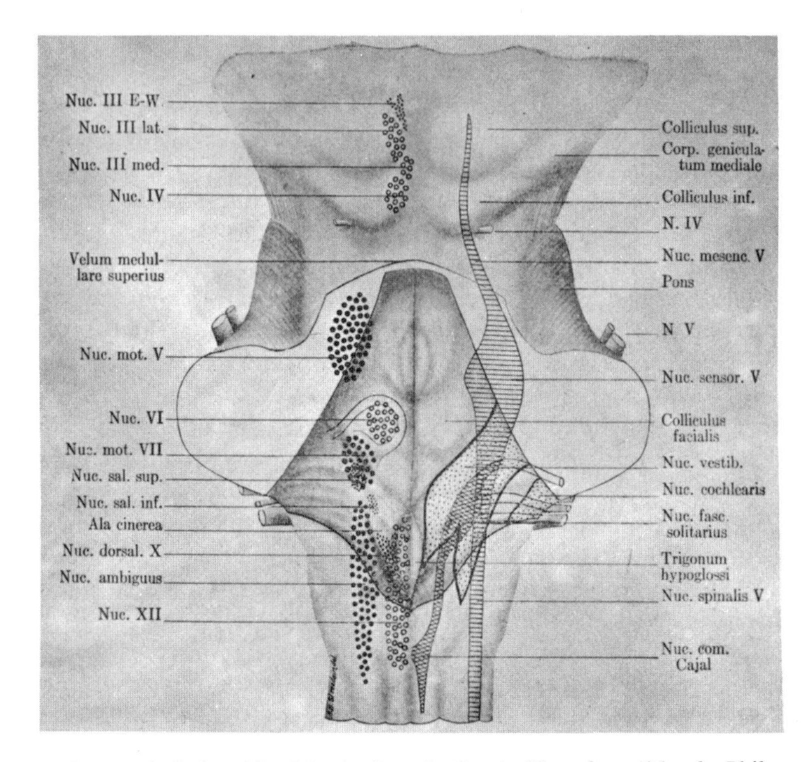

Source: C. Judson Herrick, *An Introduction to Neurology* (4th ed.; Philadelphia: W. B. Saunders Company, 1927), p. 174.

Figure 9–8. Cranial Nerve Nuclei Drawn on Dorsal Brain Stem

These bundles extend from the *interstitial nucleus of Cajal* in the midbrain caudally through the medulla and into the upper levels of the cervical cord. This band of fibers makes possible coordination between the actions of the 3rd, 4th, and 6th nerves. It also makes possible vestibular influence on eye movement and adjustments of the head and neck to shifts in equilibrium. The vestibular nuclei, to be described in detail in the next chapter, are four: superior, medial, spinal, and lateral. The lateral nucleus is the point of origin of the vestibulospinal pathway and has no connection to the MLF (medial longitudinal fasciculus). The superior nucleus has connections only rostral to its location, with fibers going to both the nuclei of IV (trochlear) and III (oculomotor). The medial nucleus bifurcates after crossing the midline and fibers connect with VI (abducens), IV, and III nuclei, as well as running caudally at least to the level of the motor nucleus of X (vagus) in

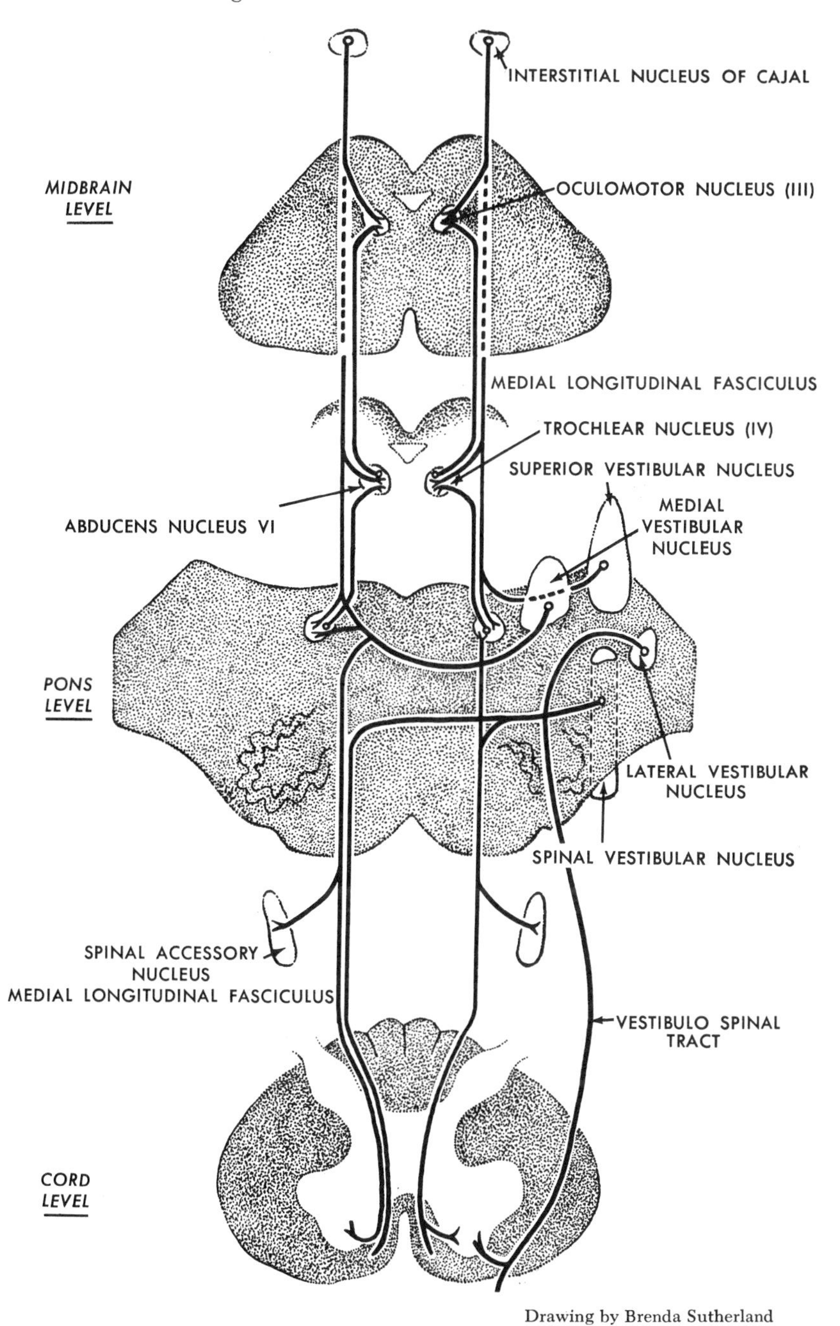

Drawing by Brenda Sutherland

Figure 9–9. Diagram of Medial Longitudinal Fasciculus

Table 9–I

Cranial Nerves

Name	*Origin and Termination*	*Function*
I *Olfactory* (Sensory)	Olfactory cells in nasal mucous membrane. Fibers through cribiform plate to olfactory bulb. Olfactory nerve divides into medial olfactory stria which ends in other bulb, subcallosal or septum, and lateral olfactory stria which ends in amygdaloid nuc. and prepyriform cortex	Smell—Depends on molecular structure of vaporous substance
II *Optic* (Sensory)	Sensitive rods and cones in retina–bipolar to ganglion cells whose axons form the optic nerve. Partial crossing in chiasm, passes lateral and dorsal to lateral geniculate of thalamus, to superior colliculus and calcarine fissure	Vision—Depends on photochemical reaction to light involving four retinal pigments: rhodopsin, porphyropsin, iodopsin, cyanopsin
III *Oculomotor* (Motor)	Nucleus just below aqueduct at level of superior colliculus. Emerges ventrally—medial of cerebral penduncles—passes out of skull to innervate superior internal and inferior rectus muscles external to eye	Eye movement—inward, upward, and downward
IV *Trochlear* (Motor)	Nucleus just below aqueduct at level of inferior colliculus. Emerges dorsally from top of midbrain, sweeps laterally and ventrally to innervate superior oblique eye muscle	Eye movement inward and downward
V *Trigeminal* (Sensory and Motor)	Touch, temperature, pain, and pressure and proprioceptive organs of face, head, upper neck, including cavities as in teeth. Terminates in spinal nuc. of V for pain and temp., main sensory nuc. of V for touch and pressure, and mesencephalic nuc. of V for proprioception	Sensory from face, head, and upper neck
	Motor Nuc. V—Somatic efferent of mandibular nerve	Motor to muscles of mastication
VI *Abducens* (Motor)	VI Nucleus, just below floor of IV ventricle (pons) to lateral rectus muscle of eye	Eye movement outward and upward

Table 9–I *(continued)*

Name	*Origin and Termination*	*Function*
VII *Facial* (Sensory and Motor)	Taste buds on anterior ⅔ of tongue to nuc. solitarius	Taste—anterior ⅔ of tongue
	Sensation from concha of ear	Skin sensation from ear
	Motor from Motor Nuc. VII to muscle of facial expression	Movement of muscles of facial expression
VIII *Vestibulocochlear* (Sensory and slight motor)	Semicircular canals, saccule, and utricle to vestibular nuc. in medulla	Sense of equilibrium
	Organ of Corti of ear to dorsal and ventral cochlear nuc. at caudal end of pons	Audition
	Superior olive to cochlea	Selective inhibition of auditory data
IX *Glossopharyngeal* (Sensory and Motor)	Sensory organs of soft palate, tonsils, pharynx, and taste buds on posterior ⅓ of tongue to nuc. salivatorius	Somesthetic sense from throat and taste from posterior ⅓ of tongue
	Nuc. ambiguus to muscles of pharynx, and parotid and salivary glands	Muscle control of pharynx and glandular secretion
X *Vagus* (Sensory and Motor)	Sensory organs of skin of external ear	Sensation from pinna of ear
	Sensory organs of lungs, heart, pharynx, stomach, and abdominal viscera to medulla	Sensation from thoracic and abdominal viscera
	Motor Nuc. X and ambiguus to lungs, heart, pharynx, stomach, and abdominal viscera	Preganglionic parasympathetic to thoracic and abdominal viscera
XI *Accessory* (Motor)	Spinal Branch Anterior gray of cervical cord to trapezius and sternocleidomastoid muscles of shoulder girdle	Movement of shoulder girdle
	Bulbar Branch Dorsal Nuc. X and ambiguus. Joins vagus and indistinguishable from it	Innervation of thoracic and abdominal viscera and pharynx and larynx
XII *Hypoglossal* (Motor)	Nuc. hypoglossal ventral to IV ventricle to muscles of tongue	Innervation of muscles of tongue

Figure 9–10 gives the 12 cranial nerves and the structure innervated.

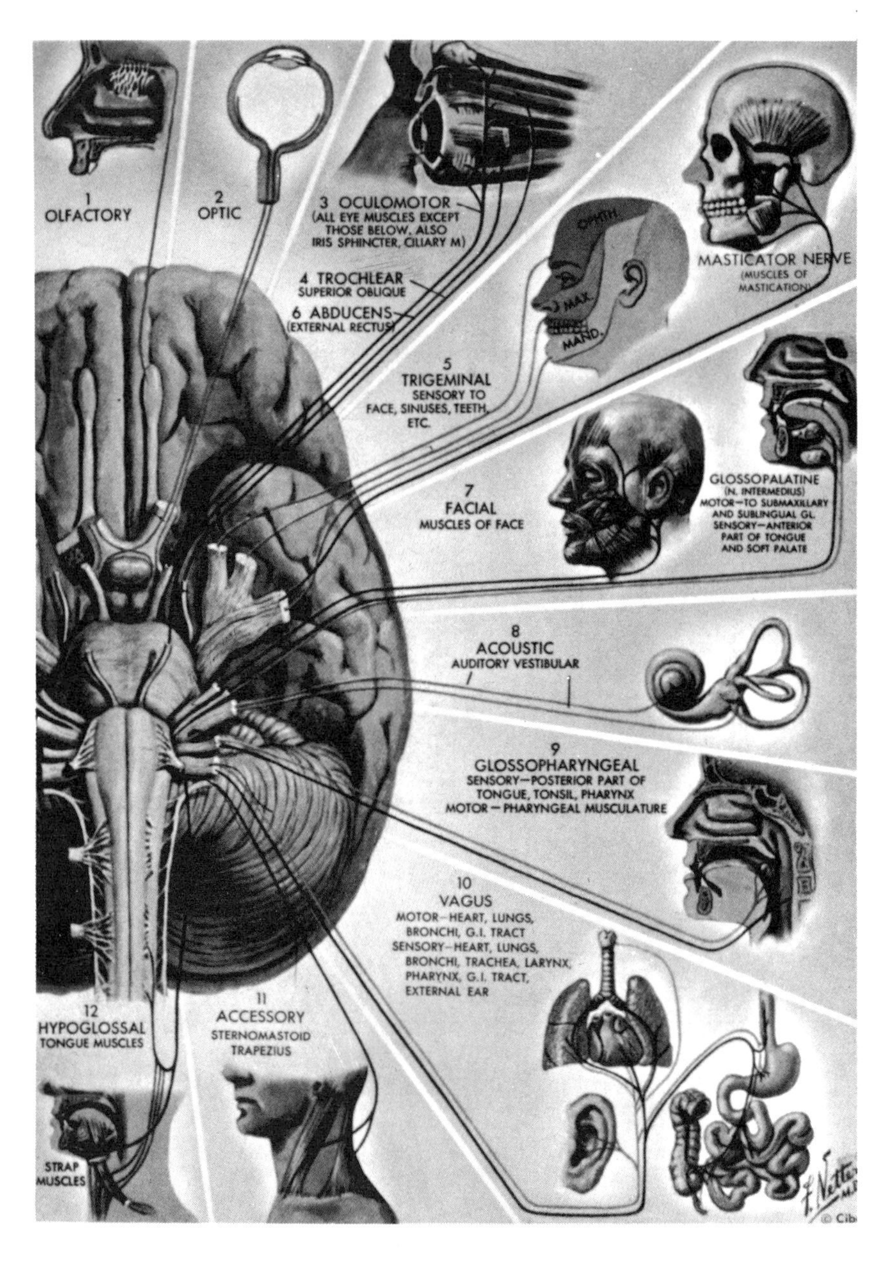

Source: *The CIBA Collection of Medical Illustrations* by Frank H. Netter, M.D. Copyright CIBA. (Vol. I, *Nervous System* [Summit, N. J.: CIBA Pharmaceutical Company, 1953], Plate 20.)

Figure 9–10. Brain Stem and the Cranial Nerves

the lower medulla. Fibers from the spinal nucleus run only caudally, passing down both MLF into the cervical cord to mediate movements of the head and neck to changes in equilibrium.

Voluntary influence on this complex series of mechanisms is mediated from cortex by way of the interstitial nucleus of Cajal. The occipital cortex has second-order connection with this interstitial nucleus, as does the frontal-eye field or area 8 of Brodmann. In addition there is a very close connection between the superior colliculus, as the reflex center for vision, and the oculomotor nucleus (III). There has been a suggestion that a direct connection exists between the frontal-eye fields and the oculomotor nucleus, but this is not yet established.

SOURCES AND ADDITIONAL READING

Brodal, A., *The Cranial Nerves*. Oxford, England: Blackwell, 1962.

The CIBA Collection of Medical Illustrations, Vol. I, *Nervous System*. CIBA Pharmaceutical Company, 1953.

Crosby, E. C., T. Humphrey, and E. W. Lauer, *Correlative Anatomy of the Nervous System*. New York: The Macmillan Company, 1962.

Fulton, J., *Physiology of the Nervous System*, Chaps. 9, 10. New York: Oxford University Press, Inc., 1951.

Ranson, S. W. and S. L. Clark, *The Anatomy of the Nervous System* (10th ed.), Chaps. 10, 11. Philadelphia: W. B. Saunders Company, 1959.

Ten

EQUILIBRIUM AND ITS CENTRAL CONNECTIONS

In an earlier section we saw that one of the three main divisions of sensory receptors was the proprioceptive. This gave the basis for muscle tone and antigravity position. Most of the sensory input for this muscle tone comes from sense receptors attached to muscle fibers, tendons, or joints. However, an important division of proprioceptive sense is not derived from muscle action, but arises in the vestibular apparatus located adjacent to the organ of hearing. The 8th cranial nerve has both auditory and vestibular divisions and hence is called vestibulocochlear.

SEMICIRCULAR CANALS

The vestibular apparatus is a part of the coiled membranous labyrinth inside the bony labyrinth which lies in the inner ear, as is indicated in Fig. 10–1. A part of the membranous labyrinth is concerned with hearing and is contained in the two and one-half turns of the cochlear duct, and somewhat resembles a snail shell. The other part of the labyrinth contains the five parts of the vestibular appartus. These are the three semicircular canals, the saccule, and the utricle. All of the semicircular ducts have the same function, but this is different from the function of the *saccule* and *utricle*. The three *semicircular canals* are set in three different planes at right angles to each other, as in A-B-C.

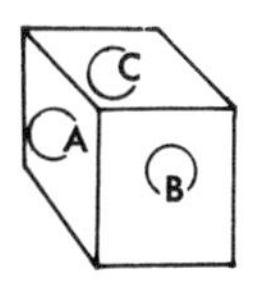

The function of these canals is to inform us of rotation of head or body in any one of these planes or in any combination of the three. Adequate stimulus for the excitation of the sensory receptors in these canals and the generation of impulses in the vestibular portion of the 8th nerve involves motion and, as we will see, is elicited in part by the inertia of the fluid when motion takes place.

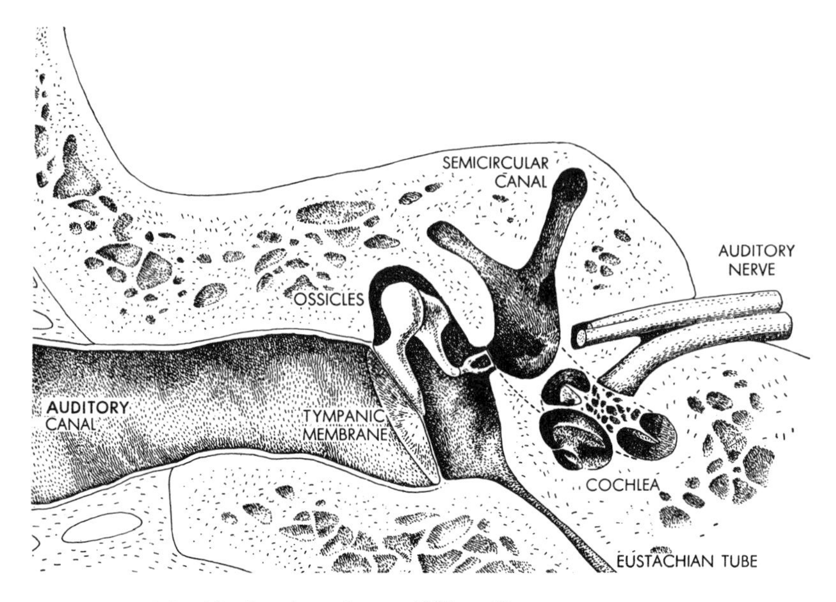

Source: *Scientific American,* August 1957, p. 67.

Figure 10–1. Semicircular Canals and the Cochlea in Place

The curved horn of each semicircular duct is filled with fluid endolymph. The sensitive receptors are in the bulbous end of each, where the three canals are attached together. This bulb is called the ampulla, and it contains the sensory epithelium which is affected by motion in the three planes. The sensitive cells are called hair cells because of the hair-like processes which project upward into a semigelatinous material. This matrix forms a crista or cupula of some size, relative to the hair cells, and extends up into the ampulla. (See Fig. 10–2.)

When the head is turned the inertia of the liquid in the canal makes it move in a direction opposite to that of the movement. This inertia bends the cupula and excites the hair cells to generate sensory impulse. When the motion stops, the interia is exerted in the opposite direction, and the cupula is bent accordingly. Thus the maximal stimulation of

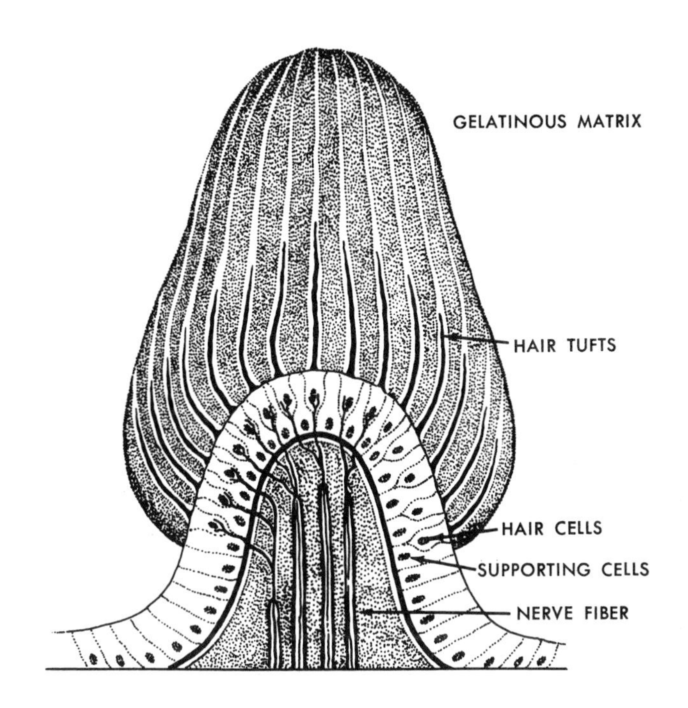

Drawing by Brenda Sutherland

Figure 10–2. Diagram of Crista Ampullaris

the hair cells occurs when the inertia is greatest, namely when motion is begun or ended. If motion is continued at a uniform rate in the same direction, as in an automobile, then almost no semicircular sensation is recorded. Excitation of this system occurs mainly from acceleration, deceleration, and change of direction.

UTRICLE AND SACCULE

In contrast to the activity of the *semicircular ducts* the *utricle* and *saccule* operate differently and give different sorts of information. This information is mainly concerned with our position in relation to the force of gravity. Because of this they respond not to motion but to static conditions. When a person is standing or sitting quietly the utricle and saccule still provide information about his position with reference to the force of gravity. The mechanism by which this is accomplished varies significantly from the action of the cupula. The same sort of hair cells are present and they are embedded in a gelatinous matrix. There is, however, no cupula or crista. The hair cells of the *utricular* and *saccular maculae* extend upward to end at the border of the gelatinous matrix. On the border of the matrix are tiny particles of calcium carbonate called *otoliths,* which exert pressure on the top of the hair cells and by varying pressure cause varying deformation of the hair cells. (The details of this mechanism can be seen in Fig. 10–3.)

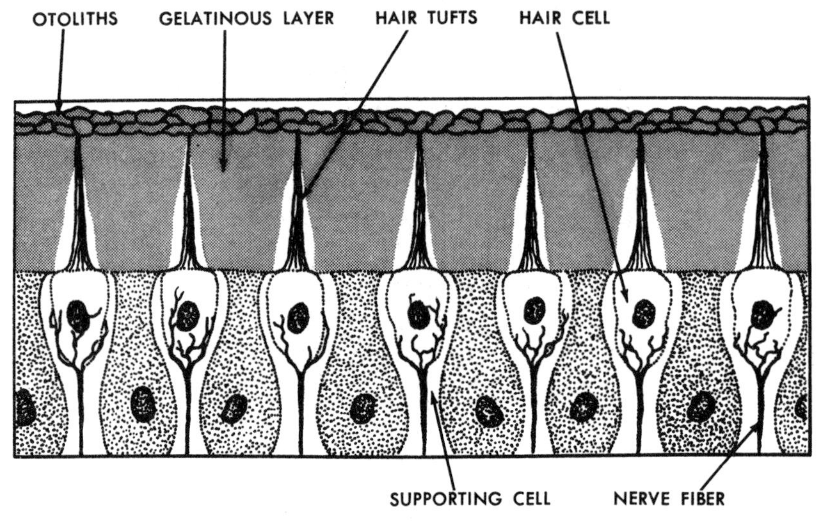

Drawing by Brenda Sutherland

Figure 10–3. Diagram of Structure of Saccular and Utricular Maculae (Sacculus is in Vertical Plane)

Again, increased pressure and deformation is translated into increased frequency of nervous impulse. The maximal stimulation of the utricle may be illustrated by the sensation received by passengers in a fast express elevator.

The utricle and the saccule, even though they function in the same way, do not provide the same sort of information. The *utricular macula* has its gelatinous membrane and its hair cells set in the horizontal plane, whereas the membrane and hair cells of the saccule lie in the vertical plane. The hair cells and otoliths oriented in a horizontal plane respond to vertical displacement, while those oriented in a vertical plane respond to lateral displacement. From these facts it is supposed that the utricle provides information of disturbances to equilibrium by tilting forward and back; while the saccule provides information of disturbances to equilibrium by tilting laterally, although this is not yet certain. A forward or backward tilt of the utricle or a lateral tilt of the saccule must include in the nerve discharge received by the brain some indication of the direction of tilt. That is, the utricle, for instance, must send a differing pulse from the point of maximum forward tilt than from the more stable portion of the maculae. In light of the structure of the macula, tilting forward pulls the forward part of the basal membrane and the hairs away from the ponderable otoliths, whereas the posterior part of the macula does not experience serious distortion of its stable relations to the posterior otoliths. Here then is a differential action of one part of the macula from that of another. Recent reports give a clear indication that under the conditions of forward tilt the hair cells of that portion of the macula give rise to a faster frequency of impulse discharge than when no tilt exists. Supposedly, too, the greater the tilt the greater the change in impulse frequency. Thus a minute deflection downward or upward of an airplane provides a basis for the vestibular apparatus to give us differential sensory information.

The behavioral responses to both kinds of sensory information are rapid adjustments of posture to a more stable position. It is by means of these receptors that our upright position is maintained and the rapid adjustments to forward acceleration or deceleration are made possible. As the most highly specialized division of the proprioceptive sensory department, the vestibular apparatus obviously must be connected very closely with the body musculature for the adjustment mentioned above. Part of these connections are made directly down the spinal cord by the vestibulospinal tract. The major control of body equilibrium is, however, mediated through the cerebellum, which coordinates most of the moves involved in orientation of the body in space. In order to understand these relations more clearly it is necessary to review the four vestibular nuclei in the medulla and pons and the connections they have with other centers.

FOUR VESTIBULAR NUCLEI

The nerve fibers, in which an impulse is induced by the generator potential in the hair cells of the maculae and cristae, form the afferent dendrites of the bipolar cells of the vestibular ganglion. The axons of these bipolar cells lead centrally to enter the medulla as the vestibular branch of the 8th cranial nerve just caudal to the pons. These axonal fibers end, with one exception, in one of the four vestibular nuclei already referred to. These nuclei form an eminence in the floor of the

4th ventricle. The four are the *superior, medial, spinal,* and *lateral vestibular nuclei.* As was indicated, with one exception the fibers from the vestibular ganglion synapse in one of these four nuclei. The exception is that some fibers from the vestibular ganglion proceed directly without synapse to the *nucleus fastigius* (medial) of the cerebellum. The second-order neurons from these vestibular nuclei proceed as follows.

1. From the *superior vestibular nucleus* the fibers ascend mainly contralaterally by way of the medial longitudinal fasciculus to make connections with the nuclei for eye muscle movement—specifically the oculomotor (III), trochlear (IV), and abducens (VI) cranial nerves. The connections of these nuclei are exemplified in Fig. 10–4.

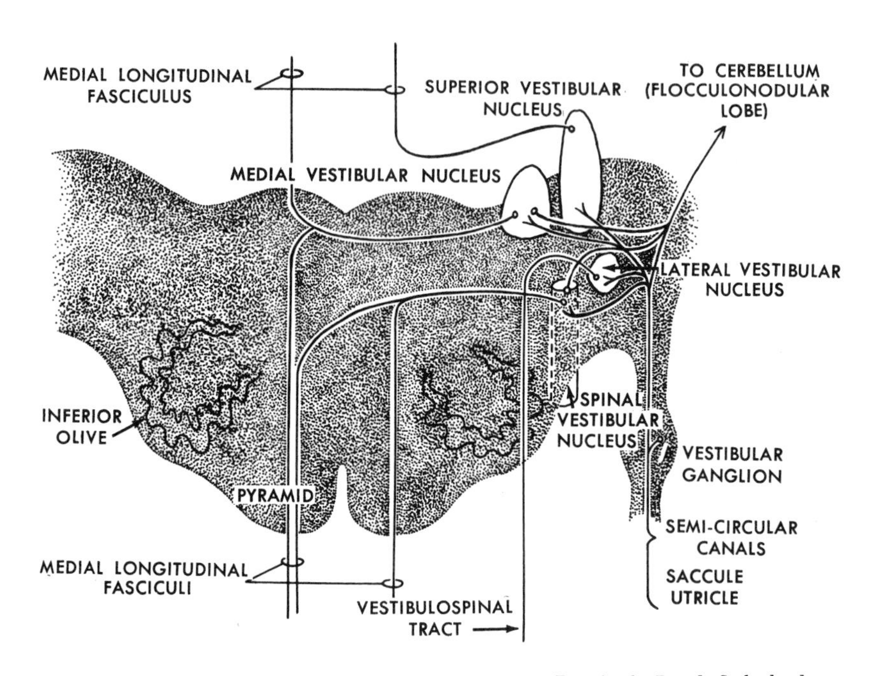

Figure 10–4. Diagram of Location of Four Vestibular Nuclei

2. Axons of the cells in the *lateral vestibular nucleus* run caudally, on the same side, to form the vestibulospinal tract. This tract continues into the lower levels of the cord and allows reflex adjustment of bodily orientation and position to vestibular stimulation. So far as is known this is the only direct connection between vestibular nuclei and the anterior motor horn cells of the spinal cord for movements of trunk and limbs.

3. The *spinal vestibular nucleus* contains neurons whose axons cross to the opposite side and descend in the medial longitudinal fasciculus for reflex coordination of eye and neck muscle movement and cerebellar adjustment of equilibrium. It also sends fibers to the cerebellum.

4. The *medial nucleus* is the largest in size and is therefore called the principal nucleus. It contains both large and small celled portions. From the large celled division fibers cross the midline and bifurcate to both ascend and descend. These fibers are a component of the medial longitudinal fasciculus and provide connections then with eye nuclei III, IV, and VI and with the cervical cord for neck and shoulder movement as well. In addition to this major connection the medial nucleus has another function. The axons from the small celled portion provide the major pathway for reflex visceral adjustment to vestibular stimulation. The fibers from this division of the medial nucleus run by way of the reticular formation of the same and opposite sides and make connection with the visceral motor nuclei, such as the dorsal nucleus of the vagus nerve. It is by means of this series of nervous connections that the reflexes of vomiting and facial pallor result from excessive vestibular stimulation. The medial nucleus sends fibers, also, to the cerebellum.

These then are the four vestibular nuclei. It is clear that no circuit has been described which mediates direct connection with the thalamus for subsequent cortical projection and, in fact, it is at present uncertain if there is any such cortical connection. Some evidence exists that vestibular information does arrive at the cerebral cortex; but this is probably by an indirect route such as the cerebellar projection upstream by way of the superior cerebellar peduncle, or a pathway that ascends along with auditory fibers. Responses have been recorded to vestibular stimulation on the upper margin of the ectosylvian gyrus, usually considered part of the auditory cortex, in cats. Most of the vestibular information, however, is used for reflex purposes. Since the medial longitudinal fasciculus has not been found below the level of the cervical cord, this avenue is limited to reflex movements of the head and neck in coordination with eye muscle movements.

LABYRINTHINE REFLEXES

The impulses from this vestibular system play a large part in the maintenance of our upright posture and general equilibruim. Particularly, the vestibulospinal and the reticulospinal impulses exert a strong tonic effect on the (antigravity) muscles opposing the pull of gravity. These impulses are normally under the modifying control of the pyramidal or extrapyramidal systems or the reticular formation. The effect of these systems is to partially inhibit the discharge of tonic impulses. When the nervous system is sectioned above the vestibular nuclei, in this way eliminating the central inhibitory control, there results an exaggerated extensor thrust or tonus characteristic of decerebrate rigidity. The righting reflexes to which the sense of equilibrium contributes are very strong in all normal animals. A blindfolded cat dropped upside down can right itself in an incredibly short distance. The labyrinthine righting reflexes (See Fig. 8–1, p. 112) are primary over other systems and take the lead in bringing the body back to an upright position. The evidence for this is that all sensory channels contributing to the righting response have to be obliterated before the animal will lie passively on its side. If an animal is blindfolded with the vestibular apparatus intact, the head assumes the horizontal position and is therefore oriented in space. This response disappears if the otoliths are destroyed. Once the head orientation occurs, the reflexes needed to orient neck, shoulders, body, and hind quarters follow in sequential order. Vision also plays a large part in the orientation of the animal in space and will bring about righting reflexes even when the visual receptive area in the occipital cortex is removed.

The semicircular canals also give rise to reflex responses. Rotation of the body and head around a fixed axis brings about reflex reactions of the eyes called nystagmus. As the body rotates, the eyes move in the opposite direction, only to swing quickly in the direction of rotation to fix on a second point for visual clarity. The slow backward movement followed by the quick forward swing is the nystagmus that is an attempt to maintain visual orientation and is important clinically. The reverse reflex sequence occurs when the rotation stops suddenly and the quick swing is in the direction opposite to that during rotation.

SOURCES AND ADDITIONAL READING

The CIBA Collection of Medical Illustrations, Vol. I, *Nervous System.* CIBA Pharmaceutical Company, 1953.

Handbook of Physiology, Sec. I. Vol. I, Chap. 22. Washington, D. C.: American Physiol. Soc., 1959.

Neff, W. D., ed., *Contributions to Sensory Physiology,* Vol. I. New York: Academic Press, 1965.

Ranson, S. W. and S. L. Clark, *The Anatomy of the Nervous System* (10th ed.) Chaps. 11, 13. Philadelphia: W. B. Saunders Company, 1959.

Rasmusson, G. L. and W. F. Windle, *Neural Mechanisms of Auditory and Vestibular Systems.* Springfield, Ill.: Charles C. Thomas, 1960.

Walsh, G., *Physiology of Nervous System,* Chap. 5. New York: Green and Co., Inc., 1959.

Eleven

THE CEREBELLUM

For many years it was considered that the cerebellum was an uncomplicated organ concerned primarily with the maintenance of equilibrium. During a large part of the phylogenetic series this was indeed true, for the cerebellum appears first in the forms which are beginning to travel on legs. In birds the homolateral spinocerebellar system is very large. This is primarily the dorsal spinocerebellar path, but might include also the ventral spinocerebellar pathway. The avian spinal cord and spinal mechanisms are more influenced by descending pathways from the vestibular nuclei, from the cerebellum, and from the optic tectum than is the case in the reptiles, amphibians, and fish. This reflects the shift in birds to balance on two legs, the dominance of the visual sense, and the needs of equilibrium in flight. The avian forms show a sudden enlargement of the central vermis of the cerebellum which coincides with the requirement for equilibrium during flight. Since the work of Snider in 1942 the simple view of the function of the cerebellum has had to be abandoned.

It became abundantly clear from the work of Snider and Stowell that the cerebellum, while it does not initiate action, monitors and reacts to six different kinds of information input. The research of Snider and his associates established the fact that stimulation of receptors of (1) touch, (2) sight, and (3) hearing resulted in recorded potentials in the cerebellum as well as in the primary receptive areas of the cerebral cortex, vision and hearing being recorded in the central vermis, while touch was recorded both anteriorly and posteriorly. In addition to touch, vision, and audition the cerebellum handles information about (4) equilibrium, (5) state of muscle and joint, and in addition it has a loop (6) connecting it to the motor area of the cerebral cortex.

These six kinds of incoming information must be coordinated and integrated in the cerebellum. One of the peculiarities of the cerebellum that makes this probable is that the efferent fibers which leave the cerebellum make up only one-third as many fibers as the number that enter it. The reduction from three to one in information channels must mean fusing, integration, and coding of several items into one for a single impulse to a muscle group.

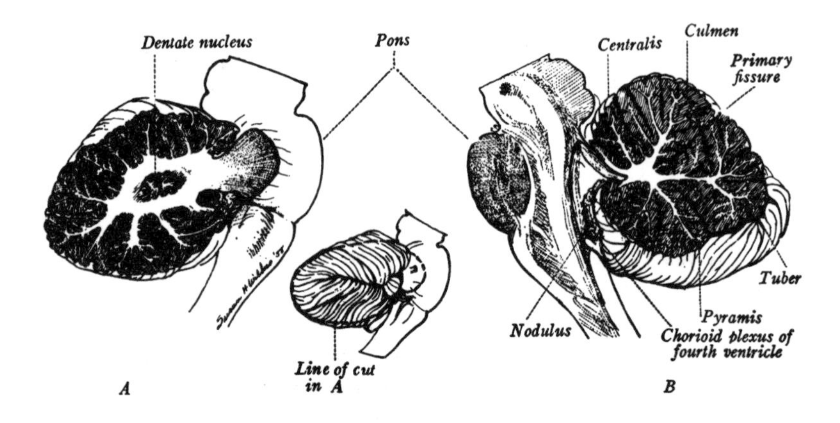

Source: S. W. Ranson and S. L. Clark, *The Anatomy of the Nervous System: Its Development and Function* (10th ed., Philadelphia: W. B. Saunders Company, 1959), p. 275.

Figure 11–1. Medial View of Cerebellum, Pons, Medulla, and IV Ventricle

THREE CEREBELLAR PEDUNCLES

The cerebellum is very convoluted, having only one-sixth of its actual surface exposed. It lies just caudal to the colliculi of the tectum, and is dorsal to the pons and medulla and separated from them by the IV ventricle. These relationships are illustrated in Fig. 11–1. It has connections with the *medulla* via the *inferior cerebellar peduncle,* with the *pons* by way of the *middle peduncle,* and with the anterior *diencephalon* by way of the *superior cerebellar peduncle.* The *inferior peduncle* or lower bridge to the cerebellum carries information of muscle sense (spinocerebellar) from the spinal cord, as well as muscle information from the head and neck via the inferior olive, and vestibular information from the semicircular ducts, utricle, and saccule. The *middle peduncle* is composed of crossed connections in the pons, carrying information from the cerebral cortex about voluntary decisions for movement or the significance of visual and auditory input. The *superior peduncle,* or a path adjacent to it, may carry much of the sensory information of vision and audition as well as some muscle sense (Golgi tendon organ) by way of the ventral spinocerebellar path. Unpublished studies of Nauta degenerative lesions in the lateral geniculate nucleus of squirrel monkeys show degenerated fibers descending medially from the geniculate into the cerebral peduncle and then clearly crossing the midline in the pons. In addition, the superior peduncle is the major efferent pathway from the cerebellum to the red nucleus and thalamus. From the thalamus the cerebellar information is projected to the cerebral cortex. The only other efferent pathway is by way of the inferior peduncle to the lateral vestibular nucleus and the vestibulospinal tract, or the parallel path to the reticular nuclei. The three peduncles are illustrated in Fig. 11–2.

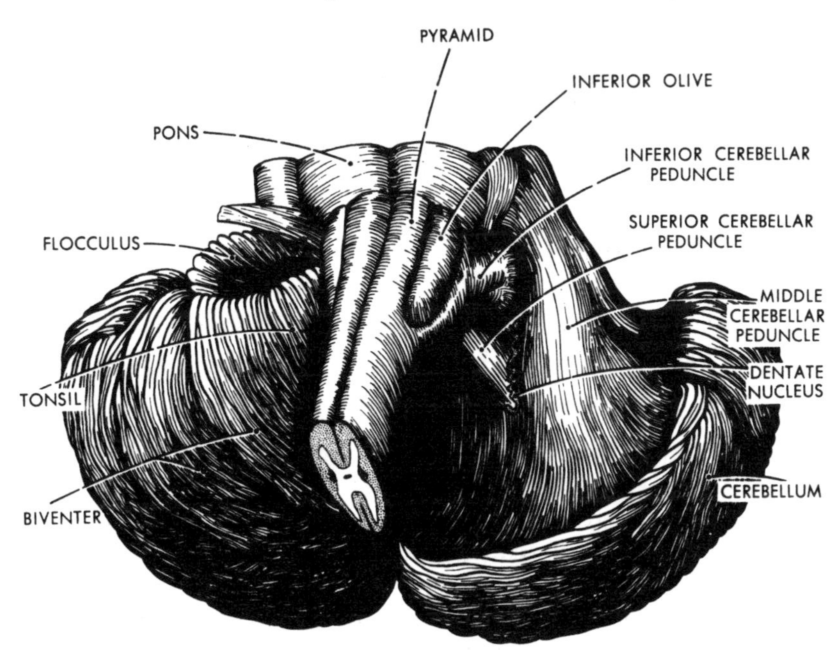

Source: Reprinted with permission of the Macmillan Company from *Correlative Anatomy of the Nervous System* by Elizabeth C. Crosby, Tryphena Humphrey, and Edward W. Lauer. © The Macmillan Company, 1962. P. 201 (labeling altered slightly).

Figure 11–2. The Inferior, Middle, and Superior Cerebellar Peduncles

LOBES OF CEREBELLUM

The lobes and fissures of the cerebellum become very complex if studied without guidelines. For purposes of anatomical and functional identification the following description and table (Table 11–I) may be

Table 11–I

Cerebellar Lobes and Functions

Anatomical Part		*Function*	*Connections*
Anterior Lobe, or Paleocerebellum	Lingula		
	Central Culmen	Receptive area for proprioception	Ventral spinocerebellar
	Rostral Part of Hemispheres	Receptive area for touch	Uncertain
Primary or Preclival Fissure			
Posterior Lobe, or Neocerebellum	Declive Lobulus Simplex Folio Vermis	Receptive areas for vision and audition	Uncertain
	Tuber Pyramid Uvula	Receptive areas for proprioception and touch	Dorsal spinocerebellar
	Lateral Hemispheres	Cortical control	Pontine-cerebellar path
Postnodular Fissure			
Archicerebellum	Flocculonodular Lobe	Equilibrium	Vesibulocerebellar path

of assistance. The most caudal portion of the cerebellum is the flocculonodular node. It is composed of the rounded *nodule* in the most posterior part of the central vermis and of two lateral extensions called *focculi* which are separate from and underlie the main cerebellar hemispheres. It is bounded dorsally by the postnodular fissure. This node is concerned with connections to the vestibular apparatus for response to changes of equilibrium, and is related to the lateral-line organs of lower vertebrates. Because it is the most primitive part of the cerebellum it is called the *archicerebellum*. The details of lobes and fissures can best be understood by reference to Fig. 11–3.

The segment of the cerebellum next both dorsal and rostral of the flocculonodular node is the neocerebellum, or new cerebellum, which

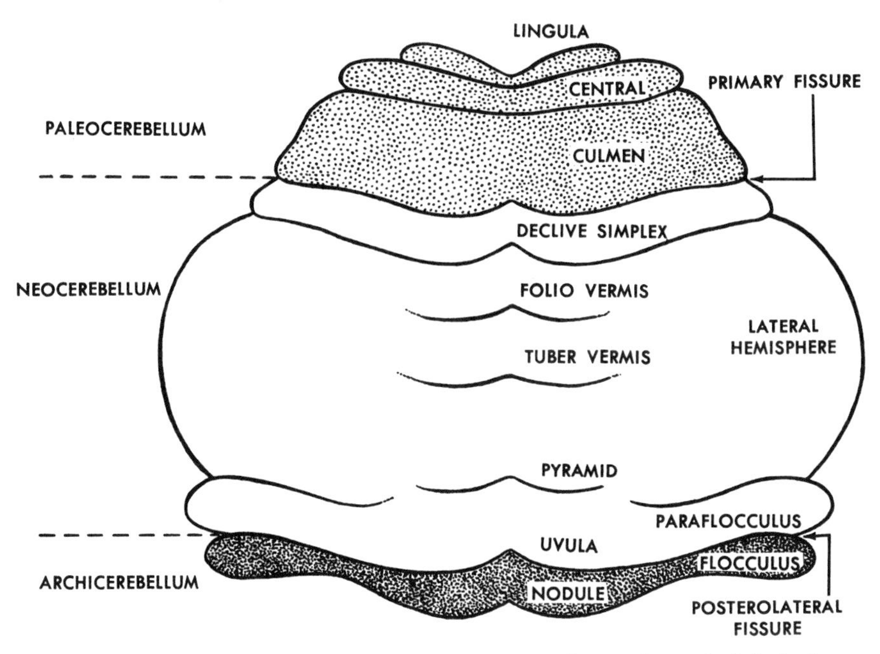

Figure 11–3. Diagram of Lobes of the Cerebellum

begins dorsal of the postnodular fissure and includes all of the posterior lobe up to the *declive* and *lobulus simplex.* This neocerebellum, particularly the large lateral hemispheres, is concerned with connections to the cerebral cortex. It developed, therefore, with the expansion of the cerebral cortex as the dominant center of coordination. The vermal and the paravermal area of the posterior lobe comprising the *folium vermis, tuber, pyramid,* and *uvula* is concerned with the pathways for proprioceptive sense by way of the *dorsal spinocerebellar* tracts and is the receptive area for touch.

Rostral from the neocerebellum is the anterior lobe or *paleocerebellum,* which is older phylogenetically than the *neocerebellum* but more recent than the *archicerebellum.* It is bounded caudally by the primary (preclival) fissure and includes in the vermis the anterior-posterior segments of *lingula, central,* and *culmen.* This paleocerebellum developed when limbs first appeared in the phylogenetic series, and receives in central and culmen the ventral spinocerebellar tract. The anterior lobe includes also the rostral part of the hemispheres where touch sensation is received. The *declive* and *lobulus simplex,* which are roughly midway from rostral to caudal, are concerned with the reception of auditory and visual information and are important for posture, walking, and other automatic movements.

MICROSCOPIC STRUCTURE

The incoming pathways for sensory information ascend through the peduncles to the cerebellar cortex and there make synapse with the *granule cells* and the *basket cells.* These cells have axons that run at right angles to and parallel to the outer mloecular layer of the cerebellum. Across the external cerebellum are found *folia* which correspond to the folds, or *gyri,* of the cerebral cortex. The organization of the cells in the cerebellum follows either a parallel or right-angle orientation to the long axis of the folia. Branching in a plane parallel to the long axis of the folia, the *granule* cells in the outer cortical layer make synaptic contact with the tight bundles of dendrites of *Purkinje cells.* At right angles to the long axis of the convoluted folia the dendrites of the Purkinje cells spread over a wide area like a banyan tree. These dendrites make contact with the many calyx-like axons of the *basket cells* to permit and enhance spatial summation. Thus an impulse reaching the basket cells will be used to fire many Purkinje cells and thus result in many efferent impulses. For the details of microscopic structure see Fig. 11–4.

DEEP NUCLEI AND THREE PEDUNCLES

The Purkinje cells in their turn carry impulses away from the surface and down toward one of the four cerebellar nuclei. These are the *medial* (fastigial), the *interpositus* (globos and emboliform), and the *lateral* (dentate) nuclei. The Purkinje cells of the flocculonodular lobe (for equilibrium) discharge into the medial (fastigial) nucleus in the medial center of the cerebellum. From here axons pass out (1) to the lateral vestibular nucleus, and so down the vestibulospinal pathway.

Fig. 11–4.

Cross section of a cerebellar fold is diagrammed to show the network of cells which transmits nerve impulses through it. Nerve impulses enter the fold through the white matter (*broken lines in center*). These impulses are drawn into the cortex, or gray matter, by the granule cells. Each granule cell (*a*) receives an impulse through its short dendrites. It transmits the impulse into the outer, or "molecular," layer of the fold through its long, T-shaped axon. In the molecular layer the impulse passes from these axons into the many-branched

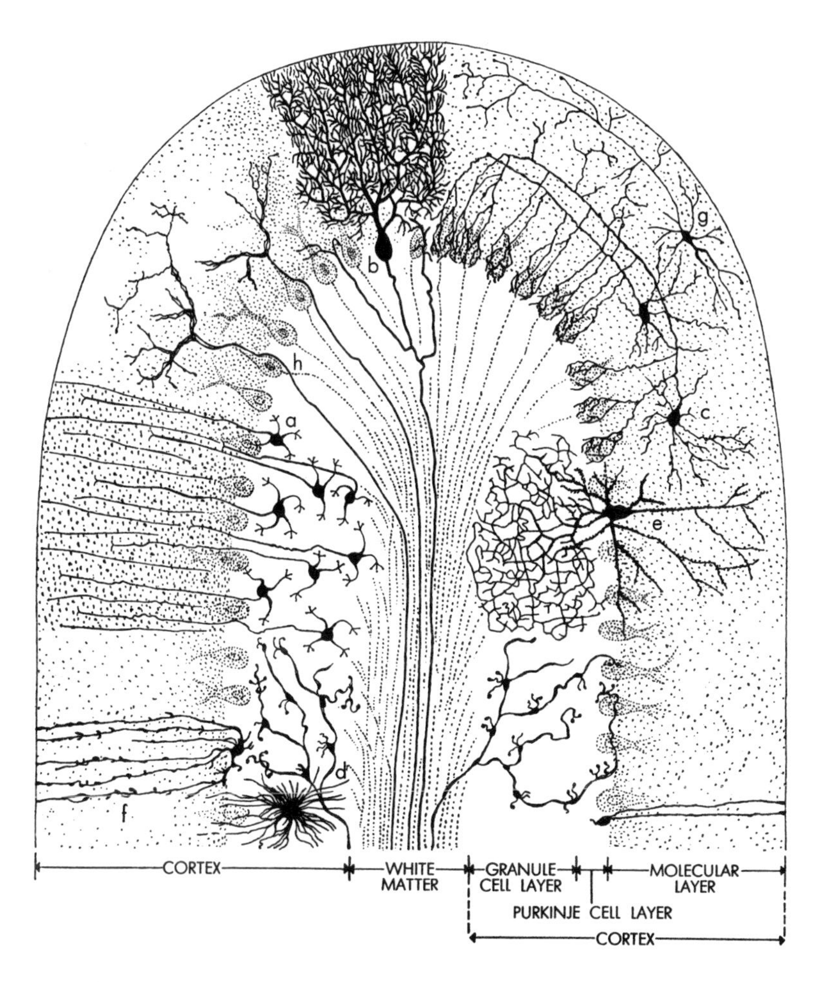

dendrites of the Purkinje cells (*b*). The impulse then leaves the cerebellar fold through the axon of the Purkinje cell, embedded in the white matter at center. The process by which impulses pass from granule cells to Purkinje cells is abetted by basket cells (*c*). Each basket cell picks up impulses from a granule-cell axon, then transmits them through a long fiber to "baskets" of fibrils which surround the cell bodies of several Purkinje cells. Other auxiliary cells are the "mossy terminals" (*d*) and Golgi Type-II cells (*e*) which help diffuse incoming and outgoing impulses respectively. Cell-types *f* and *g* are of unknown function; *h* is a climbing fiber whose axon adheres to the Purkinje cell dendrites and may serve to "switch" them on and off.

Source: *Scientific American,* August 1958, p. 87.

Figure 11–4. Diagram of Microscopic Structure of a Cerebellar Fold

Another pathway from the medial (fastigial) nucleus is (2) by the fastigiobulbar path to the reticular nuclei, and so downstream by way of the reticulospinal tract. The medial cerebellar zone consisting of the vermal cortex (the receptive area for spinocerebellar paths, equilibrium, and probably some touch) acts through the *fastigial* (medial) *nucleus* upon the central reticular formation. This sequence of structures is concerned with postural tone, equilibrium, and locomotion of the entire body. The intermediate zone of the cerebellum arises in the paravermal cortex and acts, by way of *nucleus interpositus* and the superior peduncle, upon the lateral reticular formation. This sequence of cortex and nuclei is considered to have more discrete control of ipsilateral limbs. The projection of cerebellar cortex to deep nuclei can be seen in Fig. 11–5.

As might be expected from the three-to-one ratio of incoming to outgoing fibers, most of the fibers in the inferior peduncle are afferent. The dorsal spinocerebellar pathway transmitting proprioception from the body moves dorsally along the lateral surfaces of the medulla to become one component of the inferior peduncle. This band of fibers ends in the posterior portion of the paramedian vermis, where it is joined by fibers for touch. The olivocerebellar pathway comprises the largest component of the inferior peduncle. These fibers have crossed over from the inferior olive of the opposite side, after synapse with axons of spino-olivary and thalamo-olivary fibers. The other afferent bundle in the inferior peduncle is that from the vestibular nerve directly and from the spinal and medial vestibular nuclei. These fibers end mainly in the flocculonodular lobe, but also spread thinly over the middle vermis, although very thinly in the middle portion (the declive, folio, and tuber vermis).

There is one outgoing or efferent pathway using the inferior peduncle. This is the pathway for vestibular instructions. The fibers from the cortex of the vermis and flocculus end in the deep fastigial, or medial, nucleus. From these nuclei, fibers cross to the opposite lateral vestibular nucleus in the medulla. From there the impulse, after synapse, travels down the vestibulospinal path. Connections are also made from fastigii to reticular nuclei in the medulla. Both of these pathways provide for innervation of the muscles of the body. The various efferent pathways are shown in Fig. 11–6.

The middle peduncle contains no efferent fibers, but is a heavy band of crossed connections from the cerebral cortex. These come from the frontal, temporal, and occipital as well as motor and premotor areas of the cortex to synapse in the pons (corticopontine). The other component of this band comes from collateral branches of the pyramidal

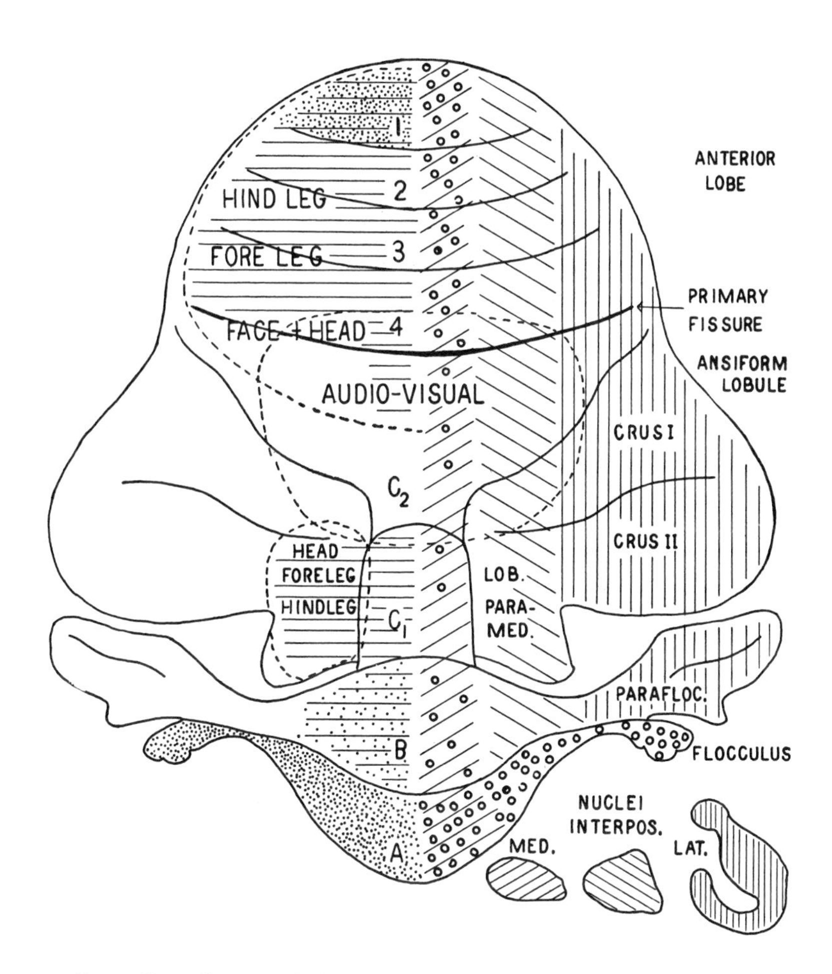

Generalized diagram of the cerebellum to show regional specialization as described from the work of various authors. On the right are represented the cerebellonuclear projections: small circles for projection to vestibular nuclei; oblique lines (/), next to midline, for projection to nucleus medialis (fastigii); oblique lines (\) for projection to nucleus interpositus (globose and emboliform); vertical lines for projection to nucleus lateralis (dentate). On the left side afferent connections are indicated: dots for vestibulocerebellar connections; horizontal lines for spinocerebellar connections; blank space for pontocerebellar projections but all other parts of the cortex except the flocculonodular receive these. The lettering and numbering of midline structures is that of Bolk.

Source: S. W. Ranson and S. L. Clark, *The Anatomy of the Nervous System,* p. 279.

Figure 11–5. Cerebellar Afferent Receptive, and Efferent Projection Zones to Deep Cerebellar Nuclei

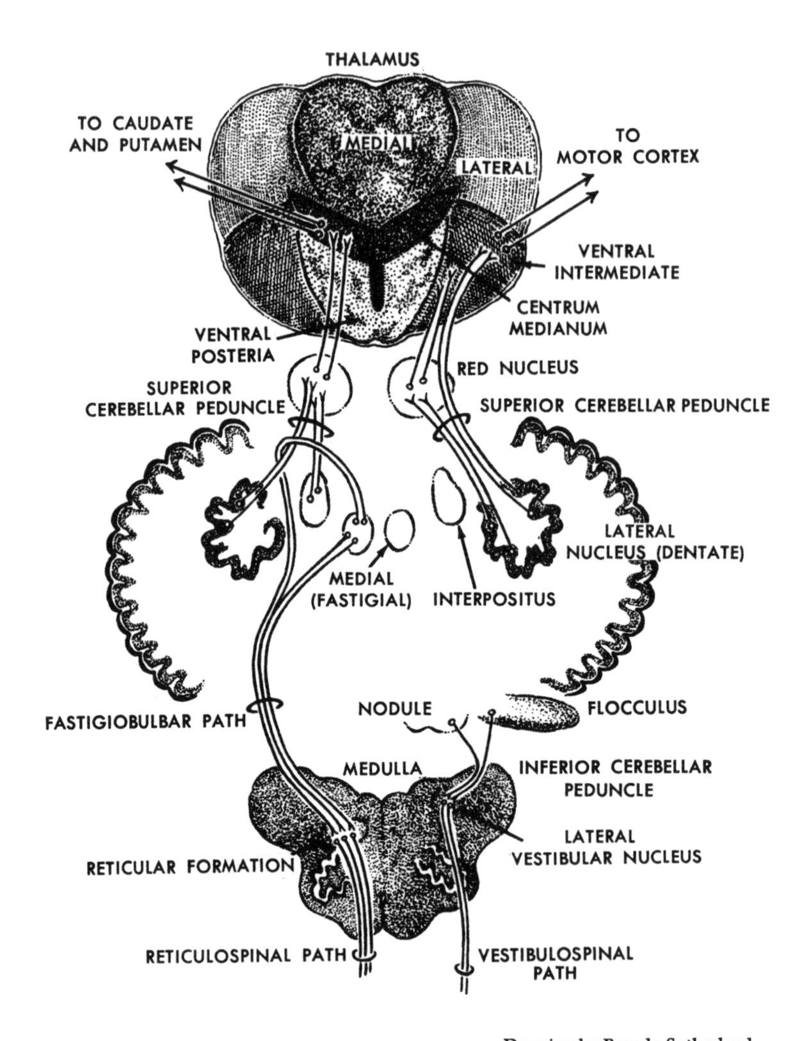

Drawing by Brenda Sutherland

Figure 11–6. Efferent Pathways from Cerebellar Nuclei to Thalamus and to Medulla; also Path from Flocculus and Nodule to Lateral Vestibular Nucleus

fibers which also synapse in the pons. After synapse the fibers from the pons to the cerebellar hemispheres form the middle peduncle, sweeping around the inferior peduncle to reach the laterally placed hemispheres.

The other afferent fibers come into the cerebellum by the superior peduncle or alongside it. These are the ventral spinocerebellar fibers. Aside from these the superior peduncle is efferent to nucleus ruber and to thalamus.

The *lateral* (dentate) nucleus is larger and more convoluted than the others. It receives fibers from the hemispheres of the cerebellum, which are the terminus of the crossed pathway from the cerebral cortex through the pons. From the *lateral* (dentate) nuclei, axons pass to the red nucleus and the intermediate ventral nucleus of the thalamus by way of the superior cerebellar peduncle. From the red nucleus, fibers go downstream in the rubrospinal tracts to the levels of the spinal cord.

The other nucleus, the *interpositus* (globose and emboliform), receives fibers from the paramedian part of the vermis, where are located the projection of touch and proprioceptive sense, at least in the anterior and posterior portions of the cerebellum. The anterior and posterior location of muscle sense follows, in part, from the point of entry of the dorsal spinocerebellar and ventral spinocerebellar tracts, the dorsal entering the cerebellum by the inferior peduncle and the ventral with the superior peduncle. The fibers from the *interpositus* nucleus pass forward via the superior peduncle to the red nucleus also. They do not seem to synapse there, but continue to the central nucleus (centrum medianum) of the thalamus. From this description it is clear that the information about muscle stretch and contraction, touch, vision, hearing, and equilibrium are integrated and coded to provide the proper instructions to the antigravity muscles involved in posture.

The location of the projection areas for touch, vision, audition, muscle sense, equilibrium, etc. is incongruous with the portions of the cerebellar cortex which project to the three deep nuclei. That is, the vermis receives vestibular, proprioceptive, and touch information, if not more; and yet the projection to the medial nucleus from the vermal zone and the efferent path by way of the vestibulospinal tract or central reticular formation involves postural tone, locomotion, and equilibrium of the entire body. This lack of complete agreement is one index of the complex integrative and coding function which the cerebellum performs. In addition to the above, in the folia of the cerebellar cortex there are reverberating circuits which bring about restimulation of the Purkinje cells to ensure a series of pulses over a long period of time to maintain a state of muscle contraction, or tonus. This may be merely the maintenance of normal muscle tone which continues even during sleep.

Students are frequently confused about the functioning of the cerebellar cortex. And this confusion is well founded. It has been shown above that proprioception and touch afferents end up on the anterior and the posterior vermis and paravermis, while audition and vision afferents end in the central vermis, and the pontocerebellar fibers end in the cortex of the hemispheres. These are the incoming paths. By contrast the efferent fibers to the deep nuclei are organized very differently. As we have seen, the middle vermis from anterior to posterior projects to the medial (fastigial) nucleus, while the paravermal zone projects to interpositus, and the hemispheres to the lateral nucleus. It will be seen that the description of afferent paths does not agree with that for efferent projections. There is clearly an undefined gap between, and this gap involves the activity of the cerebellar cortex. It is at this point and because of the cerebellar cortical activity that we have to insert an unknown (*y*) to represent the extent of fusion and coordination of incoming messages which issue on the efferent side as an integrated series of impulses to skeletal muscles. Until we are better able than at present to substitute specific neural linkage for this unknown, there is bound to be some confusion about the functioning of the cerebellar cortex.

In the relation of the cerebellum to the cerebral cortex there are not only connections by way of the thalamus to the precentral cortex, particularly to the motor cortex (area 4 of Brodmann), but there are also connections between cerebellar areas for touch, vision, audition, and possibly proprioception with the corresponding projection areas of the cerebral cortex. These connections run in both directions. In the maintenance of posture it seems clear that at least three kinds of sensory information are needed. Upright posture cannot be maintained without visual, vestibular, and proprioceptive information. The essential function of the cerebellum is to combine vestibular information and visual information about equilibrium with the state of contraction from the muscle spindles concerned, and to so integrate these data as to be able to send out over the motor fibers a coded message which will maintain the upright posture over the desired period of time.

An important part is played in this postural circuit by some very small efferent fibers to the muscle spindle called the *gamma efferents.* They constitute one-third of all the fibers in the motor roots of the cord, and innervate the intrafusal fibers of the muscle. The annulospiral endings which are the sensory organ for muscle stretch are silent during muscular contraction. Impulses carried by the gamma efferents change the shape (take up the slack) of the intrafusal fibers to which the annulospiral endings are attached, causing the annulospirals to begin to fire again. This connection allows finer modulation of effort and greater control during muscular contraction. The cerebellum has an essential role in the firing of the gamma efferent impulses.

ABLATIONS AND LESIONS

Ablations of the flocculonodular lobe result in loss in equilibrium without loss of voluntary movements. Monkeys subjected to this ablation can feed themselves but cannot stand without swaying or toppling over on the floor. In order to stay in "position" while they eat, therefore, they will brace themselves by sitting in a corner of the room where the connecting walls will hold them erect. In addition, motion sickness in dogs can be prevented by ablations in this area, but by the ablation of no other area of cerebellar or cerebral cortex.

As we have seen, the proprioceptive information is projected to both the anterior and posterior portions of the paramedian section of the vermis. Under normal conditions, stimulation of this area (median anterior lobe) inhibits extensor tonus of the antigravity muscles in particular, and decerebration always greatly increases the extensor reflexes, and rigidity results. When ablation of this cerebellar area follows decerebration the release of extensor reflexes from any inhibiting control is much greater than in a simple decerebration alone. Ablations of the posterior lobe alone bring about hypotonia, with uncertainty of gait and tremor of the head and ipsilateral limbs. Ablations of lateral and paravermal cerebellar cortex show a distinct loss in the modulation of voluntary movement.

As contrasted with ablations on the surface, lesions give other evidence of cerebellar function. Lesions in the fastigial nucleus result in both facilitation and inhibition of the antigravity muscles, the facilitation arising by lesions in the rostromedial portion and inhibition resulting from lesions in the rostrolateral portion. Lesions in the dentate nucleus bring about intention tremor and postural tremor.

As has already been indicated, vestibular reflexes are important in the maintenance of posture. But the vestibular component in this complex orientation is supervised and integrated with muscle sense by the cerebellum. For it is not enough that a certain level of activity be maintained in the postural centers of the brain stem. The posture of the body will be symmetrical only if the tonic contractions of homonymous muscles are the same on both sides of the body. Posture and locomotion are closely related, and reflexes basic to standing (extensor reflex) contribute inseparably to progression as well. Reflexes subject to, or influenced by, labyrinthine inflow are especially important in rhythmic movements of walking and swimming. In monkeys this basic motor performance is more dependent upon higher centers, and thalamic animals seem incapable of progression. The different elements of postural adaptation are all present in the different spinal reflexes. Their development of the energy adequate to overcome gravity actively, and of sequences capable of effective performance, requires the presence of the pontine and midbrain reticulum and of the cerebellum. The cerebellum is the necessary agent to coordinate these individual discharges. In addition, stimulation of the cerebellum inhibits cortically induced movements which are already under way.

SOURCES AND ADDITIONAL READING

The CIBA Collection of Medical Illustrations, Vol. I, *Nervous System,* CIBA Pharmaceutical Company, 1953.

Dow, R. S. and G. Moruzzi, *Physiology and Pathology of the Cerebellum.* Minneapolis: University of Minnesota, 1958.

Handbook of Physiology, Sec. I., Vol. II, Chap. 51. Washington, D. C.: American Physiol. Soc., 1959.

Ranson, S. W. and S. L. Clark, *The Anatomy of the Nervous System* (10th ed.), Chap. 14. Philadelphia: W. B. Saunders Company, 1959.

Ruch, T. and J. Fulton, *Medical Physiology and Biophysics* (18th ed.), Chap. 12. Philadelphia: W. B. Saunders Company. (See 19th ed., Chap. 13.)

Snider, R. S. and A. Stowell, "Receiving Areas of Tactile, Auditory, and Visual Systems in the Cerebellum," *J. Neurophysiol.,* 95 (1944), 331–57.

Walsh, G., *Physiology of the Nervous System,* Chap. 6. New York: Longmans Green & Co., Inc., 1959.

Twelve

THE PONS AND MIDBRAIN

BASILAR PONS

The function of the pons is scarcely separable from that of the cerebellum. The basilar portion of the pons (or bridge) is largely concerned with connections between the cerebral cortex and the cerebellum, although it also conducts the corticospinal fibers descending to the cord (p. 100). The basilar portion of the pons is composed of an intermixture of nerve fibers going downstream and a large number of cell groups known as the pontine nuclei, whose function is to make connection with the collaterals of the corticospinals and with the corticopontine fibers. After synapse has been made in the pontine nuclei, the axons of these neurons sweep across the midline and curve up to assemble themselves in the middle cerebellar peduncle. Since this peduncle ends in direct connection with the lateral hemispheres of the cerebellar cortex, there exists a two-neuron path by means of which the cerebral cortex can influence the activity of the cerebellum. Thus the maintenance of upright posture, which is largely a cerebellar function, is interrupted by the cortex when we lie down. And the corticopontine cerebellar pathway is the avenue used for this cortical control.

In addition to the pontine nuclei and crossing fibers, the basilar portion of the pons shows a number of compact bundles of fibers, which are divided by the nuclei and the fibers moving across the midline and into the peduncle. These bundles, which are the corticospinal fibers, become more compact at the caudal border of the pons, where they form the pyramids on the ventral surface of the medulla. (See Fig. 12–1.)

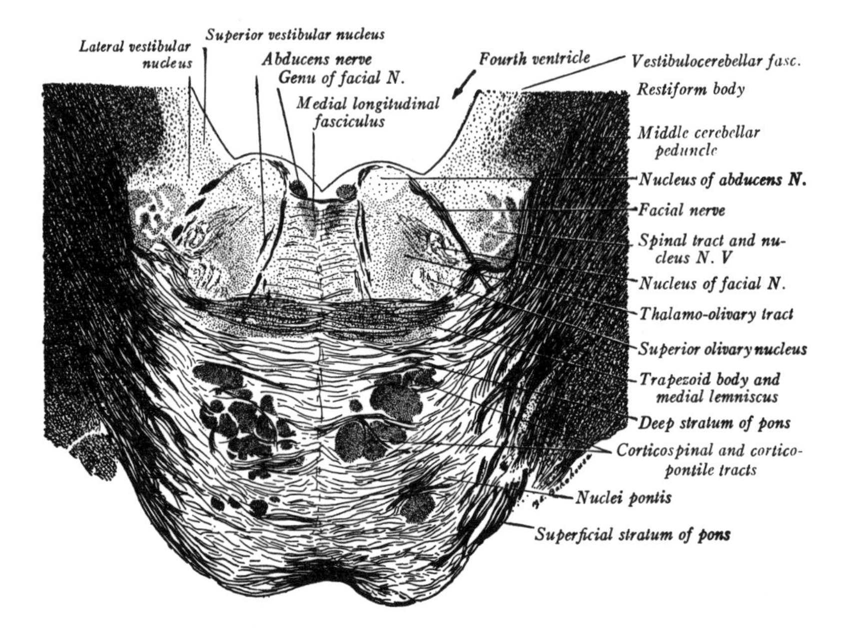

Source: S. W. Ranson and S. L. Clark, *The Anatomy of the Nervous System: Its Development and Function* (10th ed.; Philadelphia: W. B. Saunders Company, 1959), p. 219.

Figure 12–1. Basal and Tegmental Pons

TEGMENTAL PONS

Since the basilar portion of the pons represents a wholly different function than any portion of the medulla below or the mesencephalon above, all of the other pathways going up or down, as well as the cranial nerve nuclei, must be in the dorsal or tegmental portion of the pons. Here we see a number of the pathways which were present in the medulla. The *medial longitudinal fasciculus* lies on both sides of the midline and is the most dorsal of these paths. Just ventral to the medial longitudinal fasciculus the *tectospinal* pathway courses downstream from the roof of the midbrain to make connections in the spinal cord. The *medial lemniscus,* which at medullary levels was the most ventral of the midline tracts, just ventral to the tectospinals, has now changed position. The absence of the inferior olivary nucleus has allowed the medial lemniscus in the pons to flatten out laterally at the ventral border of the tegmental portion. This lemniscus is there traversed by cochlear fibers which compose the trapezoid body. The composition of the medial lemniscus here is as follows:

(right side)	sac.	lum.	thor.	cerv.

Aside from the medial lemniscus, all of the remaining ascending pathways from the body, except spinotectal and spinal lemniscus, have already reached their end station. The spinothalamic and spinotectal move upstream in the lateral segment of the pons.

In addition to the trapezoid body other segments of the cochlear pathway show up in the pons. At the junction of the pons and medulla the *dorsal* and *ventral cochlear nuclei* may be seen on the two sides of the inferior cerebellar peduncle. The *superior olive* lies just dorsal and rostral to the lateral edge of the trapezoid body, and from this same point the *lateral lemniscus* starts upstream to the *medial geniculate* of the thalamus. These pathways will be reviewed in detail in the section on audition. Two of the vestibular nuclei (superior and medial) are present in the pons, occupying a position along the lateral border of the lower lip of the IV ventricle. From here they feed into the medial longitudinal fasciculus and other pathways, such as the vestibulocerebellar fascicle, entering the cerebellum by way of the inferior cerebellar peduncle. By means of these pathways vestibular information is fed into the medial longitudinal fasciculus and thus influences reflex movements of the head and eyes, and, by the inferior peduncle, vestibular control of posture. This is the pathway, then, responsible for nystagmus from excessive rotation of the head and body.

CRANIAL NERVES IN PONS

The cranial nerves entering the pons are the 8th, 7th, 6th, and 5th, although sensory nuclei of the 5th extend into medulla and midbrain. The cochlear portions of the 8th have already been indicated as bounding the inferior peduncle as the latter leaves the medulla on the way to the cerebellum.

The 7th, or facial nerve, has its motor nucleus located in the caudal part of the pons and in the lateral part of the reticular gray matter. The nerve fibers move dorsomedially, pass all the way around the abducens nucleus (VI), and then after forming this knee, or *genu,* pass ventrolaterally to exit just rostral to the 8th.

The 6th, the abducens, is the eye muscle nucleus innervating the lateral rectus muscle of the eye. As indicated above, its nucleus lies in the bent *genu* of the fibers of the 7th. Its fibers course ventrally, but more medially than the 7th, to leave the brain close to the midline just at the junction of the pons and medulla. The abducens also has connections with the medial longitudinal fasciculus for coordination with other eye muscle nuclei and with vestibular input.

The 5th, or trigeminal, has both motor and sensory nuclei serving the muscles of mastication and sensation from the face. These main nuclei lie on both sides of the emerging 7th nerve, the motor medial and the sensory lateral thereto. Their position is in the upper lateral

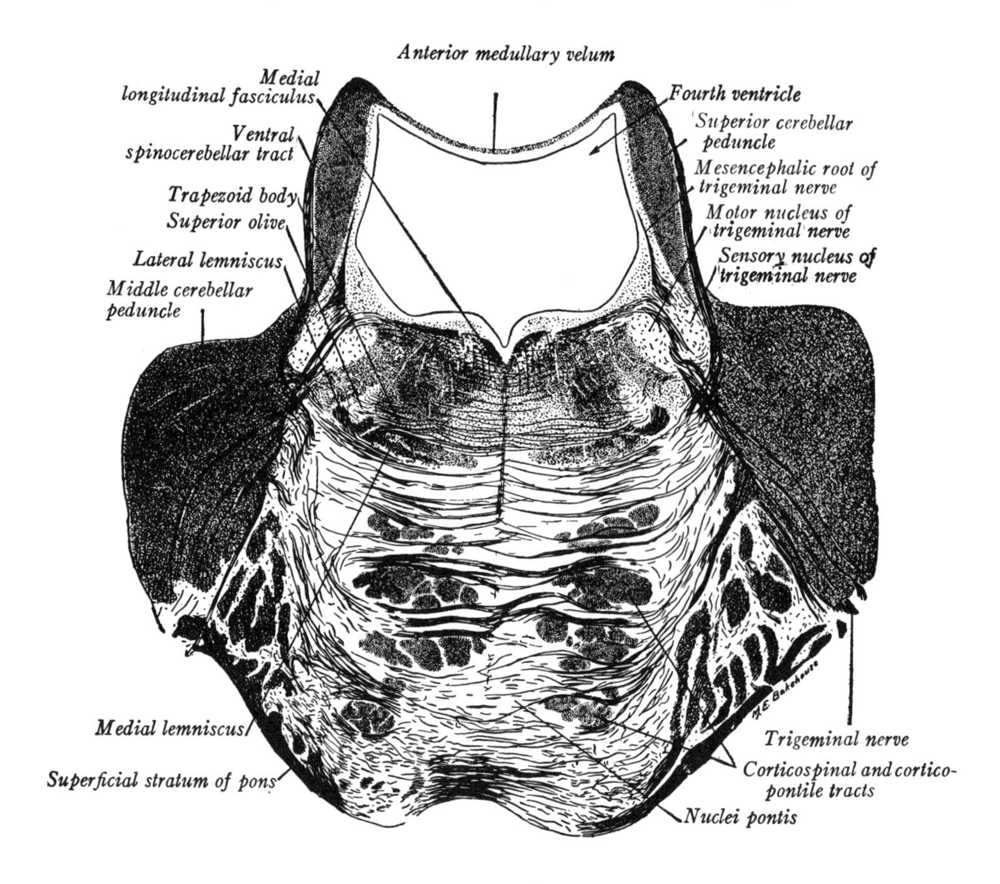

Source: S. W. Ranson and S. L. Clark, *The Anatomy of the Nervous System*, p. 223.

Figure 12–2. Rostral Pons at Level of Vth Nerve

corner of the tegmental portion of the pons, just ventral to the superior peduncle, which here has issued from the cerebellum. These structures may be seen in Fig. 12–2. The trigeminal has connections in the brain stem with other nuclei, particularly with the nuclei of VII and XII.

In the rostral portion of the pons a mass of fibers forms the lateral wall of the IV ventricle. This structure is the superior cerebellar peduncle, which is the avenue of exit from the cerebellum to the red nucleus, thalamus, cortex, etc. Accompanying this peduncle in its course, but moving in the opposite direction, is the ventral spinocerebellar tract. Its fibers stream back to the anterior lobe of the cerebellar vermis.

MIDBRAIN

Rostral to the pons and caudal to the thalamus lies a section of the brain which is dominated dorsally by the four colliculi and ventrally by the cerebral peduncles. This is the midbrain, or mesencephalon.

Four Colliculi

The inferior and superior colliculi show as four rounded prominences on the dorsal surface of the midbrain just rostral of the cerebellum. The inferior colliculus is the major reflex center for hearing, and the superior colliculus is the main reflex center for vision. Both colliculi have decussations between the two lateral prominences, and the inferior colliculus connects by a bridge to the medial geniculate nucleus of the thalamus, while the superior colliculus has a bridge to the lateral geniculate nucleus. These structures will be discussed in later sections. Fibers from the lateral lemniscus (audition) enter the inferior colliculus and the medial geniculate nucleus, while the optic tract disappears as the fibers synapse in the lateral geniculate nucleus.

Between the colliculi above and the cerebral peduncles below are found the ascending and descending pathways which have not reached their end station. These include the medial longitudinal fasciculus, the medial lemniscus, and the spinal lemniscus, as well as the terminal part of the lateral lemniscus. Lateral to the medial longitudinal fasciculus lies the descending thalamo-olivary tract, while just dorsal of the medial longitudinal fasciculus (at the level of the inferior colliculus) is found the nucleus of the trochlear nerve (IV) for eye movement. Just ventral to these nuclei and tracts (at the inferior collicular level) lies a large and distinct decussation formed by the crossing of the fibers of the

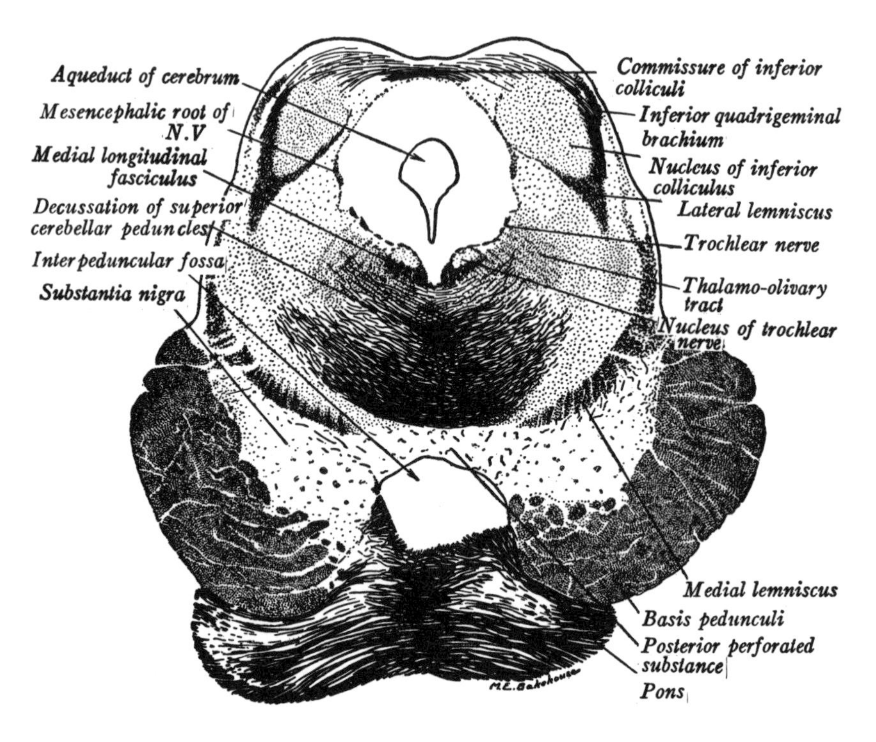

Source: S. W. Ranson and S. L. Clark, *The Anatomy of the Nervous System*, p. 228.

Figure 12–3. Midbrain at Level of Inferior Colliculus

superior cerebellar peduncle on its way to nucleus ruber and the thalamus. These relationships are exemplified in Fig. 12–3. Medial and ventral of the collicular nuclei and dorsal of the nucleus of the trochlear nerve lies a lightly staining area surrounding the cerebral aqueduct that is known as the periaqueductal gray. It is a part of the reticular formation, which is considered elsewhere. Ventral to the medial lemniscus and the decussation of the superior cerebellar peduncle lies a large mass of gray matter, the *substantia nigra,* which extends from the interpeduncular fossa at the midline nearly to the lateral surface of the midbrain. It is closed off laterally by the bulge of the cerebral peduncles, composed of corticospinals and corticobulbars, moving down from the internal capsule to the brain stem and the cord.

At the level of the superior colliculi the trochlear nucleus has ended and the oculomotor nucleus (III) has taken up its position just medial to the medial longitudinal fasciculus and just ventral of the periaqueductal gray. Fibers of the oculomotor nerve emerge from the ventral surface of the midbrain close to the midline, crossing in their passage the medial surface of the nucleus ruber. These structures can be seen in Fig. 12–4. *Nucleus ruber* lies just lateral to the dorsal and ventral teg-

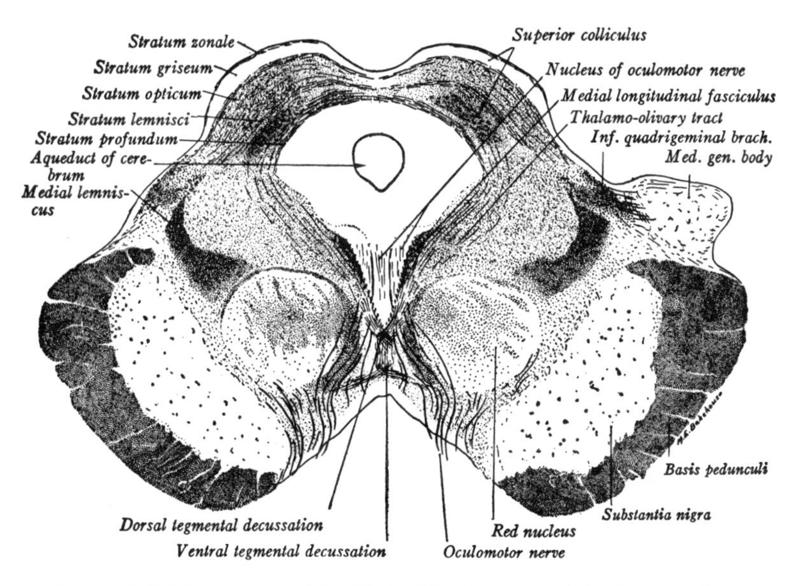

Source: S. W. Ranson and S. L. Clark, *The Anatomy of the Nervous System*, p. 229.

Figure 12–4. Mid Brain at Level of Superior Colliculus

mental decussation, the latter of which includes rubral fibers to rubrospinal and rubroreticular pathways.

Cerebral Peduncles

The cerebral peduncles carrying all cortical fibers from the internal capsule downstream may be subdivided into discrete bundles of fibers coming from specific centers. Most laterally lie the occipito- and temporopontine bundles; just inside this lies the large corticospinal tract with a small lateral corticobulbar tract on its dorsolateral edge. The frontopontile tract occupies most of the rest of the peduncle, except for a small, medially placed corticobulbar bundle. These structures are

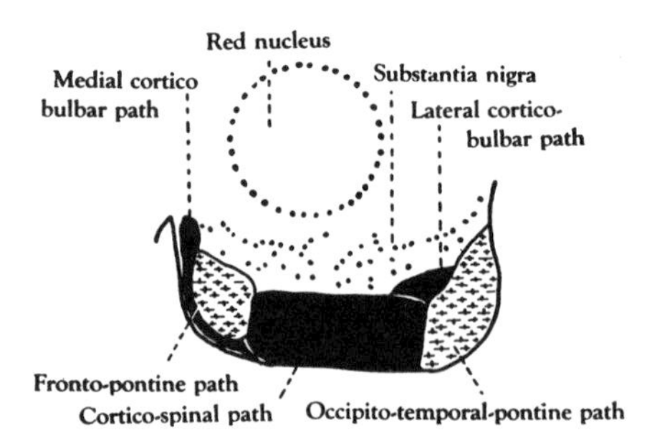

Source: C. U. Ariëns Kappers, G. Carl Huber, and Elizabeth C. Crosby, *The Comparative Anatomy of the Nervous System of Vertebrates, Including Man* (Vol. 2; New York: Hafner Publishing Company, 1960), p. 1459.

Figure 12–5. Divisions of the Right Cerebral Peduncle

illustrated in Fig. 12–5. The extent of these corticopontile bundles (temporal, frontal, occipital, and corticobulbar) indicates the importance of the fiber interconnections between various areas of the cortex and pontile and medullary centers, leading to the cross connection to the cerebellum and to cranial nerve nuclei.

The tectospinal tract has its origin in the tegmentum of the midbrain, primarily in the superior colliculus, although the inferior colliculus is believed to contribute no fibers to this fascicle. There is also a tectobulbar path which is uncrossed and runs through the tegmentum of the pons to end in the reticular formation.

DECEREBRATION

When the section of the brain stem in a decerebration passes rostral to the *superior colliculus* and passes down to the optic chiasm so as to spare the *red nucleus,* the *subthalamic,* and portions of the hypothalamus, a cat can rise to its feet and walk normally along a straight line with the body well supported and coordinated. Compared to this picture there is no coordinated movement or standing when the brain section is more caudal so as to remove the *red nucleus* and the *subthalamic nucleus.* Tone of muscle is retained but movement is deficient when the section spares only the *lateral vestibular nucleus* and portions of the reticular formation. So, muscle tone depends on vestibular and reticular facilitation, whereas locomotion requires the functional integrity of the midbrain centers of *nucleus ruber* and *subthalamicus.*

SOURCES AND ADDITIONAL READING

Crosby, E. C., T. Humphrey, and E. W. Lauer, *Correlative Anatomy of the Nervous System.* New York: The Macmillan Company, 1962.

Fulton, J., *Physiology of the Nervous System,* Chap. 11. New York: Oxford University Press, Inc., 1951.

Peele, T. L., *The Neuroanatomic Basis for Clinical Neurology.* New York: McGraw-Hill Book Company, 1961.

Ranson, S. W. and S. L. Clark, *The Anatomy of the Nervous System.* (10th ed.), Chaps. 11, 12, 16. Philadelphia: W. B. Saunders Company, 1959.

Rasmussen, A. T., *Principal Nervous Pathways.* New York: The Macmillan Company, 1945.

Riley, H. A., *An Atlas of the Basal Ganglia, Brain Stem, and Spinal Cord.* New York: Hafner Publishing Co., Inc., 1960.

Villiger, E. and A. T. Rasmussen, *Atlas of Cross Section Anatomy of the Brain.* New York: McGraw-Hill Book Company, 1951.

Thirteen

AUDITION

If we examine the extent to which different animals depend for food and protection upon specific sensory information, we cannot help but see the way this dependence shifts from one sense to another as we go up or down the evolutionary scale. The lower forms of the fish and amphibians depend largely on olfactory data; this drops out in the avian forms, comes back in the carnivores, and declines again in the primates. The main distance receptors in the primates and other mammals are hearing and sight. Hearing will be considered in this chapter and sight in the next.

The sense of hearing is dependent upon vibrations in the air of the order of 15-24,000 cycles/sec. These strike the eardrum and are transmitted by the chain of ossicles in the middle ear to the oval window and thence to the lymph of the cochlear duct. The *tympanum*, or eardrum, is at the inner end of the external auditory meatus and closes it off in the form of a concave bow. To the inner side of the upper part of this membrane is attached the first of the three ossicles that are situated in the middle ear. This is the *malleus* (hammer), whose rounded knob fits into the socket in the head of the *incus* (anvil). The small foot of the incus articulates in its turn with the *stapes* (stirrup). The foot of the *stapes* fits tightly to the *oval window* and is the agent for transmitting the oscillations to the lymph of the cochlear duct. These bones and their relation to the tympanum are depicted in Fig. 13–1.

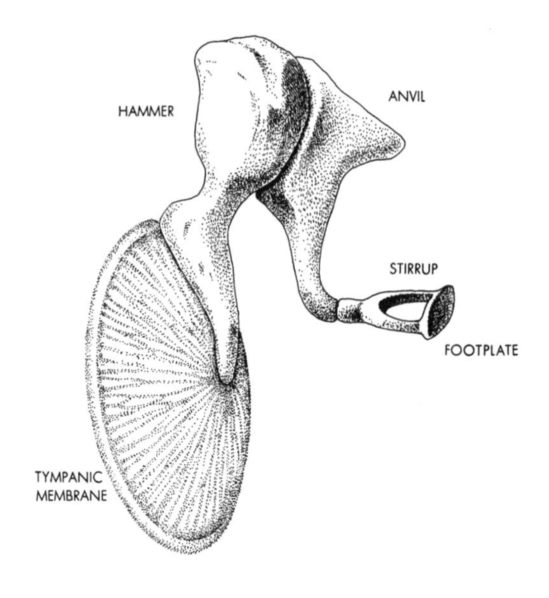

Source: *Scientific American,* August 1957, p. 68.

Figure 13–1. Bones of the Middle Ear and Tympanum

IMPEDANCE MATCHING

One of the most important functions of the middle ear is to transfer airborne vibrations into vibrations in the fluid perilymph of the cochlear canal without substantial loss of energy. The impedances to wave motion in these two media are vastly different. The middle ear mechanism is designed to overcome this difference. Part of the basis for matching or equalizing the two impedances is the relative areas of the tympanic membrane and the oval window, and the other part is the action of the three middle ear ossicles or bones. The area of the tympanum is given as 64 mm^2, while that of the oval window is 3.2 mm^2. Only 60–75 percent of the area of the tympanum is effective in this energy transfer. The other factor is the action of the ossicles, which act, not as a simple piston, but as a sequence of eccentrically connected levers increasing the pressure at the oval window. Air vibration at the tympanum displaces 44.8 mm^2 of that membrane, which is 14 times the area of the oval window. The action of the ossicles increases this, overcoming also the inertia and friction of the ossicular chain, so that there is a total pressure gain at the oval window of 17–21 times the pressure on the tympanum. This pressure gain goes a long way toward matching the impedance of the inner ear fluid to that of the air. This does not account, however, for the amazing sensitivity of the human ear as much as other features to be described later.

When the oscillation of sound reaches the oval window it becomes fluid-borne and sets up in the cochlear duct a wave pattern which affects the *basilar membrane* that divides the cochlear duct in half horizontally. The wave motion, after being transmitted to the basilar membrane, is transposed into a nerve impulse and audible sound by the tiny hair cells in the *organ of Corti*. These, then, are the transducers of mechanical energy into nervous impulse.

ORGAN OF CORTI

In the *organ of Corti*, the hair cells are surrounded by supporting cells and set in a firm framework provided by the inner and outer pillars. All this is supported on the basilar membrane. The tiny hair tufts which penetrate beyond the membrane surface of the hair cells are slightly embedded in the tectorial membrane, a thick, heavy, viscous, tongue-like structure which dorsally covers most of the organ of Corti. When sound waves cause oscillation of the basilar membrane, the hair cells are pushed against the tectorial membrane and fire an impulse. But the action of the two membranes and the intervening hair cells is not a simple reciprocating function. The basilar membrane is attached medially to the bony spiral lamina, ventral and medial to the attachment of the tectorial membrane. The basilar membrane is attached laterally, somewhat loosely, to the spiral ligament, while the tectorial membrane is attached laterally to the lateral surface of the organ of Corti. When pressure is exerted on the under surface of the basilar membrane both membranes tend to move together. However, their different axes of rotation, due to their different attachments, force the two membranes to slide across one another radially and longitudinally. Since the hair tufts are embedded in the tectorial membrane, the sliding across one another results in a shearing action between the hair tufts and the tectorial membrane.

The organ of Corti is the sound receptor mechanism wherein the transduction of fluid-borne waves to nerve impulse takes place. It rests on the basilar membrane, which divides the cochlear duct into a *scala tympani* and a *scala vestibuli*. The organ of Corti extends like a scaffold between the basilar membrane and the tectorial membrane.

The inner and outer pillars are flanked by a number of supporting cells which support the sensitive hair cells. There is usually one inner hair cell and two or three outer hair cells. As described already, the hair tufts emerging from the upper surface of the hair cell are embedded in the tectorial membrane above and when wave action pushes the basilar membrane upward, a tiny shearing action of the hairs against the tectorial membrane initiates impulses in the auditory portion of the 8th nerve. These structures can be seen in Fig. 13–2. It is this effect of even

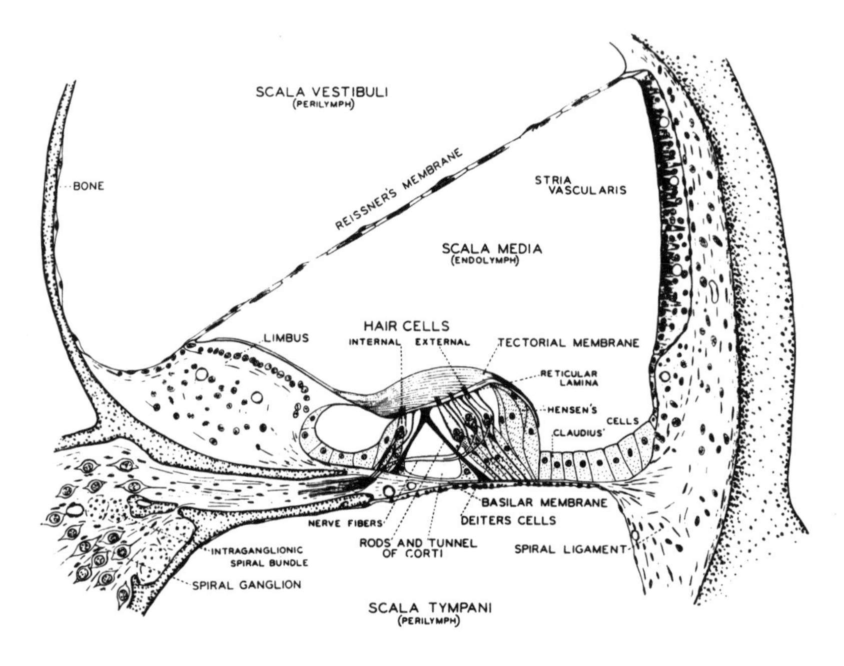

Source: *The Journal of the Acoustical Society of America,* Vol. 34, No. 8, Part 2 (Sept. 1962), p. 1379.

Figure 13–2. Organ of Corti, Detail

the most minute shearing action which gives rise to the amazing sensitivity of the ear. At the lowest intensity of audible sound a movement of the tympanic membrane of 10^{-9} dyne/cm^2, or less than the diameter of the hydrogen atom, will produce sound sensation. The double action (1) of the tympanum–chain of ossicles in matching the impedance of air pressure and fluid and (2) of the shearing action on the hair cells accounts for the fact that under the most favorable circumstances the human ear is considered to be more sensitive than many of the electronic instruments used to measure its sensitivity.

The membranous labyrinth of the inner ear shows a potential difference between the hair cells and the endolymph of the scala media, as is true of other sensory receptors. The endolymph of the scala media is polarized positively, the hair cells of the organ of Corti negatively, relative to the perilymph. Bekesy showed the potential of the endolymph to be +80mv relative to the perilymph of the scala vestibuli and scala tympani. The source of this polarization of the scala media is the stria vascularis on the lateral external edge of the scala media. If the blood supply fails, the potential falls immediately to zero. The detail of this potential difference is illustrated in Fig. 13–3. It has not been clearly demonstrated, but the presumption is that stimulation of the hair cells involves a depolarization process.

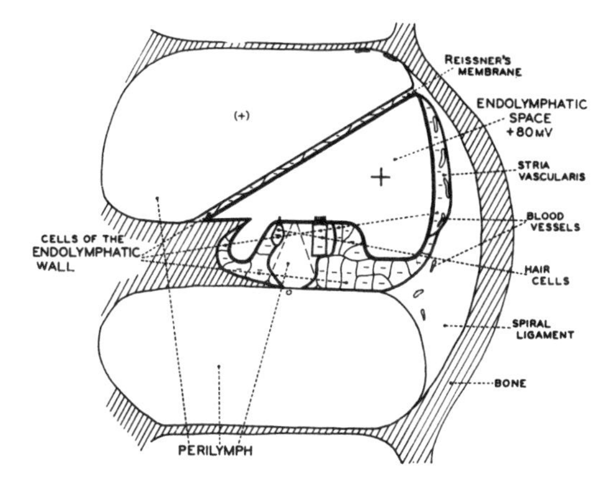

Source: *The Journal of the Acoustical Society of America,* Vol. 34, No. 8, Part 2 (Sept. 1962), p. 1377.

Figure 13–3. Difference in Potential between Endolymph and Cells of Corti

Inner and Outer Hair Cells

The inner hair cells differ in shape from the outer hair cells. The inner hair cell is slanted to lie along the inner pillar; and from the cuticular region at the top, where the neck is small, it enlarges to form a rounded flask shaped cell body at the bottom. The outer hair cells are slanted in the opposite direction to parallel the outer pillar. Their shape is like an elongated test tube with a bulbous base. (See Figs. 13–4 and 13–5.) Both the inner and outer hair cells have numerous mito-

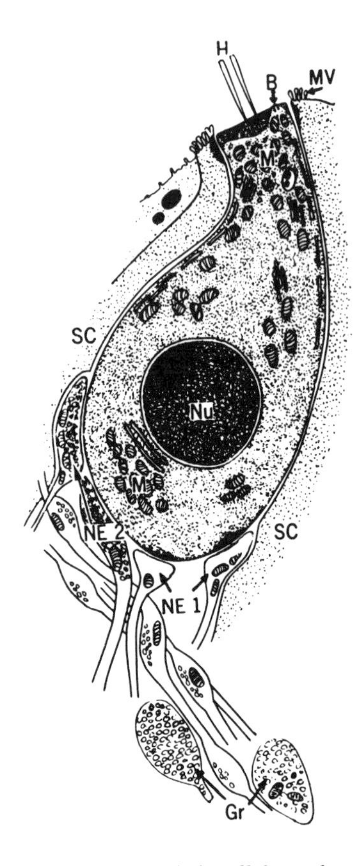

Schematic drawing of an inner hair cell from the guinea pig. At the surface hairs (H), a basal body (B) and microvilli (MV) are seen. In the subcuticular region rich accumulation of mitochondria (M) and other cytoplasmic organelles are found. Nu is the nucleus and below the nucleus are a few granulated membranes. Below the base of the cell two kinds of nerve endings are indicated (NE1 and NE2). In this region several large granulated structures (Gr) are normally found. SC represents supporting cells.

Source: William D. Neff (ed.), *Contributions to Sensory Physiology* (New York: Academic Press, 1965), p. 11.

Figure 13–4. Diagram of Inner Hair Cell

chondria both above and below the nucleus. Both of them also have *basal bodies* at their cuticular edge which are supposed to be activated by the hair tufts (stereocilia) bending against the tectorial membrane. It is believed that the hair tufts, or stereocilia, act as microlevers transmitting

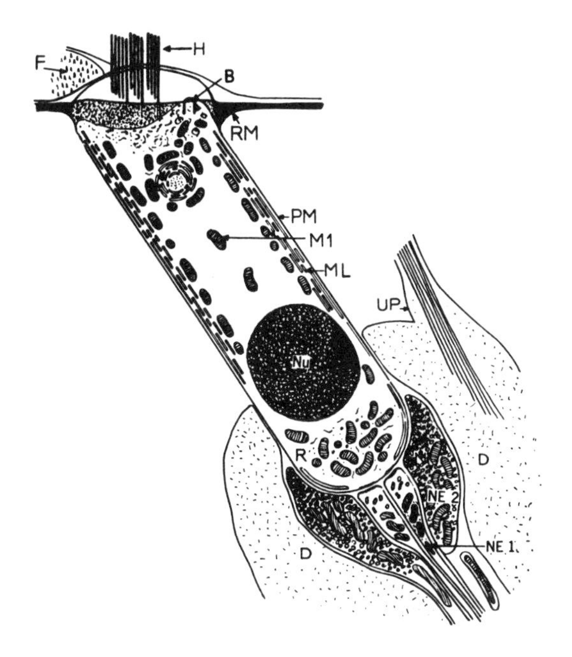

Schematic drawing of an outer hair cell and its nerve endings and supporting cells. H = hairs on the surface; B = basal body; RM = reticular membrane; PM = plasma membrane; ML = parietal membranes; Nu = nucleus; R = Retzius' body (mitochondria); D = Deiters' cell; NE1 = afferent, sparsely granulated nerve endings; UP = phalangeal process; F = microvilli; M1 = centrally located mitochondria.

Source: William D. Neff, *Contributions to Sensory Physiology,* p. 16.

Figure 13–5. Diagram of Outer Hair Cell

mechanical energy to the basal body by way of the cuticular plate. The basal body is believed, then, to be the essential excitable structure of the hair cells.

The bottom of the hair cells is rounded as the bottom of a flask and does not show the same linkage to neurons that most other sensory receptors do. The rounded bottom of the hair cell is a continuous membrane, with the nerve ending across a microgap after the pattern of the synapse. Since the nerve fiber does not enter the hair cell, the relationship of generator current to nerve impulse, found in other receptors, cannot here apply. Some investigators prefer to consider the hair cell as

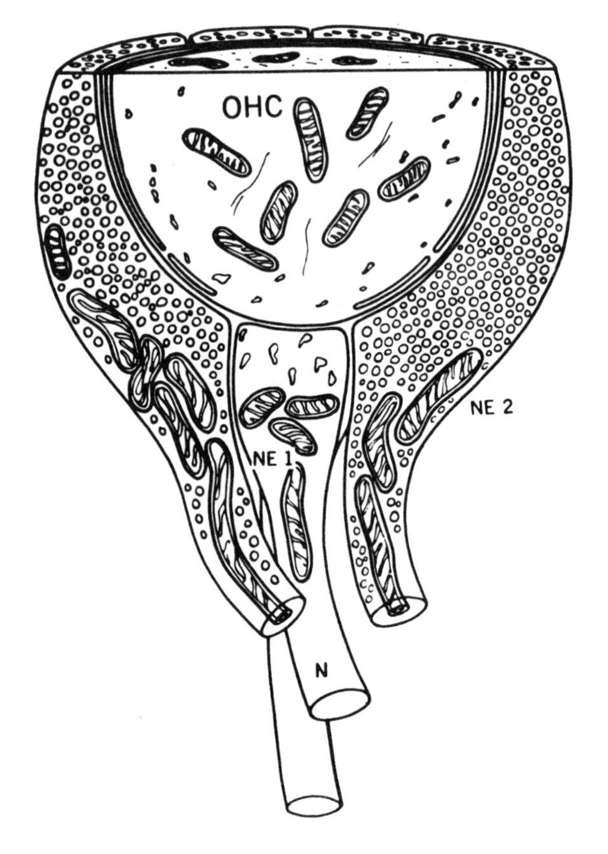

Base of outer hair cell (OHC) surrounded by two kinds of nerve endings. One form (NE1) is sparsely granulated and has a typical synaptic contact region, sometimes even a synaptic bar. It is evidently of afferent nature. The other form (NE2) is densely granulated and presumably of efferent nature. It has a double membrane inside the hair cell's plasma membrane. N is a nerve fiber.

Source: William D. Neff, *Contributions to Sensory Physiology*, p. 28.

Figure 13–6. Two Types of Nerve Endings on Outer Hair Cell

the first neuron in the auditory path. Such a consideration would imply that the connection to the neuron is a true synaptic type gap. (See Fig. 13–6.)

At the base of both inner and outer hair cells there are two different kinds of nerve endings. The nerve ending #1 is a true afferent path leading to the cochlear nuclei and temporal cortex. The nerve ending type #2 seems clearly to be efferent. It may be the end-station of the olivocochlear path from the superior olive. This ending is more granular than type #1 and approximates both sides of the rounded bottom, whereas the nerve ending #1 approximates the middle of the base of the hair cell. Type #2 ending seems to be efferent and inhibitory, and to be the only portion of the hair cell where cholinesterase is found. This makes it likely that acetylcholine is the transmitter, for strychnine will block the inhibitory action.

Excessive stimulation can severely damage the *organ of Corti,* as is seen in persons subjected to great sound intensities over extended periods. The wave pattern which is most harmful is in the low range below 1000 cps. In this range the middle ear has its own damping mechanism. Two middle ear muscles, the *tensor tympani* and the *stapedius,* will increase the stiffness of the motion of the ossicles. The tensor tympani is attached to the malleus, and the stapedius to the neck of the stapes. They both act to pull the bones to which they are attached, at right angles to the direction of motion of the ossicular chain, thus damping the vibrations reaching the oval window.

The human ear is not equally sensitive at all frequencies. It requires a greater intensity at slow vibrations of 50 cps and at fast vibrations of 16,000 cps for just barely audible sound than it does for vibrations of 1600–6000 cps. The curve illustrating the alteration of intensity with vibrations per second needed for minimal sensation is shown in Fig. 13–7.

The organ of Corti has a differential sensitivity depending on the particular frequency (cycles per second) of the sound wave. From the intensity curve it is evident that the intensity which corresponds to 10^{-9} cm movement of the tympanic membrane gives rise to audible sound only between 1600 and 6000 cps. Only in the middle range of sound waves do we have the greatest sensitivity.

SOUND INTENSITY

The intensity of sound, of which we have been speaking, is usually measured in terms of the unit known as a "decibel." This forms an arbitrary scale ranging from the faintest audible sound to the limit of the ear's endurance. A rustle of leaves in a gentle breeze has a value of 10 decibels (db), a whisper at four feet = 20, a conversational voice = 50, busy street noise = 60, riveter = 97, loud thunder = 120, limit of ear's endurance = 130. (Table 13–I.) Intensity is only one of the three qualities of the sound wave. It is a direct reflection of the amplitude of the

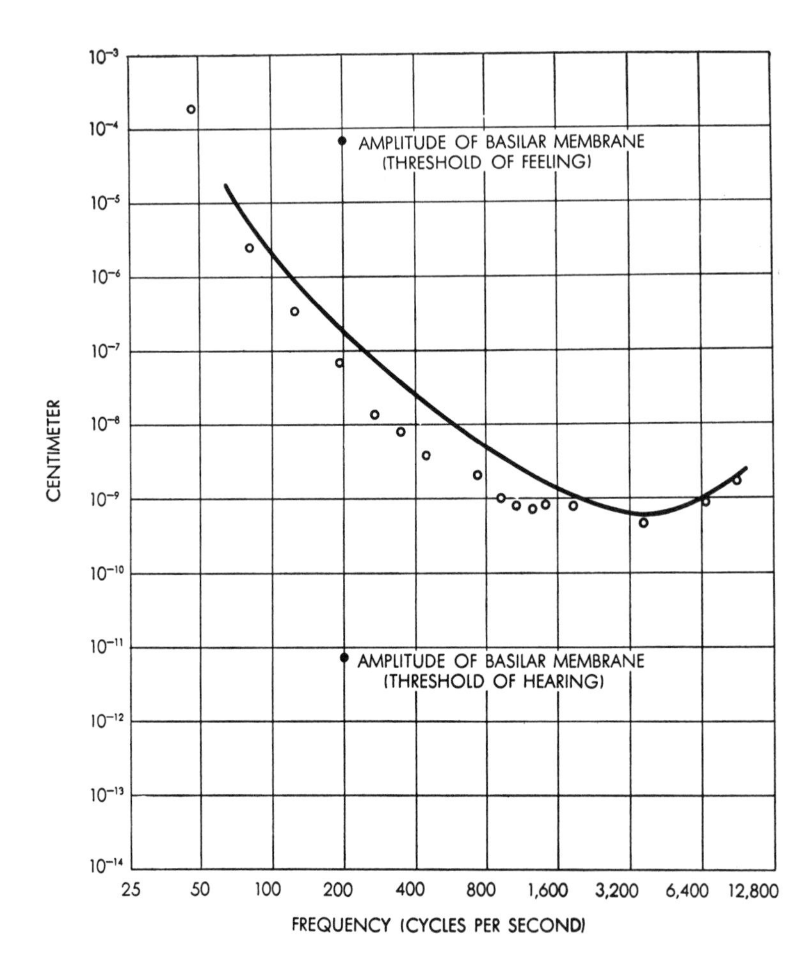

Sensitivity of the ear is indicated by this curve, in which the amplitude of the vibrations of the tympanic membrane in fractions of a centimeter is plotted against the frequency of sound impinging on the membrane. Diameter of hydrogen atom is 10^{-8} centimeter.

Source: *Scientific American,* August 1957, p. 70.

Figure 13–7. Sensitivity of the Ear

sound wave—the greater the amplitude, obviously, the greater the intensity. The other two characteristics of sound are *tone,* which depends on the frequency in cycles per second, and *timbre,* which is the quality

Table 13–I

Loudness (in Decibels)

140	Limit of ear's endurance
120	Loud thunder
100	Boiler shop
80	Pneumatic drill
50	Conversation
40	Average office noise
20	Whisper
0	Threshold of hearing

that distinguishes different instruments or different voices from each other. Timbre is dependent on the particular overtones that a voice or instrument transmits, and each instrument and most voices have different composite results. The difference between a basso and a tenor singing the same note is determined exclusively by the different overtones produced. A thin note has almost no harmonics or overtones; a full rich one has many harmonics and overtones. (See Fig. 13–8.)

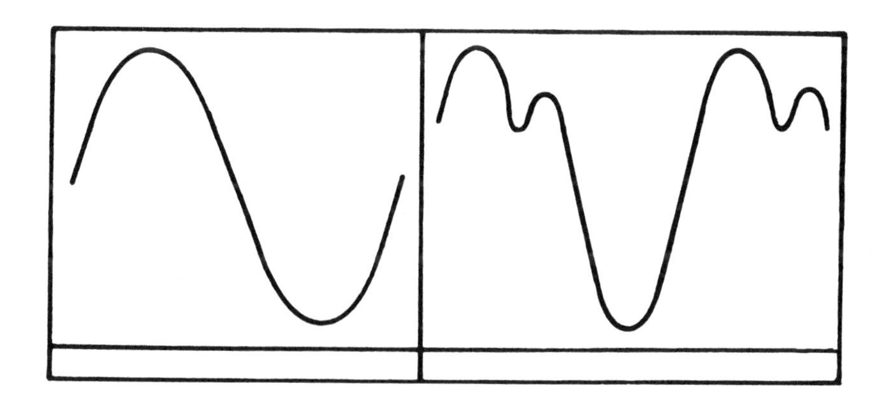

Figure 13–8. Comparison of Wave Forms Produced by Tuning Fork (Pure Tone) and by French Horn Playing the Same Note

TONE DIFFERENTIATION

The early theory of the action of the basilar membrane, developed by Helmholtz, considered this membrane as a selective resonator which responded in different locations depending on the wavelength of the sound, much as the strings in a piano. This theory assumed that the basilar membrane was under tension down its entire length, similar to a series of piano strings. Studies by Bekesy have shown that the membrane is relatively relaxed and not under tension. The most acceptable current theory is then that the membrane responds to the sound wave throughout its entire length, but responds with maximal displacement at the point corresponding to the wavelength entering from the outside. This is known as the traveling wave theory.

As we have already seen, the cochlear duct is divided horizontally by the basilar membrane. And it is this membrane which responds in different areas by maximal displacement when different tones impinge on the ear. For this to occur there must be different widths of membrane within the cochlear duct. This is actually true, for the basilar membrane is widest at the top of the cochlea and shortens progressively toward the base. This alteration in width is directly related to maximum displacement of tones of different wavelengths. The low tones are transmitted by the widest part of the basilar membrane, the high tones by the narrowest part. The topographic relation of tones to divisions of the cochlear duct is as follows: The top turn of the snail-like cochlear duct is sensitive to frequencies from about 60–500 cps, the middle turn responds to frequencies from 500 to about 1700 or 1800, while the basal turn accounts for frequencies from 1800 to about 20,000 or higher. (See Fig. 13–9.) This disproportionate spread of frequencies along the basilar membrane allows greater sensitivity in the middle range of frequencies, where the range of audible speech occurs. By contrast the lower five octaves are crowded into the short turn at the apex of the coiled canal. This topographic distribution of the sensitive areas of the cochlea is reflected by a similar topographic relationship in the medial geniculate body of the thalamus and also in the auditory part of the brain, as is indicated in Fig. 13–10. In the cat and dog, on which most of this work has been done, the low tones are recorded at the most anterior portion of the gyrus, while the high tones are recorded in the posterior part. In man the orientation is reversed, with the low tones on the posterior portion and the high tones anteriorly. The human auditory area is on the upper surface of the *superior temporal gyrus* and is separated from the parietal lobe by the lateral cerebral (sylvian) fissure.

SOUND LOCALIZATION

Sound localization is not dependent on most of the facets of audition discussed thus far. It is true that the sound has to be within the audible

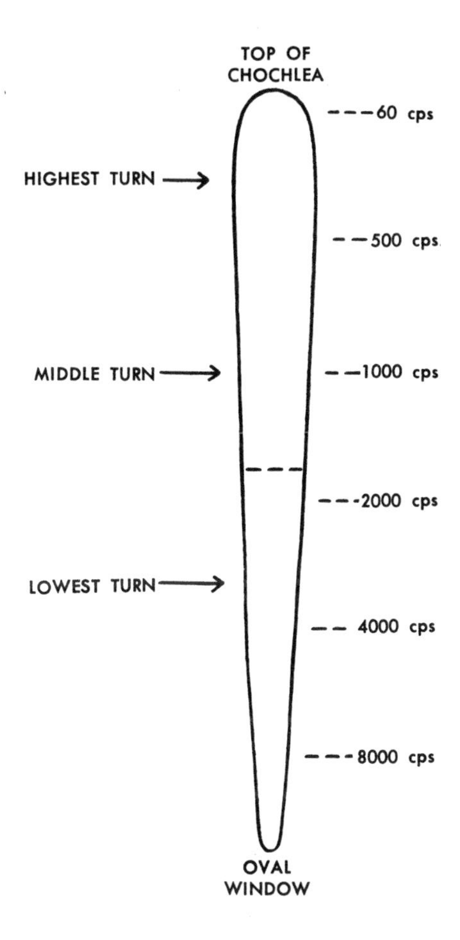

Drawing by Brenda Sutherland

Figure 13–9. Cycles per Second Superimposed on the Turns of the Basilar Membrane

range for detection, but aside from this its localization is a function of angular distance from the vertical plane or horizontal plane through the two ears. It is, then, a localization based on both a slightly different amplitude in the two ears and, more importantly, on the difference in

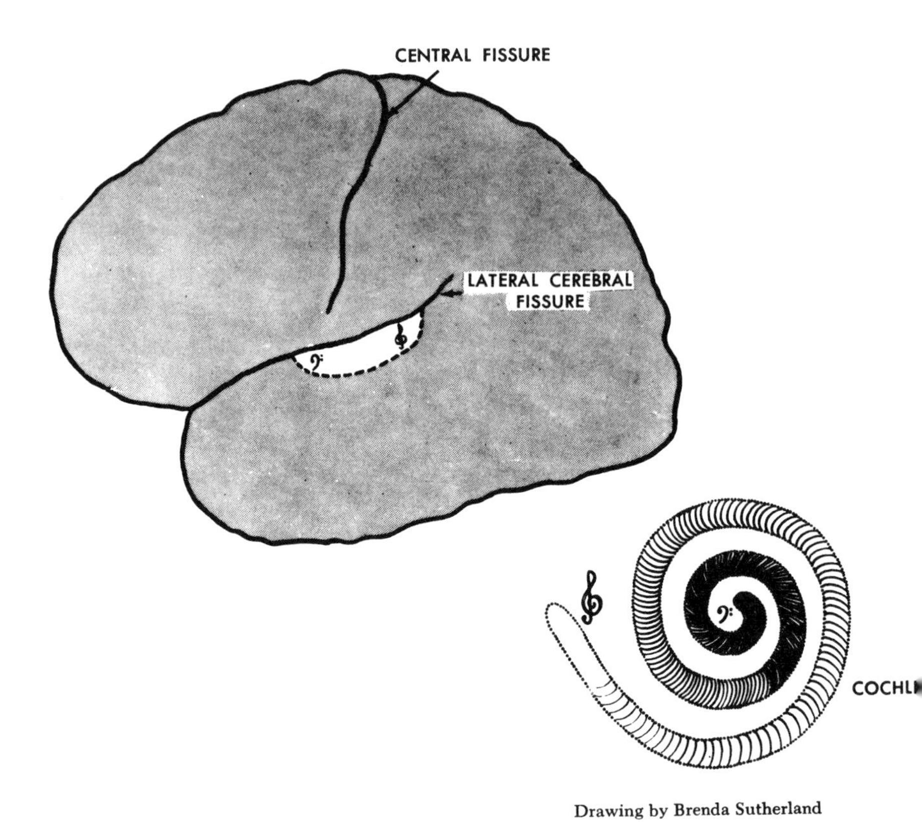

Drawing by Brenda Sutherland

Figure 13–10. Topographic Correspondence of Cochlear and Cortical Location of Different Frequencies

the time of arrival of the sound at the two ears. This localization by difference in arrival time can be very sensitive indeed. A difference in time of arrival at the two ears of 500 milliseconds is the maximum difference if the sound comes directly from the side. If the sound comes from another angle the time of interval will be even smaller. The localization, as well as the phenomenon of binocular beats, depends on the evaluation and comparison of sound received by the two ears. This must occur above the cochlear level and, as we will see, there are bilateral pathways from each cochlea to the cortex. The need for a comparison of the sounds from the two ears is shown most clearly when there is no difference in time of arrival. If an individual is blindfolded, sounds which are directly overhead, behind and in the midline, or in front and in the midline are difficult to localize accurately. Because of the added visual experience and confirmation, sound directly ahead can be localized better than those overhead or behind and in midline.

AUDITORY PATHWAYS

As was indicated earlier, the localization of sound depends upon the comparison of the auditory sensations above the level of the cochlear nuclei. An examination of this comparison requires a consideration of the auditory pathways after the 8th cranial nerve leaves the spiral ganglion, in which are located the cell bodies of the auditory nerve. Immediately on entering the brain the fibers bifurcate and pass to terminations in *dorsal and ventral cochlear nuclei.* Each fiber is reported to synapse with 75 to 100 cells of the nucleus. Each cell of the nucleus must also receive terminations from many incoming fibers, for there are three times as many cells in the cochlear nuclei as in the spiral ganglion. The different components of tone and noise are quite possibly separated in the cochlear nuclei. Tone and noise sensitivity do exist in parallel. Furthermore, we know that the cochlear nuclei of each side contain three replicas of the organ of Corti. The fibers from the *ventral cochlear nucleus* cross at this level, some fibers making a synapse in the superior olive, where many reflex connections are made. This crossing over of fibers is called the *trapezoid body.* The fibers from the ventral nucleus also have synaptic connections in both superior olives. The fibers that leave each superior olive, or which pass through it, represent, then, sensory impulses from both the contralateral and ipsilateral auditory hair cells.

The axons from the *dorsal cochlear nucleus* cross the midline dorsal to the inferior cerebellar peduncle, and after crossing sweep down to pass through, if not to synapse in, the superior olive of the opposite side. The afferent fibers from the cochlear nuclei form a bundle lying on the dorsolateral surface of the midbrain. They sweep rostrally and dorsally through the midbrain as the *lateral lemniscus,* to provide for a synapse in the *nucleus of the lateral lemniscus,* and then enter the *inferior colliculus.* The inferior colliculus is the starting point for many automatic reflex circuits, particularly those dependent on auditory information. With the *superior colliculus,* it forms the midbrain roof or tectum in which the tectospinal pathway originates.

In forms lower in the phylogenetic scale than mammals the lateral lemniscus terminates chiefly in the *nuclei isthmi* and in the counterpart of the *inferior colliculus,* the *corpus posterius.* Some of the fibers that

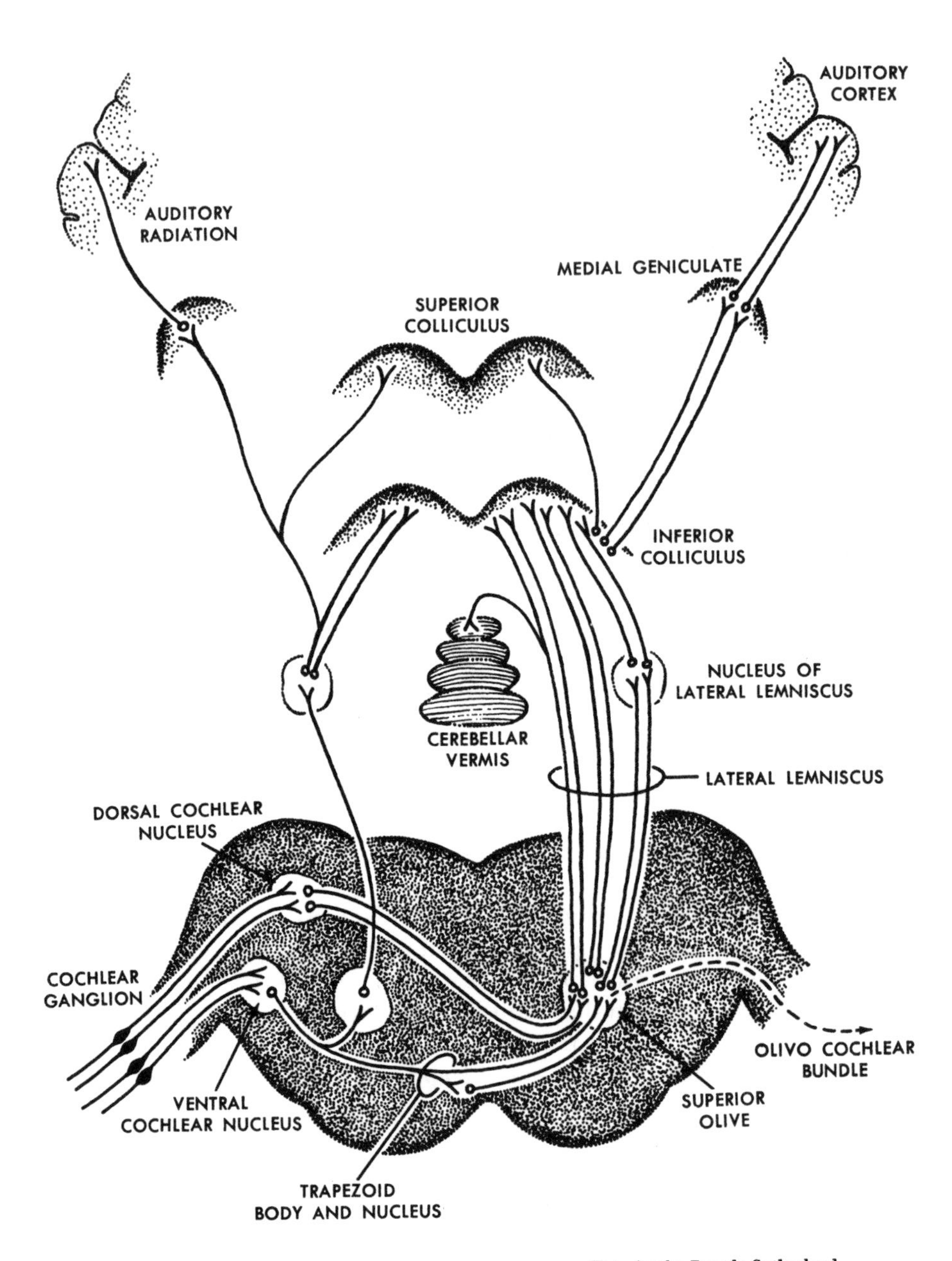

Drawing by Brenda Sutherland

Figure 13–11. Elements of the Auditory Pathway

enter the inferior colliculus do not synapse there. Some pass through directly to the *medial geniculate* body of the thalamus. All auditory fibers synapse in the *medial geniculate* nucleus. From there, after synapse, the impulse continues laterally to end on the upper rounded surface of the *superior temporal gyrus,* partly hidden behind the lateral cerebral fissure. These connections are indicated in Fig. 13–11. The reflex connections from the *inferior colliculus* include, besides connections to the *superior colliculus,* connections to the *trochlear (IV) nucleus* and thus to the *medial longitudinal fasciculus* and the other nuclei for eye movement. The fiber system which carries auditory information to the vermis of the cerebellum possibly arises as a branch of the lateral lemniscus.

Rasmussen has demonstrated that an efferent bundle of fibers, arising within the superior olivary nucleus, passes out to terminate within the cochlea of the opposite side. They appear to make contact with the type #2 nerve ending on the inner and outer hair cells discussed above. Stimulation of this olivocochlear bundle will suppress the auditory response to standard clicks. In its turn the superior olive receives fibers from the auditory cortex, the medial geniculate nucleus, and the inferior colliculus. In each cochlear nerve there are 25,000 nerve fibers, which is approximately the number of hair cells, and gives a 1:1 ratio of hair cells to nerve fibers. By contrast there are only 500 olivocochlear fibers, making their ratio to hair cells 1:50. When the olivocochlear bundle is stimulated by a pulse of 100 cycles per second, the threshold for the afferent neural response is raised over the normal, after a slight delay, by as much as 25db. This rise in threshold becomes the measure of inhibition.

This inhibition provides a selecting and organizing mechanism which can screen out from the auditory receptive area sensory data which is of little significance to the animal at that moment. As is true in vision also, this selective control of incoming messages rests upon the significance to the organism. And the significance at one period may screen out data which, under different conditions and patterns of significance, would be transmitted to higher centers.

SOURCES AND ADDITIONAL READING

Bekesy Commemorative Supplement, "*J. Acoustical Soc. America*, Sept. 1962, Pt. 2.

The CIBA Collection of Medical Illustrations, Vol. I, *Nervous System.* CIBA Pharmaceutical Company, 1953.

Handbook of Physiology, Sec. I., Chaps. 23, 24. Washington, D.C.: American Physiol. Soc., 1959.

Neff, W. D., ed., *Contributions to Sensory Physiology,* Vol. 1. New York: Academic Press, 1965.

Rasmussen, G. L. and W. F. Windle, *Neural Mechanisms of Auditory and Vestibular Systems.* Springfield, Ill.: Charles C. Thomas, Publisher, 1960.

Ruch, T. and J. Fulton, *Medical Physiology and Biophysics* (18th ed.), Chap. 17. Philadelphia: W. B. Saunders Company, 1961. (See 19th ed., Chap. 18.)

Walsh, G., *Physiology of the Nervous System,* Chap. 8. New York: Longmans Green & Co., Inc., 1959.

Wever, E. G. and M. Lawrence, *Physiological Acoustics.* Princeton, N.J.: Princeton University Press, 1954.

Fourteen

VISION

The visual sense is one of the three distance receptors, and is the one on which primates and man depend most heavily. The degree of dependence on vision is seldom evident until visual sensory information is not available. Blind persons have to substitute either hearing or olfaction or both for vision. And when such substitution is unavoidable, it is surprising how much sensory discrimination is latent, and usually unrealized, in olfaction, hearing, and touch. The well known reports of Helen Keller and other blind persons make this abundantly clear. Distinctive identification on the basis of olfactory or auditory information is just as certain as it is with visual cues. But for all of us except the blind this substitution seldom occurs. To understand the importance of visual sensory input, it will be necessary to consider three major subdivisions: 1) the mechanics of the eye, including its dioptrics; 2) the physiology of its function; and 3) the neural pathways needed for both reflex and voluntary response to visual information.

MECHANICS OF THE EYE

Dioptrics

The eye as an optical instrument is made up in part of two separate chambers: a smaller one in front of the lens, the *aqueous chamber;* and a larger one behind it, the *vitreous chamber.* The *cornea,* on the outside of the eye, and the *lens* are concerned entirely with the refraction of light so that an image falls on the sensitive retinal receptors at the back of the eyeball. The cornea is curved in a convex bow so that light rays are partially refracted before they pass through the lens. After striking the cornea the light ray passes through the aqueous humor, a clear watery fluid that lies between the cornea and the lens. This fluid is replaced periodically and is a blood plasma filtrate which is drawn off through canals, the canals of Schlemm, adjacent to the *ciliary muscles* and the *iris,* and is then reabsorbed back into the venous system.

Lens and Accommodation

The lens is the most important functional element in the dioptric mechanism. This is shaped like a small onion with the front face flattened so that there is a different curvature on the front face from that on the back. The internal structure of the lens shows a laminated series of layers similar to the layers in an onion. The lens is not rigid in shape, and its shape and relative curvatures on the two faces change as the distance of objects away from the eye alters, so as to insure that the image falls on the retina whatever the distance of the object from the eye. This process of adjustment by the lens system is called accommodation and is carried out by the *ciliary muscles,* by which the lens is attached to the transparent filament capsule (zonule fibers) which surrounds it, and to the inside of the eyeball. These structures are depicted in Fig. 14–1. The ciliary muscles have their attachment to the sides of the eyeball at the point closest to the anterior edge of the vitreous humor, adjacent to the iris. When the ciliary muscle contracts, therefore, it moves toward its attachment and acts to relax the tension on the zonule fibers. This action allows the lens to assume its most rounded shape for visual accommodation of close objects. When the ciliary muscle relaxes it puts tension on the zonule fibers, thus flattening the lens for accommodation to distant objects. The mechanism of accommodation can be more easily understood by reference to Fig. 14–2. As a person gets older the lens stays flatter and is unable to assume a more rounded shape to bring near objects into sharp focus. This is the basis of the farsightedness of middle-aged and older persons. This farsightedness is called presbyopia. Nearsightedness, based upon the difficulty of ciliary muscles relaxing sufficiently for sharp focus, is called myopia. Hypermetropia is a form of farsightedness caused by the eyeball being a flattened sphere at

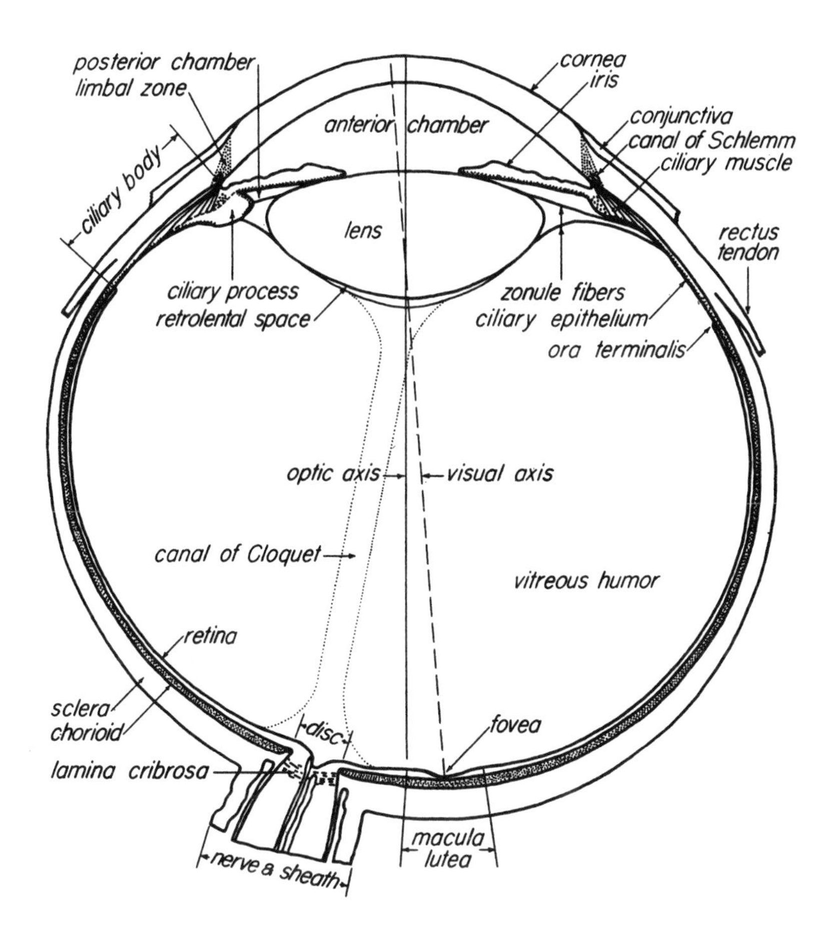

Source: Gordon Lynn Walls, *The Vertebrate Eye and Its Adaptive Radiations* (Bulletin No. 19, Cranbrook Institute of Science [Bloomfield Hills, Mich., 1942]), p. 7.

Figure 14–1. Horizontal Section through a Human Eye (Right Side)

the posterior, retinal surface. This is an abnormality of shape not dependent on lens action.

This action of accommodation produced by contraction or relaxation of the ciliary muscle is, of course, a response to nervous impulses which are triggered by the excitation of visual receptors. As we will see in considering the nervous pathways of the visual system, the reflex connections and activities based upon visual information are very extensive. These connections allow automatic adjustment of the accommo-

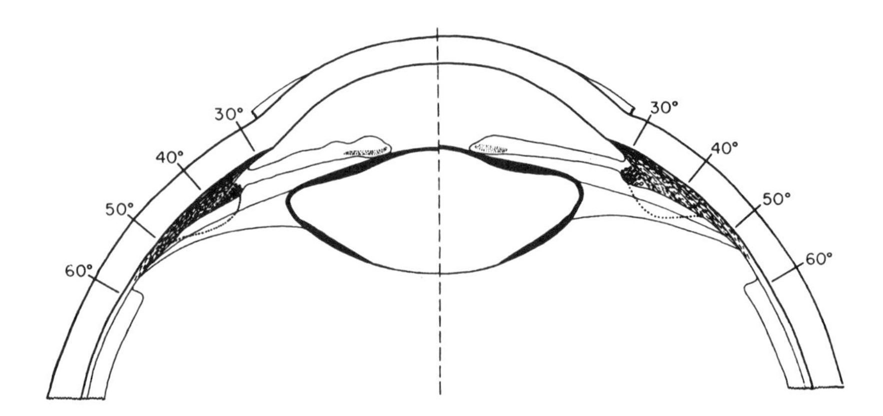

The left half of the diagram shows the structures in relaxation. The thickness of the lens capsule has been exaggerated one hundred times to bring out its local variations. On the right, accommodation; by reference to the angular scales, the movements of the various parts can be discerned. Note that the contraction of both the radial and circumferential portions of the ciliary muscle has stretched forward the smooth orbicular region of the ciliary body (to which most of the zonule fibers attach) and has bunched up the coronal region (bearing the ciliary processes, whose profiles are indicated by the dotted lines). The relaxation of the zonule fibers has permitted the elastic lens capsule to mold a bulge of sharpened curvature on the anterior surface of the lens. Note also that the sphincter muscle of the iris has contracted, closing down the pupil in its "accommodation reflex."

Source: Gordon Lynn Walls, *The Vertebrate Eye,* p. 31.

Figure 14–2. The Mechanism of Human Accommodation

dating mechanism by way of special nuclei in the midbrain. The accommodation reflex is dependent on impulses reaching the *visual cortex (area 17)* and then back to the *superior colliculus* and the *Edinger-Westphal nucleus.* The reflex of accommodation is triggered by visual impulses reaching the sensory receptive area in the occipital cortex, with an index that the retinal image is not clear. But how that visual sensation is coded to instruct the ciliary muscle to contract or relax is not known.

Light rays entering the eye first strike the cornea and are there partially refracted. The rays pass through the aqueous humor and enter the pupillary opening in the iris. After entering the iris they immediately strike the lens and are bent twice, once by the front face and, again, by the back face. Leaving the back face, the light rays transverse the vitreous humor and, successively, the accumulating fibers of the optic nerve, the ganglion cells, and the bipolar cells before they impinge on the light sensitive transducers, the rods and cones. In addition to the mere refraction of light rays, the lens inverts the image which falls upon the retina so that the image is not only a mirror image of the real object but is upside down as well.

Pupillary Reflex

While the lens-ciliary muscle system of accommodation takes care of the necessary refraction of light rays to focus the image on the retina, it does not control the amount of light entering the eye. This control is exercised at the pupil by both circular and radial muscle fibers in the iris. The iris lies just in front of the lens. When too much light or too much bright light enters the eye the circular fibers of the iris contract, reducing the size of the pupil—if need be, to a mere pinhole. The contraction of the pupil and the accommodation of the lens are almost always joined. In darkness or at dusk the radial fibers contract, opening up the pupil for the maximum admission of available light. The mechanism of the pupillary reaction, like that for accommodation, is triggered by reflex reactions to visual sensory input. The pupillary reflex is active at or before birth, while the accommodation reflex does not appear for several months after birth. These reflexes will be considered again under the section on nervous pathways. The pigment in the pigmented epithelium adjacent to the radial and circular muscles of the iris gives the eye color, blue, green, or brown.

Retina

Behind the lens lies the vitreous humor that fills the posterior chamber. It is a heavier and more gelatinous substance than the aqueous. It is clear and remains permanently without replacement. Posterior to the vitreous humor and opposite to the lens are the light sensitive elements in the retina. These sensitive transducers extend over the posterior half of the eyeball and slightly more forward than its equator. The elements are of two kinds, one for daylight vision and for color vision, called the *cones,* and the other for degrees of brightness only and for vision in dim light, called the *rods*. The distribution of the cones is different from that of the rods, the cones being concentrated on the central part of the back of the sphere and becoming sparser as they are distributed more peripherally. The rods, by contrast, are more numerous on the periphery and become scarcer toward the center of the retina. This distribution is correlated with daylight and dim light vision, for the most accurate daylight vision is in the center of the retina at the fovea (to be considered just below), while the most acute vision in dim light or dark is on the periphery of the retina. The optic nerve is displaced eccentrically toward the medial side of each eye to facilitate the junction at the optic chiasm. The part of the retina centered behind the lens is the "macula lutea," or yellow spot, in the center of which is the *fovea centralis*. Through built-in reflex circuits the function of the whole mechanism of accommodation is to project the image of an external object on the *fovea centralis*. This subtends an angle of 2 degrees and is the point of sharpest vision. It is also the point where there are no rods. In fact the fovea centralis, in its 0.3mm diameter, contains only cones, about 50,000 in number, and is therefore useless in the dark. Furthermore, the fovea has a second peculiarity. The supervening layers of cells in the remainder of the retina place the rods and cones farthest away from the light, with the bipolar and ganglion cells between them and the lens. The light rays coming into the eye have to pass through the ganglion and bipolar cell layers before reaching the layer of rods and cones. In the fovea, by way of contrast, the bipolar and ganglion cells are drawn aside at an oblique angle so that the cones are more directly exposed to the light rays. In this way much of the diffusion of lights rays, which characterizes other portions of the retina because of the supervening cell and fiber layers, is avoided, and the sharpest possible image is thrown on the most sensitive receptor site.

The diurnal retina is composed of both cones and rods intermixed, but predominantly cones. The nocturnal retina, by contrast, is almost entirely rods with only very occasional cone shaped elements in it. (See Fig. 14–3.) Whether there is a fovea in the nocturnal retina is not certain.

In addition to the straight line transmission in the retina from rod-cone to bipolar to ganglion cell, there are connections horizontal to the plane of the retina between various retinal elements. *Horizontal cells*, lying between the rod-cone layer and the bipolar layer, have their axons directed centrifugally and transmit impulses back up to the surrounding rods and cones. In addition, a cell with a horizontal plane of action, the *amacrine* cell, appears between the bipolar and ganglion cell layers. The amacrine cell may spread part of the bipolar impulse over the adjacent ganglion cells.

There is some evidence that there are centrifugal fibers in the retina running back from bipolar or ganglion cells or from the brain itself to *centrifugal bipolars* for subsequent transmission to the rods and cones. The details of these retinal layers can be seen in Fig. 14–4.

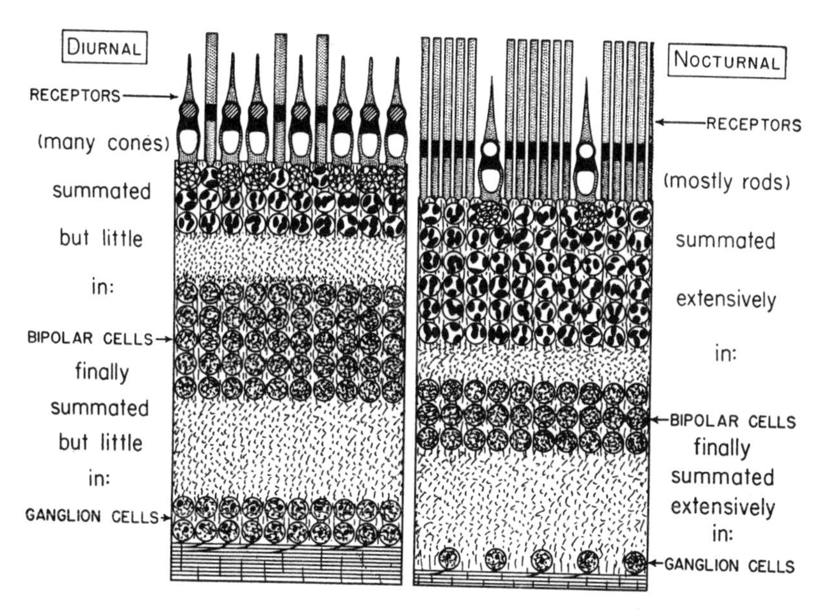

The diagrams represent two related species, one of which is diurnal and the other nocturnal. The characteristic differences in the relating thickness of the nuclear layers are the result of the visual-cell patterns and the differing extents of summation in optic nerve fibers.

Source: Gordon Lynn Walls, *The Vertebrate Eye,* p. 177.

Figure 14–3. Diurnal and Nocturnal Retina

In humans the retina is bounded externally by a choroid coat of fine vascular network. In the cat and other nocturnal animals this choroid coat is backed by a *tapetum,* which is a reflecting surface, to retain in the eye all available light rays during nighttime conditions.

The evidence from embryological development makes clear that the retina is an extension of the brain. The retina with its four cell layers has many of the characteristics of the cerebral cortex, including synapses between its neural elements. In embryonic development the optic vesicle pushes out from the brain and then folds back upon itself to form the optic cup. This double folding to form the optic cup is the anatomical reason that the bipolar and ganglion cell layers are between the light source and the rods and cones.

Convergence

When the two eyes are used together a third factor, *convergence,* is added to the agents of iris and lens in giving a sharp image. Convergence assures that the same object will be seen by the two eyes. Since the eyes

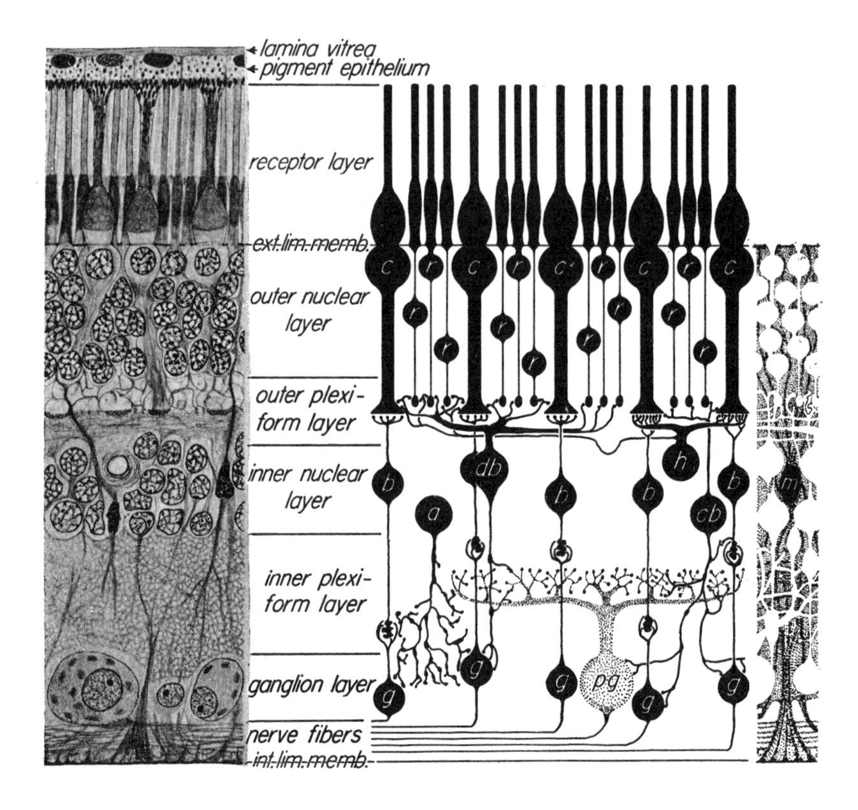

At the left, a vertical section through the retina in the nasal fundus, as it appears in ordinary histological preparations (fixation in Kolmer's fluid; nitrocellulose embedding; Mallory's triple stain, Heidenhain's hematoxylin and phloxine). x 500. (Note cross-section of capillary in inner nuclear layer).

At the right, a "wiring diagram" of the retina showing examples of its principal elements, as revealed in material impregnated with silver by the methods of Golgi. Based largely upon the work of Polyak.

a amacrine cell (diffuse type); *b, b-* bipolar cells (ordinary "midget" type); *c, c-* cones; *cb-* "centrifugal" bipolar, believed by Polyak to conduct outward through the retina rather than inward; *db-* diffuse bipolar, connecting with many visual cells—chiefly rods; *g, g-* ganglion cells (ordinary "midget" type); *h-* horizontal cell—its dendrites connecting only with cones and its axon with both rods and cones at some distance from the cell-body; *m*-Muller fiber—its ends forming the limiting membranes and its substance serving to insulate the nervous elements from each other except at synapses; *pg-* "parasol" ganglion cell (one of several giant types, connecting with many bipolars); *r, r-* rods.

Source: Gordon Lynn Walls, *The Vertebrate Eye,* p. 43.

Figure 14–4. Retinal Layers of Human Retina

usually are separated by a distance of from 55-70 mm, the two eyes see slightly different images of the one object. This gives roundness and shape to objects which are otherwise seen in one plane. The convergence of the two eyes and their integrated movement together is one of the primary functions of the neural pathway known as the *medial longitudinal fasciculus* mentioned in the sections on the pons and medulla. This integration is critical in the use of the visual horizon and orientation in space.

The distance apart of the eyes and their regular convergence provides, in addition, the basis for accurate perception of depth, and particularly relative distance away. The two eyes, since they see slightly different images of the same object, also see even greater differences between two or three different objects which are in view at the same time. This difference in image is interpreted as relative difference in depth. This disparity and the principle of convergence may be seen in Fig. 14–5. Primates and humans become very accurate in making this

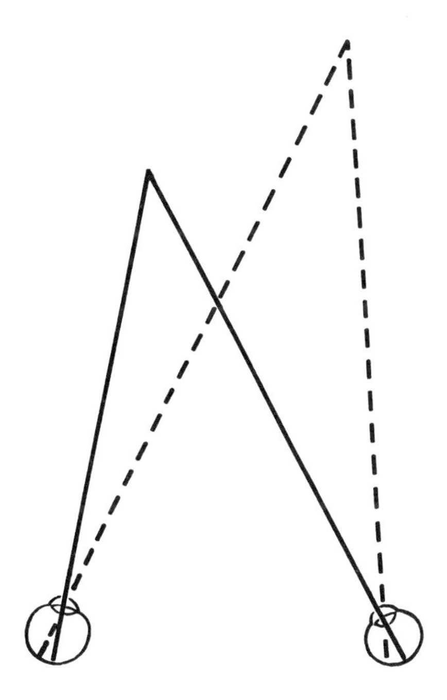

Drawing by Brenda Sutherland

Figure 14–5. Diagram of Binocular Convergence and Binocular Parallax

judgment; a difference in depth of 0.5 mm can be judged quite accurately at a distance of 10–15 feet, if the distance between the eyes is large. It can readily be seen that the difference in image depends entirely on the separation of the two eyes. The ability to discriminate above the horizontal plane, or to the left or right, again depends on the slight variation in the separation of the eyes under these different conditions.

PHYSIOLOGY OF VISION

In structure the rods and cones are tiny filaments which extend, from their cell nuclei, beyond the external limiting membrane toward the pigment layer, which is just inside the choroid coat of the eye. They are from 400-700 millimicra (mμ) in diameter, the cones being the thicker of the two. In terms of density on the retina there are many more rods than cones, there being 7-10 million cones out of a total of 115 million rods and cones combined. But each of these light sensitive elements does not have its own nervous channel to the brain receptor areas. The most reliable estimate has placed the figure for the number of optic fibers in each optic nerve at 1 million. With 115 mil-

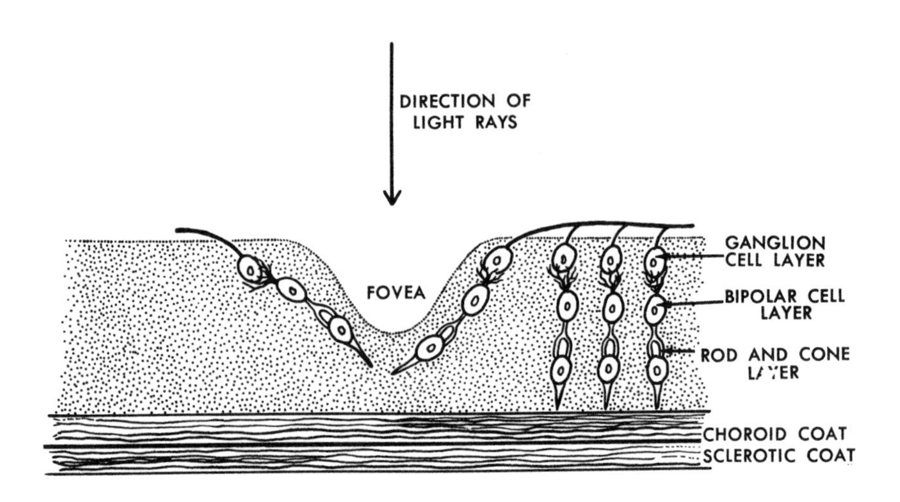

Drawing by Brenda Sutherland

Figure 14–6. Foveal Cones, Bipolar and Ganglion Cells

lion sensitive elements there has to be a substantial amount of concentration or funneling of several cone or rod fibers into a single bipolar or ganglion cell. There is also the convergence of more than one bipolar cell onto a single ganglion cell, especially from the rods. The axons of the ganglion cells form the optic nerve; and the point, nasal of the *fovea,* where the optic nerve leaves the eye is the blind spot, since there are no sensitive rods or cones at that point. The foveal cones, in the center of the *macula lutea,* do not exhibit this progressive concentration on fewer bipolar and ganglion cells and fibers. (For an illustration of foveal cones, see Fig. 14–6.) In fact, the fovea alone shows a strict 1:1 ratio of cones to bipolar cells and thence to ganglion cells and to fibers of the optic nerve. The two-point differentiation in visual acuity which measures less than 1 minute of angle is aided, then, by individual nerve fibers for each foveal cone.

Color Vision

The adequate stimulus for color vision is a narrow band of wavelengths extending from the short ultraviolet rays at below 397 mμ to the longer infrared heat waves above 723 mμ. This range of wavelengths contains the full color range of visual phenomena and the whites and grays as well. The wavelengths of the principal colors are: red, 723-647 mμ; orange, 647-585; yellow, 585-570, green, 521; blue, 480; indigo, 455-424; violet, 424-397. Many more hues are experienced than this limited list, but they are combinations of these principal hues or wavelengths. When all colors are combined we experience the sensation of white, and when white light is broken up by a prism we can see the color spectrum of which it is composed. (See Fig. 14–7.)

Colors are spoken of as unsaturated or saturated, depending on the presence or absence of white light in them. Pale pastels are unsaturated colors. When two colors fall on the same retinal element the result is different from the effect of either one alone. In addition, when two colors which are complementary fall on the same element, they will produce gray or grayish white. That is, each color process seems to cancel out the other.

In physiological function the cones and the rods respond differently. In order to account for the trichromatic basis of color sensation the cones must each exhibit three different color processes, or there must be three different kinds of cones. There are four photosensitive retinal pigments—rhodopsin and porphyropsin in the rods, and iodopsin and cyanopsin in the cones. These are all carotenoid proteins. They are continuously reformed after bleaching by light, with the help of vitamin A and enzyme activity.

Recent reports of experimental microelectrode studies give curves of spectral sensitivity corresponding to three retinal cone pigments, at 450, 540, and 590 mμ. It is likely then that there are three types of cones, each one containing principally one of these pigments, rather than (as supposed by some color theories) four or five types of cones. The chromatic response is made up of two or more distinct components, whereas the luminosity or brightness response is unitary. The retinal evidence favors a three-color, three-receptor system of color. This three-color system at the retinal cone level is processed in the retina so that it is encoded into a two-color, "on-off" signal at the color sensitive ganglion cell for transmission to the lateral geniculate nucleus. The density of the retinal cone pigment is 1 million molecules per cubic micron (the same as rhodopsin), and the pigment is present throughout the outer cone segment rather than being concentrated in a restricted spot.

The rods, by contrast, show only one qualitative scale—that of brightness, from black through the shades of gray to white. The action of light on rhodopsin (and possibly the other carotenoid proteins), in addition to splitting off carotenoid, profoundly affects the reactivity of the opsin. In the structural context of the rod's outer limb, these or like changes are probably the source of the excitation. Rhodopsin comprises one of the principal structural components of a rod. It accounts for from 14-40 percent of dry weight of the outer limb, depending on the species. The outer segments of the rods and cones are layered structures composed of hundreds or several thousand layers 40-160 Å thick, apparently composed of protein.

Figure 14–7. The Wave Lengths of the Solar Spectrum

Dark Adaptation

The models show that rhodopsin (and presumably the other carotenoid proteins as well) has the capacity to translate the absorption of a quantum of light into an electrical event. One quantum of light is absorbed by one molecule of visual pigment, and a rod or cone is so constructed that so small a change can excite it. The outstanding peculiarity of the rods is their increase of sensitivity in dim light or darkness. This can be graphed as the threshold of sensitivity and shows a decided drop in threshold with reduction of illumination. The dark adapted eye (rods) is approximately 1000 times more sensitive than the light adapted eye (cones). The physiological basis of this change in

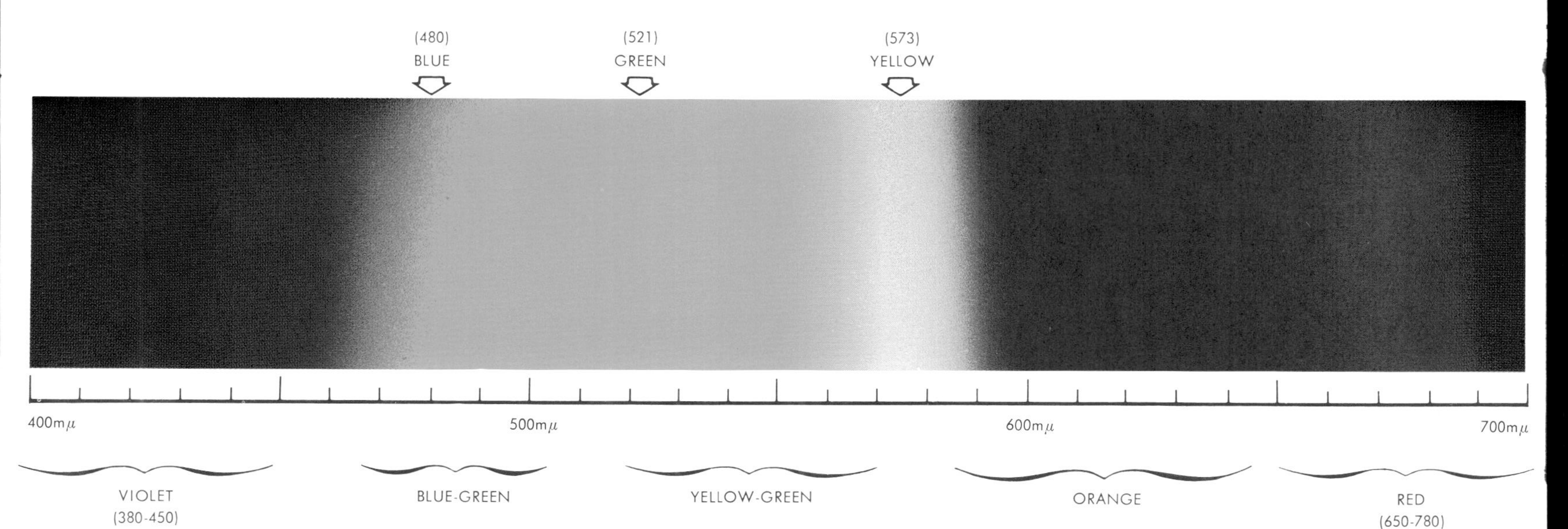

THE SOLAR SPECTRUM

The colors are in the order of the rainbow, as seen when sunlight is sent through a prism.

Eastman Kodak Company

sensitivity is the presence of rhodopsin, or visual purple, which is attached to the rods. It is bleached by intense light and has its maximum point of absorption in the green part of the spectrum at about 520 mμ, which is the point of lowest threshold in dim light. By contrast, the lowest threshold, or point of greatest sensitivity of the light adapted, or photopic eye, is in the yellow at about 570 mμ. The shift in sensitivity from green to yellow with progressive increase in illumination is called the Purkinje shift after its discoverer.

Because of the anatomical features mentioned earlier this shift does not take place at the fovea, where there are no rods, or at the extreme periphery of the retina, where there are no cones. In the process of dark adaptation the rhodopsin on the rods is bleached at the beginning. As the dark adaptation proceeds over time the rhodopsin recovers gradually from the effects of bleaching, and this results in increased sensitivity. It is this increase in sensitivity which accounts for the sensitivity of peripheral, or rather eccentric, vision at night. For the curve of dark adaptation, see Fig. 14–8. The acuity at night may, in a

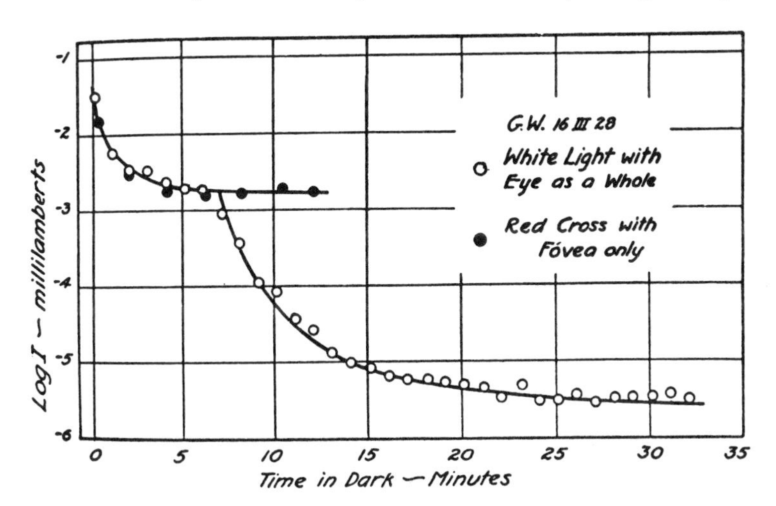

Initial limb of curve for whole eye *(circles)* is due to cones; lower portion is due to rods. To obtain complete curve for cones alone *(black dots)*, stimulation of the more sensitive rods was avoided by employing red light and foveal fixation.

Source: Theodore C. Ruch and John F. Fulton (eds.), *Medical Physiology and Biophysics* (18th ed. of Howell's *Textbook of Physiology;* Philadelphia: W. B. Saunders Company, 1960), p. 430.

Figure 14–8. Curve of Dark Adaptation Obtained by Plotting Visual Threshold Against Time Spent in Darkness

young person, amount to being able to see a lighthouse beacon at 25 miles, or a candle at 5 miles. For the acuity of central and peripheral vision, see Fig. 14–9. By contrast, the acuity of the light adapted eye will

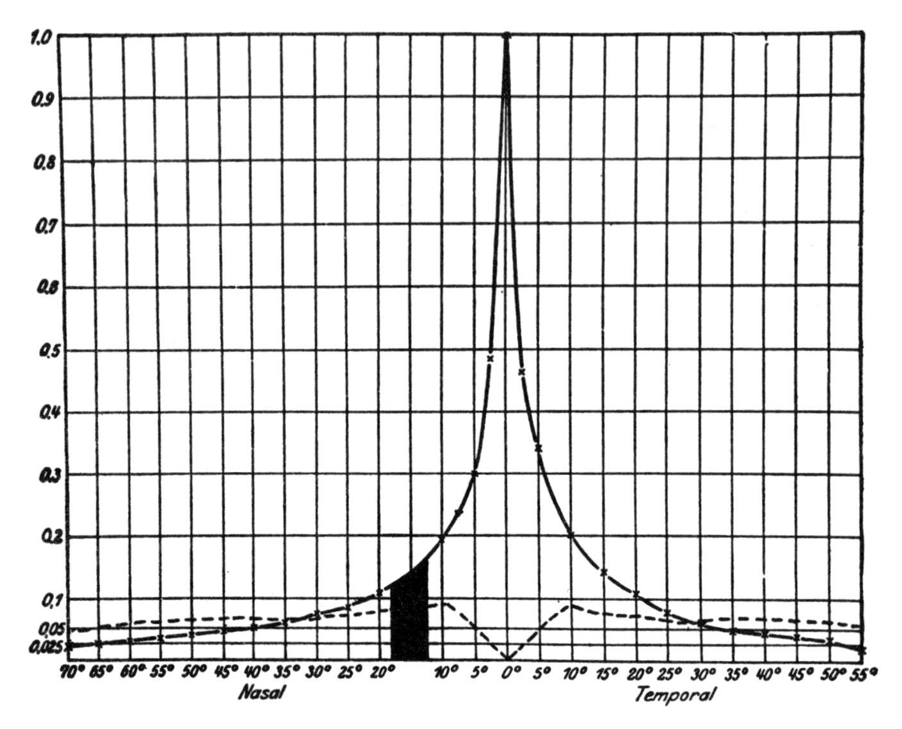

Solid line represents acuity of cone vision (light-adapted eye), and dotted line represents acuity of rod vision (approximate). Black area is the blind spot. (After Wertheim, *Z. Psychol.,* 1894, 7:177–187.)

Source: Theodore C. Ruch and John F. Fulton (eds.), *Medical Physiology and Biophysics,* p. 441.

Figure 14–9. Curve of Relative Acuity of Vision in Central and Peripheral Fields of Retina

allow us to see a telephone wire at a quarter-mile distance or a single strand of spider web in the sun at 20 yards. A moment's calculation will make it clear that the visual angle, which is a function of the size of the image and the distance away from the observer, subtended by these images is smaller than the diameter of the individual rods and cones. The acuity of vision under both light intensities depends then upon something besides the rods and cones. This addition, which assures clear resolution of such small visual angles, is twofold. First, the line or image falls on a tightly packed grid of rods and cones, stimulating some differently from others and thus producing the effect of scanning. Secondly, there may be small eye movements which increase this scanning effect.

Table 14–I

Visual Acuity for Parallel Lines

Diurnal Animals	*Visual Angle (in Minutes)*
Human Adult	0.58
Human Child	0.62
Chimpanzee	0.57
Rhesus Monkey	0.67
Squirrel Monkey	0.84
Cebus Monkey	0.95
Homing Pigeon	0.38
Nocturnal Animals	
Cat	5.50
Opossum	11.00
Rat, pigmented	26.00
Rat, albino	52.00

Stereoscopic Vision and Chiasm

Stereoscopic vision, which aids primates and other mammals in depth perception, depends on overlapping fields of vision. The critical cue in this depth perception is slight differences in the image in one eye from that in the other. The comparison of these two images is a cortical function involving the two hemispheres. Only in animals with overlapping fields of vision and some degree of stereoscopic vision do we find incomplete crossing in the chiasm. In the lower nonmammalian forms all optic fibers cross. There is a progressive decrease in the percentage of crossed fibers depending on the extent of overlapping fields of vision. Humans have the smallest percent of crossed fibers, about 50 percent; the other primates have slightly more crossed fibers. The birds have all fibers crossed, but interwoven, while the fishes' optic fibers are completely crossed, but not interwoven.

NEURAL PATHWAYS

The neural pathways from the retina fall into two divisions, one of reflex connections, and the other of pathways reaching the visual receptive area of the cortex. In some ways the reflex connections are more complex than the cortical pathways. We will examine, therefore, the pathways underlying visual sensation first and the reflex connections later.

The optic nerves pass backward and upward from their exit from the nasal part of the eye. They join at the optic chiasm, and here part of the fibers cross to the other side. The fibers from the nasal half of each eye cross over in the chiasm to join the fibers from the temporal half of the other eye. Thus the information from the corresponding portions (left or right sides) of the two eyes will be projected on the same brain hemisphere. Fibers from the left portion of both eyes pass up the left optic tract to the left *lateral geniculate nucleus,* to the *superior colliculus,* and from the lateral geniculate to the *calcarine cortex.* In analogous fashion, impulses from the right portions of the two eyes will be received by the same brain structures in the right hemisphere. Since the images are reversed on the retina, the image received and transmitted from the right portion of both eyes originates in the left visual field of the observer. This crossing of fibers in the chiasm varies greatly in different animal forms. In humans approximately 50 percent of the fibers cross, but the percentage increases as one goes down the evolutionary scale. About 60 percent cross in the cat, whereas the fish has completely crossed optic nerves. There is, therefore, no real chiasm in the fish, and nothing corresponding to primate binocular field of vision which depends upon crossing fibers.

Topographic Projection

One other characteristic of the visual system is that the particular topographic arrangements in the retina are projected faithfully in point-by-point correspondence to the *lateral geniculate nuclei* and to the *calcarine cortex.* This topographic correspondence begins in the optic nerve, where the fibers are arranged like a sandwich: the upper retinal fibers on top, the lower retinal fibers below, and the macular and foveal fibers in the middle. Likewise, in the chiasm itself the main fibers cross over anteriorly, while the macular and foveal fibers form the posterior portion of the chiasm. (See Fig. 14–10.) Because of this geographic separation a tumor in the anterior chiasm may leave the macular and foveal chiasm undisturbed, resulting in maintenance of clear vision from the center of the retina.

From the chiasm the optic tract passes laterally and upward, rotating medially 45°, to the *lateral geniculate* body, where all visual fibers

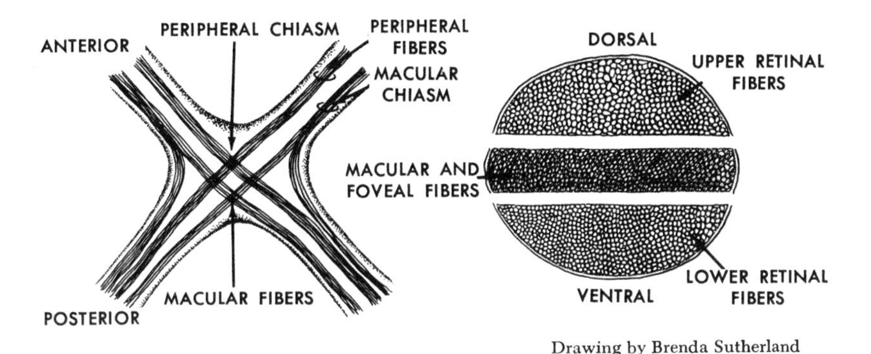

Drawing by Brenda Sutherland

Figure 14–10. Separation of Macular and Peripheral Fibers in Optic Nerve and Chiasm

synapse. In the lateral geniculates the same arrangement of optic fibers is demonstrated as in the chiasm: the upper retinal elements on one side, the macular fibers in the middle, and the lower retinal elements on the other side. The same topographic relationship is evident in the calcarine cortex as is seen in the lateral geniculate nucleus. In the geniculate nuclei fibers from the upper retinal quadrants end in the medial portion, and fibers from the lower quadrants in the lateral portion of the nucleus. The macular fibers end between the upper and lower retinal elements in the lateral geniculate. They are few at the anterior border, but increase in proportion as they proceed posteriorly, until at the extreme posterior border there are mostly macular fiber synapses and almost none from the peripheral retina. There is a similar and precise topographic relation between the geniculate nucleus and the calcarine cortex. The fibers from the medial portion of the geniculate, and consequently the upper retinal quadrants, go to the dorsal lip of the calcarine fissure, while the fibers from the lateral portion of the geniculate nucleus (lower retinal quadrants) end in the ventral lip of the calcarine fissure. This projection can be seen in Fig. 14–11.

The macular elements, after synapse in the lateral geniculate, project by way of the optic radiations mostly to the posterior portion of the lips of the calcarine fissure, with very few ending anteriorly. In primates below man a substantial portion or all of the macular projections are on the external occipital pole of the brain.

In this way the topographic divisions in the retina are reflected faithfully in both the lateral geniculate body and in the visual cortex along the calcarine fissure. The rod (brightness) function of the retina is not

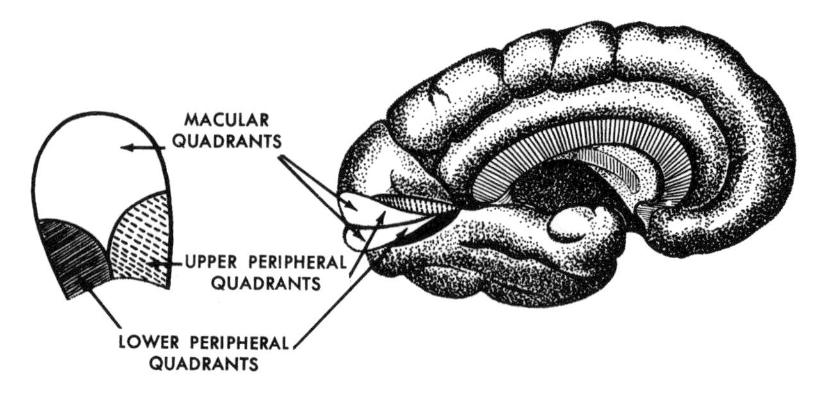

Drawing by Brenda Sutherland

Figure 14–11. Projection of Retinal Quadrants to Calcarine Fissure

eliminated in the monkey, however, by removal of the visual cortex. There is a residue of sensory awareness of brightness data at the thalamic level, and possibly in the superior colliculus as well.

In addition to the lateral geniculate nucleus, which is a part of the specific thalamic nuclear group, the pulvinar has an important role in the use of visual information which involves associations with auditory input. The pulvinar receives from both lateral and medial geniculates and projects to the visual and auditory association areas, the interparietal gyri as well as the angular and the superior marginal gyri.

Geniculate Laminations

The lateral geniculate body and the superior colliculus, which we will consider below, both exhibit a clear series of laminations or rows of cells alternating with fiber layers. The exact function of the six laminated layers in the geniculate nucleus is not entirely clear. Walls, in 1942, likened the lateral geniculate nucleus to a piled up series of maps of the retina, each recording different information. On each of the laminations or sheets of cells one-half of the field of view is represented in a point-to-point manner. Each lamina contains a different organization of visual information than the others. Whether this is analogous to the cartographic categories of geodetic, climatological, and agricultural which Walls suggested does not need to be settled now. Recent investigations indicate, by contrast to these earlier suggestions, that the laminations are concerned in color vision and in coordinating the ipsilateral and contralateral eye fields which end in the same geniculate nucleus. Studies involving microelectrode insertion in cells of the lateral geniculate nucleus show the following results. The laminations, numbered from ventral to dorsal, function as follows: laminations 1, 4, and 6 receive fibers from the ganglion cells of the contralateral eye, while laminations 2, 3, and 5 receive fibers from the ipsilateral eye. Each section of the central retina projects to each of the three segments (1 and 2, 3 and 4, 5 and 6). It is presumed that the different types of ganglion cells lying in the same region of the retina produce different patterns of response, and that the projections of these different ganglion cells are sorted out by type in the various laminated layers of the lateral geniculate nucleus. The large cells in layers 1 and 2 are inhibited by light of all wavelengths and therefore fire "off" responses when the light stimulation ceases. Layers 3 and 4 both increase and decrease their rate of firing, depending on wavelength. The individual cells which are excited by one spectral band are inhibited by another band. There are reported to be "red-on, green-off" cells and "blue-on, yellow-off" cells. The cells in layers 5 and 6 give excitatory responses to diffuse light and no inhibition at any wavelength. The cells in these outside dorsal layers (5 and 6) respond to narrow bands of spectral light. The single cells respond to only single narrow bands divided into five categories at 440, 510, 550, 580, and 620 mμ. For an illustration of these laminations, see Fig. 14–12.

The ventral layers (1 and 2) show a Purkinje (brightness) shift with different wavelengths, and might possibly be the pathway for brightness information.

The cells in the middle geniculate layers (3 and 4) give an opposite reaction when the colored light is turned off than when the light is on. It is as though one color process was inhibited by the light and fired at the light termination. They are, therefore, called "on-off" cells. Each "on-off" unit transmits two kinds of information, whereby excitation transmits one color of a pair and the removal of inhibition (by light) transmits the other of the pair by means of some process analogous to a rebound phenomenon. This provides a physiological explanation of negative afterimage where red excitation produces a green afterimage when the stimulus is removed. These cells of the middle geniculate layers show both negative afterimage and simultaneous contrast. There is an additive effect of the afterimage of red when a green stimulus is presented immediately following. In similar fashion, geniculate cells which fire for red and are inhibited by green will fire as though for red when stimulated by white light with a green "surround." These characteristics do not show up in the pure "on" cells of layers 5 and 6.

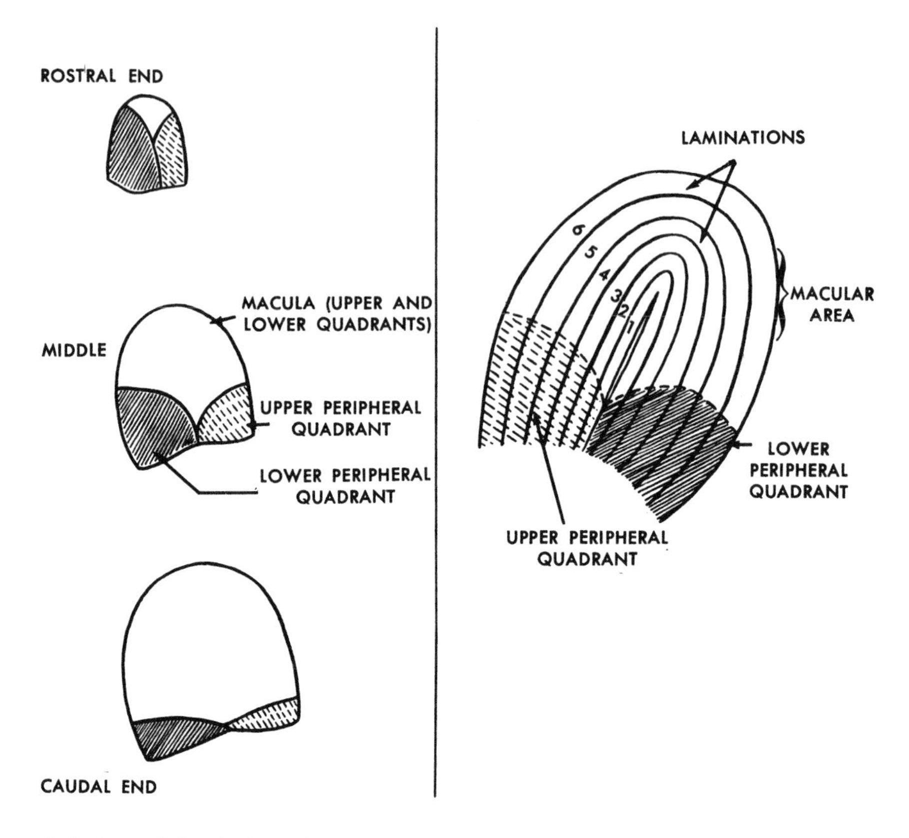

Left Lateral Geniculate, Showing Shift in Macular, Peripheral Segment

Right Lateral Geniculate, Showing Laminations and Macular and Peripheral Areas

Drawing by Brenda Sutherland

Figure 14–12

It is possible, then, that visual information is encoded in two different ways in the primate retinal-nervous system, the cells in layers 5 and 6 being wavelength specific and each responsive to only one narrow band of wavelengths. This evidence follows the Young-Helmholtz theory of color vision. The activity of the cells in layers 3 and 4 showing excitatory and inhibitory reactions from the same cell seems to provide support in the complementary color relations for Hering's color vision theory.

There is also growing evidence that the visual information is reorganized between the lateral geniculate cells, referred to above, and the optical cortex. At the cortex it is different, and recombined as though there had been fusion of the information from the three types of layers (1 and 2, 3 and 4, 5 and 6).

The laminations of the superior colliculus are seven in number. Unfortunately we do not know as much about the function of the collicular laminations as about those of the lateral geniculate body. For relation of lateral geniculate and superior colliculus, see Fig. 14–13.

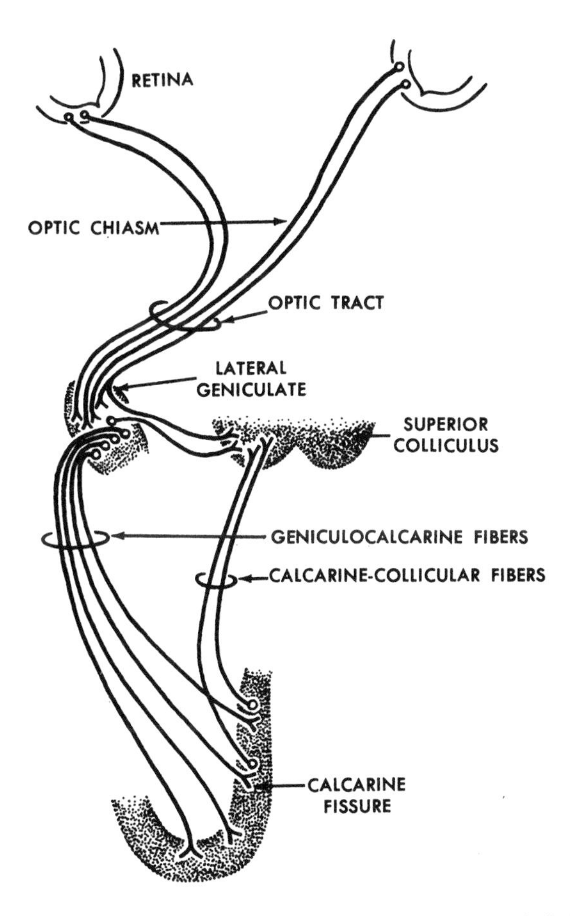

Drawing by Brenda Sutherland

Figure 14–13. Pathway of Optic Fibers to Geniculate, Superior Colliculus and Calcarine Cortex

Reflex Connections

The reflex connections and circuits of the visual system are quite complex. The fibers in each optic tract split into three branches and end in alternate layers of the geniculate nucleus. The two layers relay optic impulses, in part, after synapse to the superior colliculi for optic reflexes. From the superior colliculi fibers pass medially to the reflex centers for light and accommodation reflexes as well as for conjugate movements of the two eyes. The pupillary constrictor and accommodation reflexes are mediated by a small visceral motor nucleus, the *Edinger-Westphal,* which lies just dorsal to the oculomotor nucleus, III, in the midbrain. From here small fibers pass out with the 3rd nerve, to end in the ciliary parasympathetic ganglion in the ophthalmic region, and second-order neurons proceed thence to the internal muscles of the eyeball. This connection innervates both the circular pupillary muscles for constriction of the pupil and the ciliary muscle contraction for changing the shape of the lens. Apparently the change in lens shape in the opposite direction is the result of an absence of nerve impulse, allowing the relaxation of the ciliary muscle. The dilator muscles of the pupil are innervated by impulses of the sympathetic division of the autonomic system which travel down the brain stem to make synapse in the *intermediolateral column* in the *thoracic cord.* From there they proceed to the *superior cervical sympathetic ganglion,* where they synapse and proceed through the ciliary ganglion without synapse to the radial fibers. For the details of these connections, see Fig. 14–14.

The conjugate movements of the two eyes are mediated by the *central nucleus of Perlia.* Eye movements are generally the result of following a moving object or bringing into focus an image that is on the periphery, or farther or nearer than the focused distance. These movements then are responses to sensory information from the retina. The information must pass by way of the lateral geniculate nuclei to the calcarine fissure. From there the pathway goes to Brodmann (visual association) areas 18 and 19 and thence by association fibers to the frontal eye fields, Brodmann area 8, just anterior to the motor and premotor areas. From these cortical areas the directions go to the central nucleus of Perlia. From this nucleus, after synapse, connections are made with the interstitial nucleus of Cajal and the eye muscle nuclei (III, IV, VI) by way of the medial longitudinal fasciculus. Since vestibular nuclei also connect with the medial longitudinal fasciculus, this

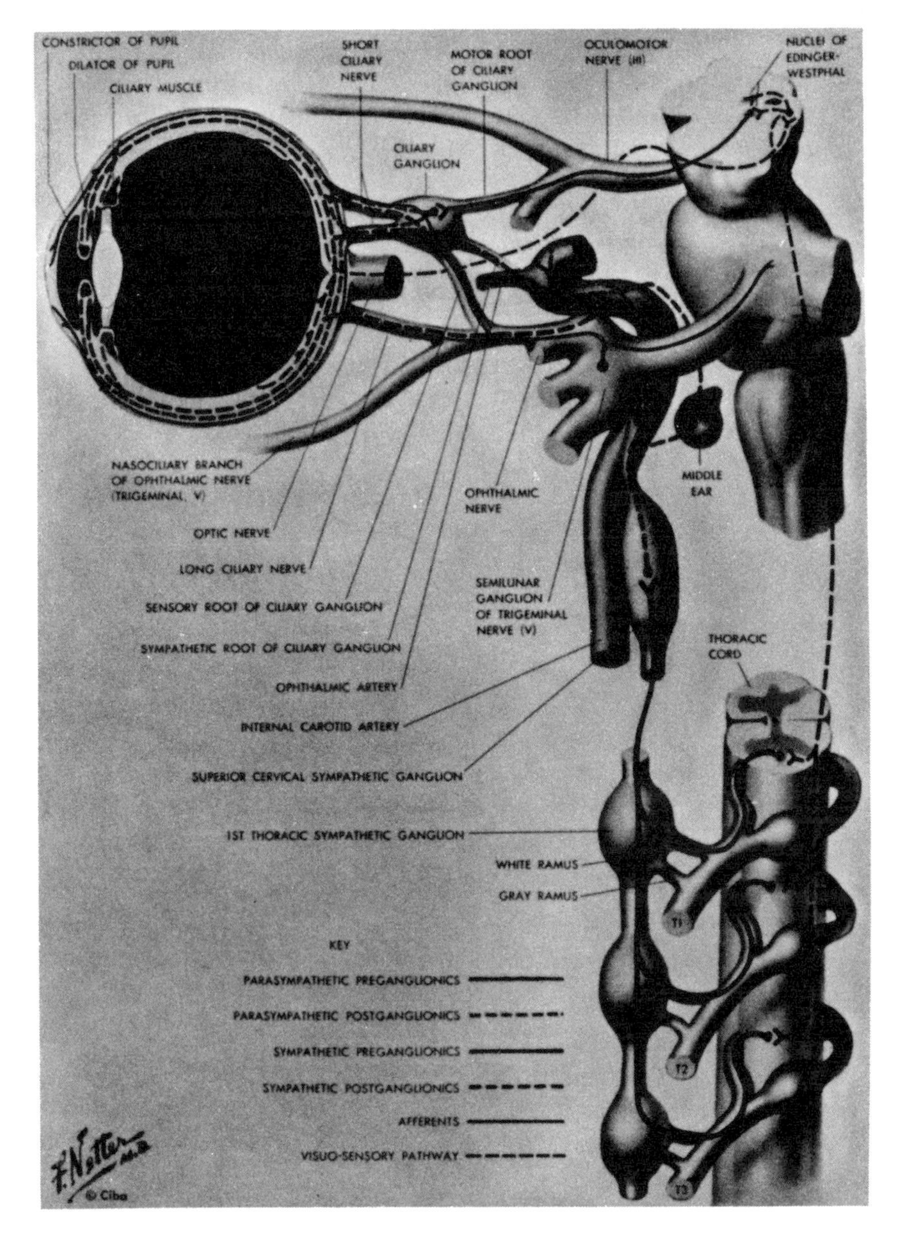

Source: *The CIBA Collection of Medical Illustrations* by Frank H. Netter, M.D. Copyright CIBA. Vol. I, *Nervous System* (Summit, N. J.: CIBA Pharmaceutical Company, 1953), Plate 65.

Figure 14–14. Pathway for Pupillary and Accommodation Reflexes

provides the neurological basis for nystagmus. The medial longitudinal fasciculus mediates, in addition, reflex movements of muscles of the neck and shoulders in response to visual stimulation. Various reflex connections are illustrated in Fig. 14–15.

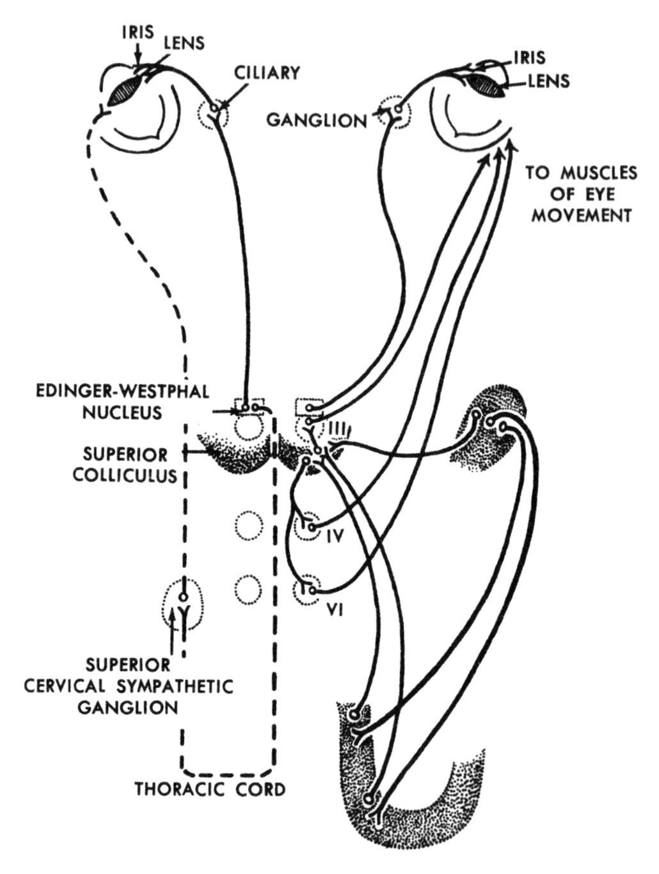

Drawing by Brenda Sutherland

Figure 14–15. Pathway of Visual Reflex Connections to External (R) and Internal (L) Eye Muscles

The connections of the superior colliculus, as well as those of the central nucleus of Perlia, include fibers returning from the calcarine fissure. There are returning pathways from calcarine to both the lateral geniculate nucleus and the superior colliculus. The information, on the basis of which changes of lens shape are made, relies then on an evaluation of sensory information originating in the retina but evaluated elsewhere. These connections are undoubtedly crucial in facilitating this sensory evaluation. The lens adjustment seems to be a learned mechanism rather than a built-in one. If it were automatic and inborn, then the information from the calcarine fissure to superior colliculus would have to be coded to indicate whether the ciliary muscles should be contracted or relaxed.

Central Control of Sensory Transmission

Recent findings seem to indicate a selective control process which affects the data transmitted to lateral geniculate and visual cortex. Stimulation of the brain stem reticular formation, or behavioral distraction by nonvisual stimuli, was associated with a reduction in amplitude of the nonhabituated photic responses. This sensory control mechanism appears to provide the perceptual process with an active organizing or selecting principle, including an element of purpose, which tends to select and modify sensory messages in their earliest stages of transmission. The inner plexiform layer, which forms a network of dendrites between ganglion and bipolar cells interspersed with amacrine cells, also is the end-station of the centrifugal axons. Experiments have shown that it is possible to obtain centrifugal effects on the discharge of ganglion cells. These impulses are partly excitatory, partly inhibitory, and sometimes mixed, excitation being followed by inhibition.

If overt behavior provides a reliable index of purpose, then this sensory control mechanism is designed to reduce the engagement of the higher centers with those sensory data that have the least significance for the person or animal at that moment and in that context. At other times and in other contexts what is significant will be different. Significance to the organism appears to be the guiding principle in the operation of this sensory control mechanism.

SOURCES AND ADDITIONAL READING

Bender, M., ed., *The Oculomotor System.* New York: Hoeber, 1964.

Handbook of Physiology, Sec. I, Vol. I, Chaps. 25–30. Washington, D.C.: American Physiol. Soc., 1959.

Jung, A. and H. Kornhuber, eds., *The Visual System.* Berlin: Springer, 1961.

Neff, W. D., ed., *Contributions to Sensory Physiology,* Vol. I. New York: Academic Press, 1965.

Ruch, T. and J. Fulton, eds., *Medical Physiology and Biophysics* (18th ed.), Chaps 18–20. Philadelphia: W. B. Saunders Company, 1961. (See 19th ed., Chaps. 19–21.)

Walls, G., *The Vertebrate Eye.* New York: Hafner Publishing Company, 1964.

Walsh, G., *Physiology of the Nervous System,* Chap. 9. New York: Longmans Green & Co., Inc., 1959.

Fifteen

OLFACTION

The sense of smell is one of the three distance receptors located in the head. It is called a distance receptor because an animal can detect from a considerable distance the presence of food, or rotting offal, or source of danger. It is not difficult to understand then why such a sense would be important under wild conditions where wolves, mountain lions, and men might all be hunting the same deer.

This same sense of smell is a very primitive one, being of primary importance in fish and amphibians. As we go up the phylogenetic scale, the reptiles and birds make very little use of smell and depend for both safety and food on other senses such as vision. The mammals below the primates show again a heavy dependence on smell information. Thus rodents and dogs and cats correct by sense of smell some of their inadequacy in form perception. The primates, by contrast, use smell rather sparingly and depend on vision and hearing, although accuracy and refinement of olfactory perception may need only training and attention.

In a barely perceptible dilution of odorous material a single sniff contains millions of molecules. When these molecules arrive at the olfactory hairs in the nose they must produce a reaction in the olfactory cells giving rise to nervous impulse. To be smellable a substance must fulfill two conditions: 1) be volatile or vaporous at ordinary temperatures and 2) be soluble in fat or water solvents. Most inorganic substances do not satisfy these conditions, being salts, and are not odorous, except for substances like sulfur dioxide, ammonia, etc. Organic substances, by contrast, are mostly odorous.

PHYSIOLOGY OF OLFACTION

The method of olfactory fatigue has been used to show whether two odors belong to the same class. Thus camphor and cloves produce fatigue for each other, hence belong to the same subclassification. If camphor and cloves produced fatigue for each other, it seemed as though odor might be related to the shape of the molecule. Camphor, for instance, could be converted to minty odor by substituting one ethyl group for a methyl group (CH_3) in the camphor structure. Mint odor, as well as camphor, cedar, lemon, musk, and civet are closely related because they have close similarity in the hydrocarbon part of the molecule. Chemical structure, then, can account for various classes of odors. But, for the fine distinctions of which olfactory cells are capable there must be a mechanism in the nose for detecting small differences in the carbon skeleton or hydrocarbon molecule. Even though two substances have somewhat different molecular structure, similarity of essential parts such as the carbon skeleton produce olfactory sensations which are essentially the same.

Subsequent investigations have led to the stereochemical theory of odors, which classifies odors into seven classes. These are: (1) camphorous, (2) musky, (3) floral, (4) pepperminty, (5) ether-like, (6) pungent, and (7) putrid. Each of these seven has an individual molecular shape or an electric charge to differentiate it from the others. The molecular shapes are:

1. Camphorous—spherical of 7Å diameter
2. Musky—oval disk of 10Å diameter
3. Floral—round disk with a tail
4. Pepperminty—wedge shape plus a hydrogen bond
5. Ether-like—thin rod shape
6. Pungent—no shape, but + electrical charge
7. Putrid—no shape, but — electrical charge

By the use of synthetic chemistry it was possible to test a panel of experienced persons on the correctness of these seven classes. When the molecular shape approximated the outlines indicated above, the reported odor fell into the appropriate class according to the theory. Complex odors in nature must depend on a combination of these primary odors, and supposedly on olfactory receptors which respond to the different molecular shapes. Only in the frog, thus far, have there been identified receptors of different shapes which corresponded to a majority of the classes of odors in this stereochemical theory.

STRUCTURE OF OLFACTORY ORGAN

The olfactory sense is much more sensitive than taste, which is the other chemical sense, and much of the sensitivity of taste is really an addition from olfaction. For many substances, perception by taste requires 3000 times the minimum concentration which is adequate for olfaction. This greater sensitivity is accounted for partly by some special neural connections which we will see constitute the function of the olfactory bulb. The olfactory sense organ is composed of slender olfactory cells, sandwiched between thicker supporting cells, which extend down into the mucous membrane in the upper nasal passage. The tip of the olfactory cell has protruding from its distal end tiny hairs which extend beyond the limiting membrane. The olfactory cells in the *olfactory epithelium,* because it is a neuroepithelium, are almost the only sensory cells in the body which do not develop a generator potential to stimulate nerve fiber, but which conduct the nerve impulse directly, without intervening process, to the *mitral cell* synapse. At the base of these olfactory cells the unmyelinated fibers continue, to group themselves in about 20 small bundles, and these bundles pass through openings in the cribiform plate of the ethmoid bone to enter the *olfactory bulb,* which lies just dorsal to this plate. The olfactory bulb performs the function of summating the impulses which enter it. A number of olfactory fibers end together, in synapse with the second-order neurons, in a dense entanglement called a *glomerulus.* (See Figure 15–1.) There are approximately 1 million olfactory axons entering the bulb, but only one-tenth as many fibers in the olfactory tract. This re-

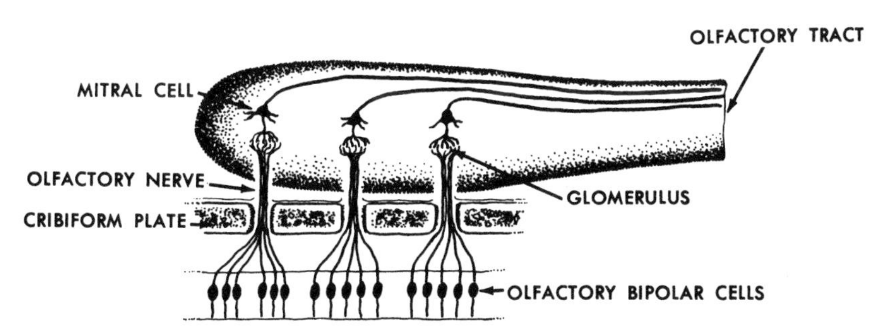

Figure 15–1. Diagram of Olfactory Bulb

duction from 10 to 1 results in summation of substantial magnitude. In this way a number of faint subthreshold olfactory stimuli are able to fire the second-order neuron.

NERVOUS CONNECTIONS

The internal structure of the olfactory bulb also increases olfactory sensitivity. The cells whose dendrites form glomeruli with the dense entanglement of olfactory fibers are called *mitral* and *tufted cells.* The axons of these cells pass upward and form the olfactory tract. Before they form the olfactory tract, however, the axons of the mitral cells in particular send off a number of recurrent collaterals which probably connect with the *granule cells.* The axons of these granule cells, moving in direction opposite to the mitral and tufted axons, end on a glomerulus and make possible a repetitive firing of the mitral and tufted cells, or inhibition of succeeding pulses. The axons of the *mitral cells* of the olfactory bulb form the major part of the *olfactory tract,* which lies on the ventral surface of the frontal lobes. This tract runs back and laterally to form three separable olfactory stria, the medial, the intermediate, and the lateral. The medial goes to the other olfactory bulb and possibly to the septum; the intermediate synapses in the anterior perforated substance, or tubercle, for reflex connections; and the lateral passes backward and more lateral still, curving out into the uncus of the temporal lobe to penetrate the *amygdaloid nuclei* and *prepyriform cortex.* The axons of the mitral cells are thicker than those of the tufted cells and pass into the lateral olfactory stria, while the finer axons of the tufted cells pass to the bulb of the other side and possibly to the septum by way of the anterior commissure. (These relations will be made clearer by reference to Fig. 15–2.) This *medial stria* from the tufted cells connects not only with the other bulb but also probably with the *subcallosal gyrus* and the *septum.* The *intermediate olfactory nucleus* in the anterior perforated substance (tubercle) is the major olfactory reflex center. From this intermediate nucleus, fibers of third-order neurons pass directly 1) by way of the *median forebrain bundle* to the *mammillary bodies* and 2) by way of the *stria medullaris* up and over the thalamus, to end in the *habenular nucleus* of the epithalamus. By means of habenular and mammillary nuclei the integration of olfactory information with touch and taste is made possible. From the habenular and the mammillary bodies the fourth-order neurons make connections with the midbrain tegmentum, where they synapse with major cranial nerves concerned with movements of the mouth and face, and the ac-

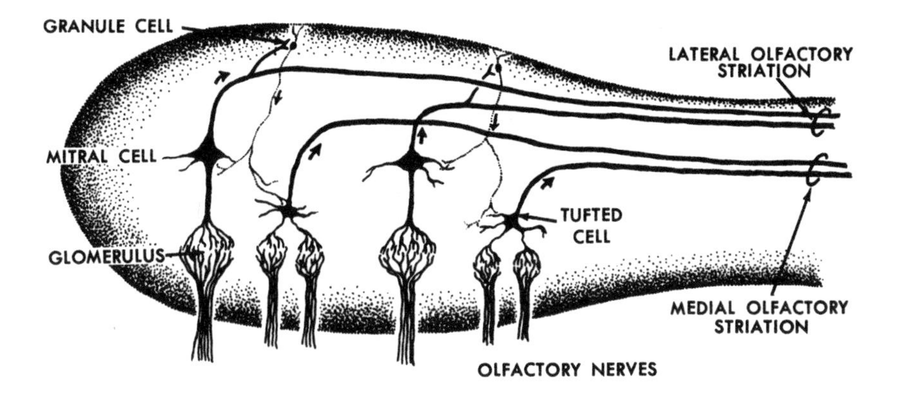

Drawing by Brenda Sutherland

Figure 15–2. Schematic Drawing of Internal Structure of Olfactory Bulb

tivity of the digestive tract. From the mammillary nuclei, pathways lead by way of the *mammillotegmental* tract to the *dorsal tegmental nucleus* and from there to nuclei of the trigeminal (V), facial (VII), vagus (X), etc. From the habenula the connections run ventrally to the interpeduncular nucleus on the floor of the midbrain. From there connections are made again with the dorsal tegmental nucleus. For the details of these connections, see Fig. 15–3. Thus in the olfactory responses, the tegmental nuclei, which in turn connect with the cranial nerves, function as coordination centers of substantial magnitude. From the mammillary nuclei the connections may be of reflex type to tegmentum, habenula, and cranial nerves concerned with eating or digestive activity; or the connections may fan out into the more diffuse rhinencephalon, or *limbic system,* which will be examined in Chapter 16.

After a synapse in the *lateral olfactory nucleus* the impulses transmitted by mitral cells continue by third-order neurons into the uncus of the temporal lobe. The fibers from the lateral olfactory stria reach the *amygdaloid nuclei* and the *prepyriform* area.

Olfactory impulses have not been traced electrically to any part of the hippocampus. Removal of the olfactory bulb in the monkey and rabbit was followed by the degeneration of fibers running in the lateral olfactory stria and ending in the olfactory tubercle, prepyriform cortex, cortical and medial amygdaloid nuclei, and the nucleus of the stria terminalis. The receptive olfactory cortex, then, is prepyriform. No degeneration was seen in the hippocampal formation or the en-

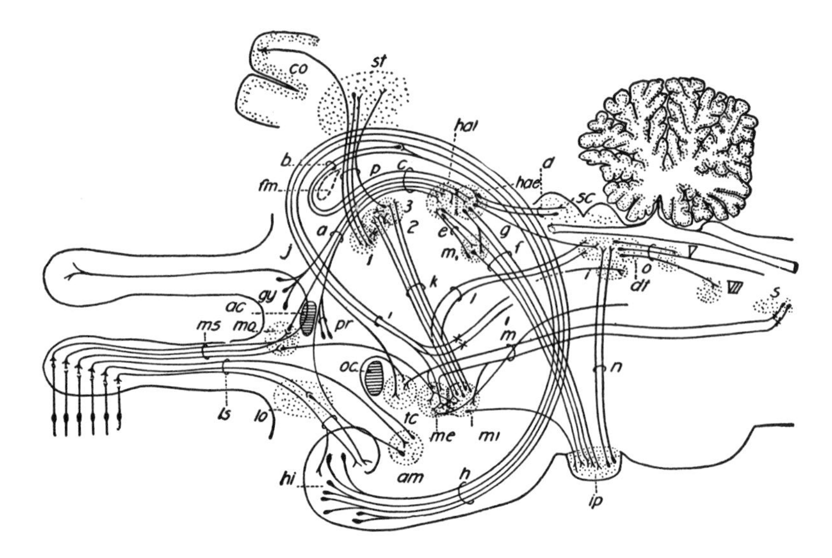

a, Olfactohabenular fibers; *ac,* anterior commissure; *am,* amygdaloid nucleus; *b,* septohabenular and corticohabenular tract; *c,* stria medullaris; *co,* cortex; *d,* tectohabenular and habenulotectal fibers; *dt,* dorsal tegmental nucleus; *e,* habenulodiencephalic and thalamohabenular fibers; *f,* habenulopeduncular fibers; *fm,* interventricular foramen; *g,* habenulotegmental fibers; *gy,* gyrus subcallosus; *h,* fimbria; *hae,* external habenular nucleus; *hai,* internal habenular nucleus; *hi,* hippocampus, *i,* fornix; *ip,* interpeduncular nucleus; *j,* corticohypothalamic (and septohypothalamic) fibers; *k,* mammillothalamic fibers; *l,* mammillotegmental fibers; *lo,* lateral olfactory area; *ls,* lateral olfactory stria; *m,* mammillary peduncle; m_1, nucleus of Meynert's habenulopeduncular tract; *me,* external mammillary nucleus; *mi,* internal mammillary nucleus; *mo,* medial olfactory area; *ms,* medial olfactory stria; *n,* pedunculotegmental fibers; *o,* dorsal longitudinal fasciculus of Schultze; *oc,* optic chiasm; *pr,* preoptic area; *s,* bulbar centers; *sc,* superior colliculus; *st,* striatum; *tc,* tuber cinereum; *V,* motor nucleus of the fifth nerve; *VII,* motor nucleus of the seventh nerve; *1,* anterior dorsal nucleus; *2,* anterior medial nucleus; *3,* anterior ventral nucleus. (Huber and Crosby.)

Source: S. W. Ranson and S. L. Clark, *The Anatomy of the Nervous System: Its Development and Function* (10th ed.; Philadelphia: W. B. Saunders Company, 1959), p. 345.

Figure 15–3. Olfactory Connections of the Diencephalon

torhinal area (posterior pyriform). Connecting pathways to the hippocampus and the remainder of the limbic system for emotional response are probably of long latency and therefore circuitous. The olfactory cortex is primitive, being called the archipalleum. It is composed of only three layers of neurons as contrasted with six layers in the other sensory receptive and motor cortical areas.

SOURCES AND ADDITIONAL READING

Amoore, J. E., J. W. Johnston, Jr., and M. Rubin, "The Stereochemical Theory of Odor," *Sci. American*, Feb. 1964.

Handbook of Physiology, Sec. I, Vol. I, Chap. 21. Washington, D.C.: American Physiol. Soc., 1959.

Ruch, T. and J. Fulton, eds., *Medical Physiology and Biophysics* (18th ed.), Chap. 16. Philadelphia: W. B. Saunders Company, 1961. (See 19th ed., Chap. 17.)

Walsh, G., *Physiology of the Nervous System*, Chap. 7. New York: Longmans Green & Co., Inc., 1959.

Sixteen

THE LIMBIC SYSTEM

The examination of the cerebral cortex in Chapter 21 includes a review of the function of the cerebral mantle on the dorsal and lateral surfaces and to some slight extent on the ventral surface, especially in the inferior frontal region. There is, however, a primitive kind of transitional cortex on the ventral surface of the temporal lobe and rolled up in the infolding of the temporal cortex as this approximates the brain stem. This transitional cortex belongs to a system separate from the connections through the thalamus to neocortex and the return paths by one of the motor systems. Because this older cortex is separate from the neocortex, and transitional to it, it has been called a part of the "limbic system". The limbic system, however, includes much more than the transitional cortex. It is a very complex system containing many subcortical centers, as well as cortex and parts of the olfactory system as well. This limbic system is believed to be concerned with motivational and emotional activities, and much of it developed in phylogenetic history before the elaboration of thalamocortical relations.

The hypothalamus is considered to be the main neural center for mediating expression of emotion through its connections with the autonomic nervous system. The hypothalamus does not, however, share in the experiencing of emotional or motivational states. The thalamus participates in crude somesthetic awareness as in pain, but does not participate in the complex affective states such as fear, love, and anger. Except for some substantial contributions from dominant sensory modalities the limbic system is relatively separate from the strictly informational aspects of cortical function. It is, then, concerned with the affective aspects of experience.

THREE RHINAL[1] SYSTEMS

The limbic system, as it has become elaborated by investigators, contains three subsystems beginning with the olfactory sense. The importance of olfaction in food getting, mating, etc. in lower animals is evident to anyone who has observed cats or dogs.

I. The first system includes the following:

a) olfactory tubercle (anterior perforated substance)
b) area of diagonal band of Broca
c) prepyriform cortex
d) corticomedial nuclei of the amygdaloid

These structures are connected to the primary olfactory system on the basis of direct fiber connections to the olfactory bulb.

II. The second system includes subcortical as well as cortical structures, and is connected with the first system but not with the olfactory bulb. These structures are as follows:

a) subcallosal cortex
b) frontotemporal cortex
c) septal nuclei
d) basolateral nuclei of amygdaloid

This system has been implicated in diverse activities such as olfactory-gustatory, metabolic, and socioemotional. Whether this variability of function implies that the system takes part in several larger systems of interconnections must be determined by future investigations.

III. The third system is connected with the second system, but not with the first or the olfactory bulb. It comprises:

a) Ammon's formation (hippocampus and dentate fascia)
b) entorhinal cortex (pyriform)
c) retrosplenial cortex (at caudal end of callosum)
d) cingulate cortex (just dorsal to callosum)

The third system contains only various cortical areas. Whether these form the neural basis of emotion is not yet certain. An illustration of these systems can be seen in Fig. 16–1.

---

[1] The terms *rhinal* and *limbic* are approximately equivalent.

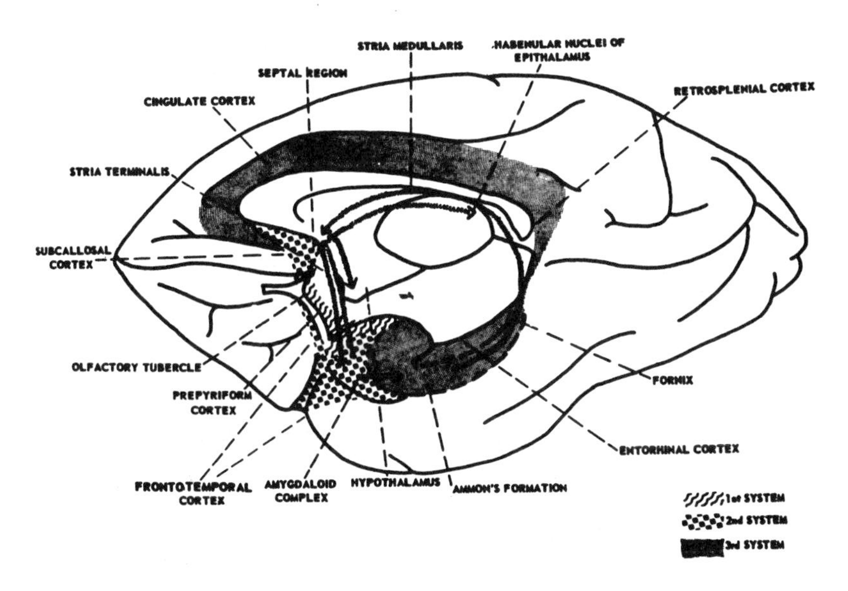

Source: Karl H. Pribram and Lawrence Kruger, "Functions of the 'Olfactory Brain,'" *The Annals of the New York Academy of Sciences* (Vol. 58), Fig. 1, p. 116, in Robert L. Isaacson (ed.), *Basic Readings in Neuropsychology* (New York: Harper & Row, Publishers, 1964), p. 222. Figure reprinted by permission of The New York Academy of Sciences and Dr. Pribram.

Figure 16–1. The Three Rhinal Systems and Their Relation to One Another

FIBER CONNECTIONS

In addition to the cortical and subcortical centers the limbic system includes many fiber bundles connecting one structure with another. (1) The lateral olfactory stria, as was indicated in the last chapter, leads to the corticomedial nuclei of the amygdaloid and to the prepyriform cortex. The corticomedial nuclei of the amygdaloid of the two sides of the brain are interconnected by way of the anterior commissure. (2) The main efferent pathway from the basolateral amygdaloid is the *stria terminalis,* which makes a loop caudal, dorsal, rostral, and ventral to terminate in the septum and in the anterior hypothalamus. The most prominent efferent pathways lead into hypothalamic nuclei. (3) One of the largest efferent bundles is the *fornix,* which arises in the posterior part of Ammon's formation (hippocampus) and, passing caudal, rostral, and ventral around the thalamus, ends primarily in the mammillary bodies, but with branches to the septum and the median forebrain bundle. (4) From the mammillary bodies fibers proceed by the mammillothalamic tract to the anterior thalamic nucleus and from there to the cingulate gyrus. It has been stated that the preservation of nervous pathways from the mammillary bodies through the anterior thalamic

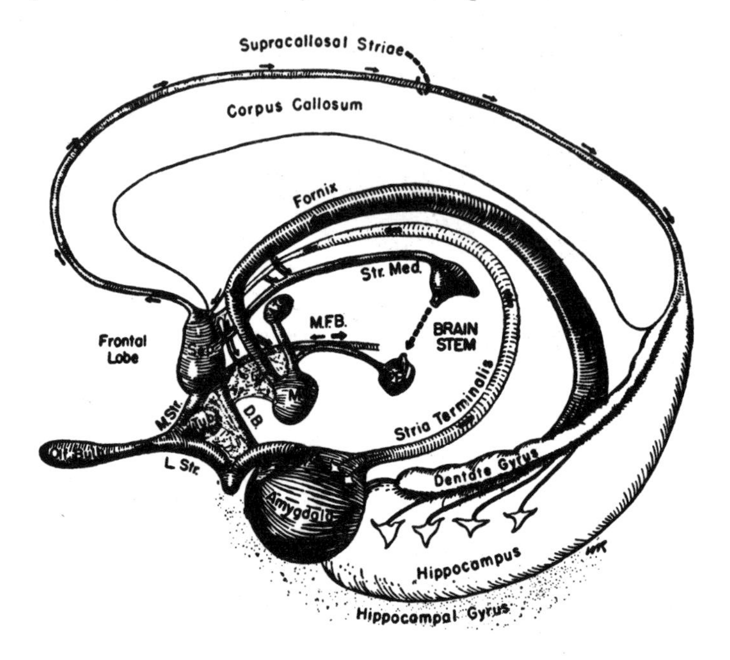

[The schematic representation] is drawn as though all of them could be seen from the medial aspect of the right hemisphere, with the intervening tissue dissolved away. The composite was suggested by illustrations from W. J. S. Krieg's *Functional Neuroanatomy* (Philadelphia: Blakiston, 553 pp.), but for diagrammatic purposes some of the added or altered connections have been given an arbitrary course. Abbreviations: A.T., anterior nucleus of thalamus; D.B., diagonal band of Broca; H., habenula (a part of the epithalamus); I.P., interpeduncular nucleus; L. Str., lateral olfactory stria; M., mammillary body (a part of the posterior hypothalamus); M.F.B., medial forebrain bundle; M. Str., medial olfactory stria; Olf. Bulb, olfactory bulb; Sep., region of the septal nuclei; Str. Med., stria medullaris; Tub., olfactory tubercle (head of the caudate immediately underneath).

Source: Paul D. MacLean, "Psychosomatic Disease and the 'Visceral Brain': Recent Developments Bearing on the Papez Theory of Emotion," in Robert L. Isaacson (ed.), *Basic Readings in Neuropsychology,* p. 189.

Figure 16–2. A Schematic Representation of the Relationship of the Main Subcortical Structures and Connections of the Rhinencephalon

nucleus to the cingulate is essential for a state of vigilance and wakefulness. This path may then be a part of the diffuse thalamocortical projection system. (5) The major return path is the *supracallosal stria* from the septum, following the dorsal aspect of the corpus callosum caudal and ventral to enter the dentate gyrus of the hippocampus (Ammon's formation). The dentate gyrus was probably the first cortical association area for smell, taste, mouth, and viscera, since it receives afferents from septal nuclei which are implicated in smell, taste, and visceral activities. The dentate gyrus is the only part of the hippocampus which is absent in anosmic animals. The hippocampal cortex, Ammon's formation, has changed little in its structure from mouse to man. These interconnected elements can be seen in Fig. 16–2.

AMYGDALOID NUCLEI

The amygdaloid group of nuclei lying just dorsal to the entorhinal (pyriform) cortex is an important correlating center of the limbic system. It is considered to be a thalamus-like relay center for olfactory and other visceral impulses to the archipalleum. The amygdaloid group is divided into a corticomedial division and a basolateral division. Fibers of the lateral olfactory stria terminate in the corticomedial division, whereas the basolateral division developed parallel with the development of the association nuclei of the thalamus and reached its largest size in man. The two corticomedial groups are connected bilaterally by way of the anterior commissure.

The afferent input to the amygdaloid includes olfactory and somatosensory signals, which may even converge on the same amygdaloid cell. In addition, fibers feeding into the various amygdaloid nuclei originate in (1) the brain stem reticular formation, (2) the striatum, (3) the temporal pole cortex, (4) the anterior insular cortex, (5) posterior orbital cortex, and (6) primary motor cortex (Brodmann 4). The efferent fiber pathways have already been indicated above.

STIMULATION AND ABLATIONS

Respiratory, cardiovascular, and gastrointestinal motility are altered (stimulated or inhibited) by stimulation of the different amygdaloid nuclei, as is also the release of the gonadotrophic hormone by the anterior pituitary. The entire second system, including the amygdaloid (basolateral), septal nuclei, and the subcallosal and frontotemporal cortex, is believed to be concerned with motivational reinforcement of behavior patterns. A review of the stimulation and ablation studies of the structures contained in the second and third systems, outlined above, may provide a better understanding of the differential functions of the nuclei and cortical areas involved. The second system contains (1) septal nuclei, (2) basolateral nuclei of the amygdaloid, (3) subcallosal cortex, and (4) frontotemporal cortex; the third system includes (1) cingulate cortex, (2) retrosplenial cortex, (3) entorhinal cortex, and (4) Ammon's formation (hippocampal formation).

Stimulation of the amygdaloid and periamygdaloid structures leads to various responses related to eating and the upper end of the gastrointestinal tract. Implanted electrode stimulation in the basal nuclei leads to licking, chewing, sniffing, swallowing, panting, and accelerated respiration, along with dilation of the pupil. Stimulation of the central nucleus of the amygdaloid gives rise to meowing, swallowing, and inhibition of respiration; while stimulation of the medial nucleus gives rise to hissing, growling, pawing, and pupillary dilation. Thus, in the amygdaloid nuclei we find that stimulation elicits important parts of the food connected activities, defense or fear reactions, flight reactions, and visceral responses such as changed respiration. A graphic representation of these changes can be seen in Fig. 16–3.

Stimulation studies of the septal region have been carried out for a number of years. Electrodes implanted in the septal area have allowed the carrying out of self-stimulation studies without food reward. The very high rates of responding by frequent self-stimulation of low voltage electric current seems to indicate that the septal area is an integral part of an important reward mechanism.

Ablations of these same structures show sharply contrasting results from the stimulation studies. Ablations of the septal region result in a reduction of anxiety and fear in the experimental animals. The preoperative tame rats become aggressive and savage after the ablation and even attack bars of steel. Ablations of the amygdaloid nuclei and the overlying cortex in cats and monkeys make the animals unusually docile and placid. Even the lynx and agouti, naturally savage animals, become very docile postoperatively.

These affective changes seem to be sequentially related, or there seems to be a clear order of dominance between the several structures. An animal which has been made savage by septal lesions can be made placid by subsequent amygdaloid ablations. In somewhat similar fashion, animals rendered placid by amygdalar ablations have subsequently been made savage by lesions in the ventromedial nucleus of the hypothalamus. Hypersexuality is induced by a lesion restricted to a small area

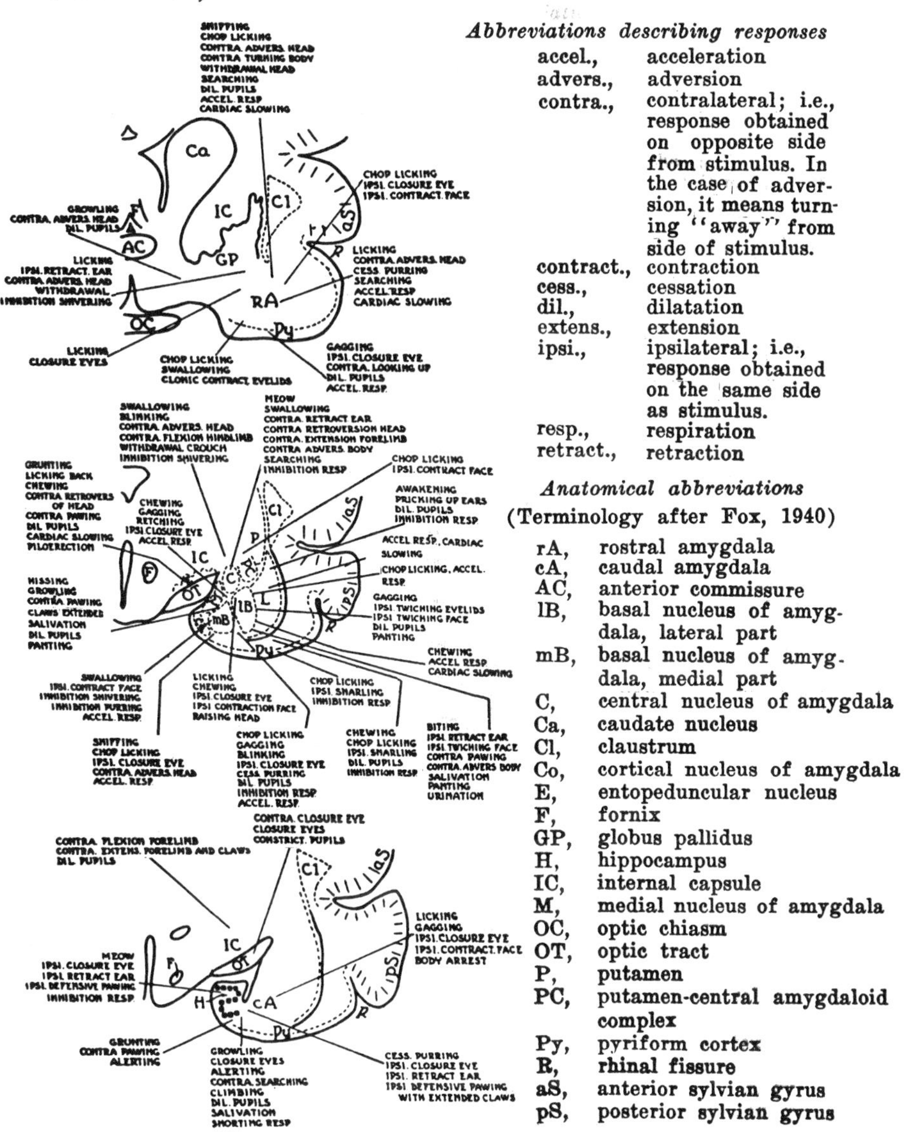

[These drawings] are representative frontal sections of the cat's brain through the rostral, middle, and caudal parts, respectively, of the amygdale. . . . The responses to electrical stimulation at various points are listed. . . .

Source: Paul D. MacLean and José M. R. Delgado, "Electrical and Chemical Stimulation of Frontotemporal Portion of Limbic System in the Waking Animal," *The EEG Journal: Electroencephalography and Clinical Neurophysiology,* Vol. V (1953), p. 92.

Figure 16–3. Amygdaloid Nuclei and Their Function

in the posterolateral part of the pyriform cortex beneath the basal and lateral amygdaloid. Hyperphagia without hypersexuality is produced by lesions more dorsal near the junction of the basal and lateral amygdaloid nuclei. In cats, lesions of 2 mm in diameter near the junction of the lateral and basal amygdaloid nuclei were followed by signs of hyperphagia and increase in weight.

With respect to the third system, there is the same lack of concurrence between stimulation and ablation studies. Stimulation of the anterior cingulate cortex or the ventral portion of the orbitoinsulotemporal cortex results in profound inhibition of respiratory movements. In monkeys the inhibitory area corresponds to the anterior agranular cingulate and extends ventrally into the subcallosal and posterior orbital cortex. The point of maximum effect is in the region of the genu of the corpus callosum. The inhibitory effect is an instantaneous damping of the inspiratory movements. Acceleration of respiration results from stimulation of the cingulate gyrus posterior to the inhibitory area, and of the rostral pyriform cortex. Generalized cardiovascular changes follow stimulation of many of the above neural structures in the third system. A rise and a drop in arterial pressure may result from stimulation at points only a few millimeters apart.

The behavioral results of ablations in the cingulate, posterior orbital, and anterior temporal areas have been reported from numerous studies. In general neither unilateral or bilateral ablations of cingulate or orbitoinsulotemporal cortex interfere with the basic integration of somatomotor or autonomic mechanisms, except for an increase in restlessness, nor with functions essential to survival. From ablations, there are no changes in respiratory, cardiovascular, gastrointestinal, or pupillary activities. This contrasts with the generalized changes in these cortical areas from stimulation studies. The influence of these areas, then, is probably not a tonic one. The only changes following ablation operations are an increase in motor restlessness and some affective changes. Anterior cingulate ablations result in greater tameness and a lessening of preoperative fear and rage levels. Posterior orbital ablations result in motor restlessness, as though the animal was released from some inhibition regulating activity levels. It was suggested, however, that profound restlessness results only when the subjacent head of the caudate nucleus is damaged. Ablations of the anterior temporal region which involve bilateral removal bring about profound changes in behavior. This observation is based on the well known Klüver-Bucy operation, which removed most of the entire temporal lobe including the amygdaloid and hippocampus. The behavioral changes include visual agnosia, excessive tendency to examine objects visually, tactually, and orally, decrease in aggressive behavior, loss of fear, bizarre sexual behavior, and change in dietary habits. Later investigations seem to indicate that much less extensive changes occur if the ablation is limited to the ventral orbitotemporal region. Visual discrimination was found to depend on the integrity of the medial occipitotemporal region. Careful behavioral studies suggest that the posterior orbital cortex is concerned with locomotion, the anterior insular area with taste, and the temporal polar and amygdaloid areas with food intake, temperature regulation, and excessive examination by visual, tactual, and oral means. Recent studies seem to show that central areas of the pyriform (entorhinal) cortex are involved in hyperexpression of sexuality, sometimes indiscriminately as to sex, age, or species. This is depicted in Fig. 16–4.

In addition to the cortical and subcortical centers and their connections summarized above, parts of this limbic system have connections with midline and intralaminar nuclei of the thalamus. The anterior hypothalamus sends fibers to the midline and intralaminar nuclei of the thalamus. These thalamic nuclei in turn project to prepyriform, subcallosal, cingulate, and entorhinal cortices. These cortical areas in their turn send afferents to Ammon's formation. There is, therefore, a series of recurrent loops between these structures, involving structures in the second and third systems and the anterior and midline thalamus.

An analysis of the three systems, which are interconnected but with different functions, shows the following characterization. The first system is largely olfactory, or olfactory connected reflex circuits. The second system involves olfactory and gustatory behavior—food intake, temperature regulation, sleep-activity cycles, and defense-flight reactions. This is the system which comes closest to comprising the emotional-motivational behavior. The third system has no such clear relationship to specific types of behavior. The cingulate cortex is not involved in emotional behavior, but rather the amygdaloid and entorhinal cortex are primarily involved in emotional activity. The hippocampus (or Ammon's formation) is clearly involved in memory fixation, for the fixation of memory of current events is impossible if the hippocampus is removed. The cingulate gyrus, together with its connections to mammillary bodies through the anterior thalamic nucleus, is essential for vigilance and wakefulness. None of these activities is directly related either to olfactory reactions or to emotional and motivational behavior, except that some motivational level is necessary for either wakefulness or memory fixation.

It is clear from the above discussion that the transitional cortex has very diffuse relationships with peripheral structures, in contrast to the

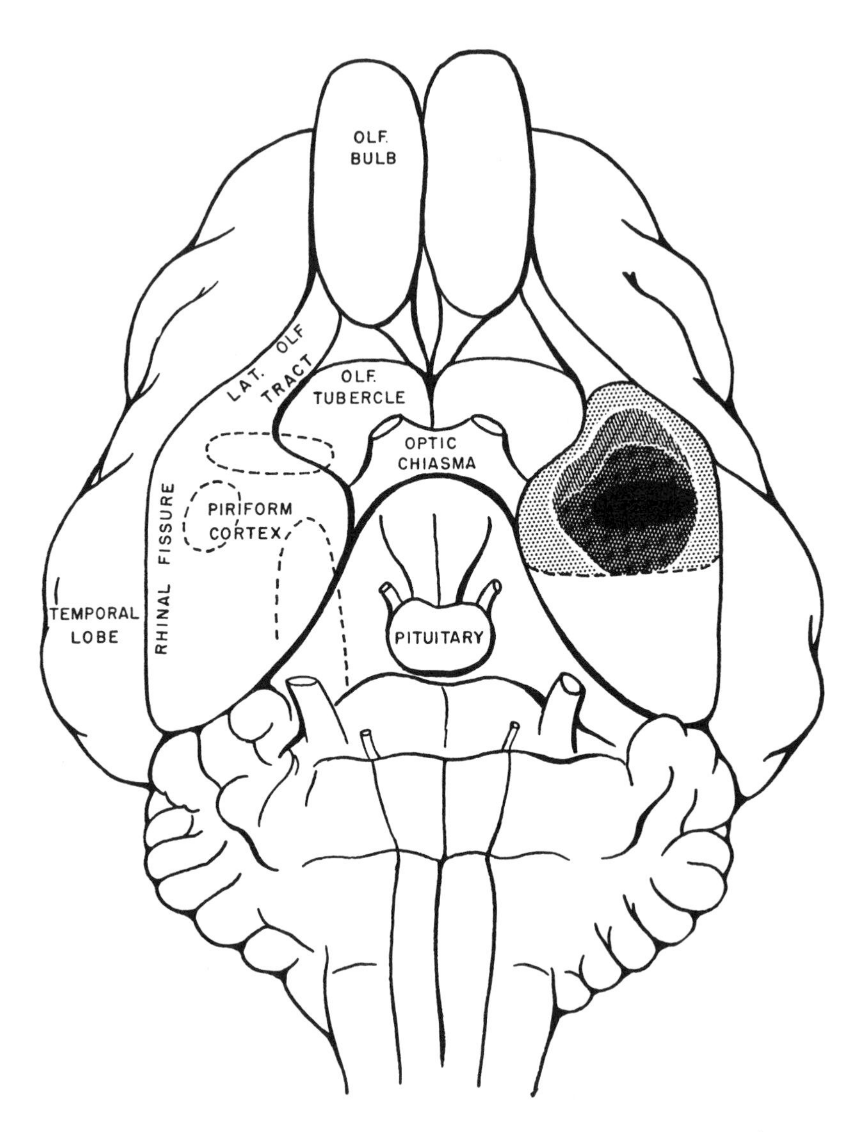

Source: Figure 2, J. D. Green, C. D. Clemente and J. De Groot, *J. Comp. Neur., 108*:522.

Figure 16–4. Ventral Brain Surface and Pyriform Cortex Associated with Hypersexuality

discreteness of relationships between the afferent and efferent projection systems and the neocortex. It is probable that this diffuse relationship may provide the basis for fitting into a number of diverse behavior patterns, for the functions of neocortex and transitional cortex are clearly different. One area of the second or third system may be part of two differently organized cerebral systems. A static conception of "a" function would be replaced under this point of view by a dynamic concept involving different functions for one area under different conditions of afferent input.

SOURCES AND ADDITIONAL READING

The CIBA Collection of Medical Illustrations, Vol. I, *Nervous System.* CIBA Pharmaceutical Company, 1953.

Handbook of Physiology, Sec. I, Vol. II, Chaps. 55–58. Washington, D. C.: American Physiol. Soc., 1960.

Isaacson, R. L., ed., *Basic Reading in Neuropsychology.* New York: Harper & Row, Publishers, 1964.

Ranson, S. W. and S. L. Clark, *The Anatomy of the Nervous System* (10th ed.) Chap. 17. Philadelphia: W. B. Saunders Company, 1959.

Ruch, T. and J. Fulton, *Medical Physiology and Biophysics* (18th ed.), Chap. 22. Philadelphia: W. B. Saunders Company, 1961. (See 19th ed., Chaps. 25, 26.)

Walsh, G., *Physiology of the Nervous System,* Chap. 12. New York: Longmans Green & Co., Inc., 1959.

Seventeen

THE THALAMUS AND INTERNAL CAPSULE

In preceding sections we have considered the transmission of information from the sense organs into the spinal cord or other coordinating center before traveling to higher centers for integration with other modalities of incoming sensation. Much of the proprioceptive information ends in the cerebellum, where it is integrated with data about touch, equilibrium, etc. In contrast to cerebellar pathways all of the sensory data which reaches the cortex, except olfaction, pass through a common coordinating center, the thalamus. Here, added fusion and integration occur, and from the thalamus the sensory data are directed to particular receptive areas of the cerebral cortex. The thalamus is then the last relay station on the afferent, or incoming, limb of sensory pathways below the cortical level. The term "relay station" might give the impression that the thalamus was like a junction point or switching point in a railroad line, but this would be incorrect. The thalamus functions rather as a huge shunting yard where different "combinations of freight cars" are made up for different destinations. There is, then, considerable fusion and coordination of sensory data in the various thalamic nuclei. In the spinal cord and higher up in the spinal lemniscus it is possible to separate the fibers for pain and temperature from those for touch and pressure. Above the level of the thalamus this separation is no longer possible, and one cannot isolate any of these sensory modalities from the others. For a general view of the thalamus, see Fig. 17–1.

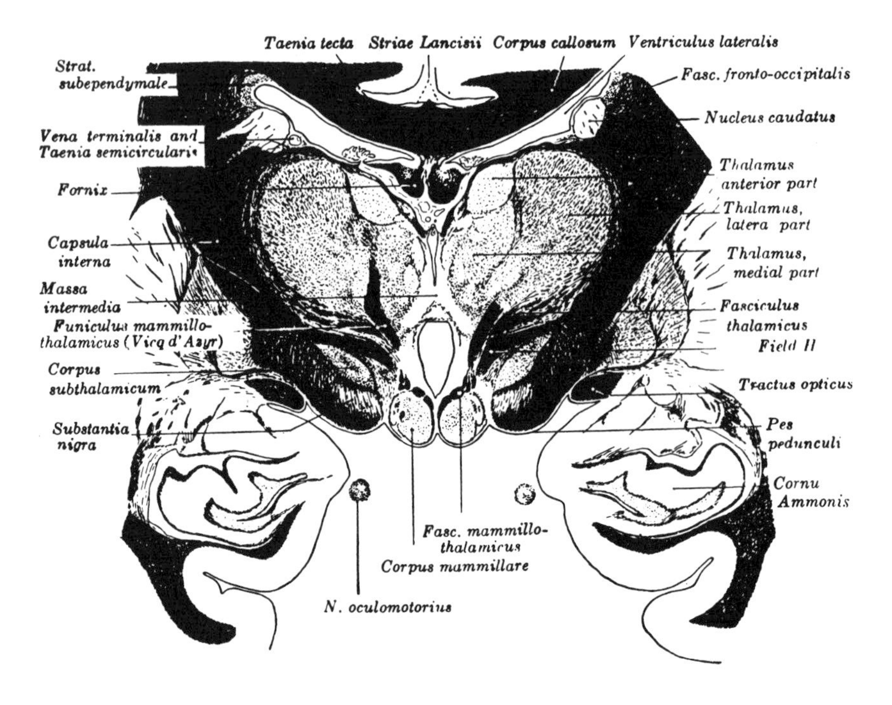

Source: S. W. Ranson and S. L. Clark, *The Anatomy of the Nervous System: Its Development and Function* (10th ed.; Philadelphia: W. B. Saunders Company, 1959), p. 300.

Figure 17–1. Cross Section of Thalamus at Level of Mammillary Bodies

THALAMIC NUCLEI

The bilateral thalamus lies dorsal to the hypothalamus and ventral to the lateral ventricles, anterior to the superior colliculus, and largely posterior to the basal ganglia. It is bounded laterally by the internal capsule and medially by the III ventricle. The thalamus is composed of a series of different nuclei—some receiving direct sensory input, others sending efferent fibers to lower centers, and still others having more direct cortical connections. The nuclei receiving sensory fibers are located largely in the ventral and lateral segments of the thalamus. These are the *ventral-posterior* (V.P.L.) for body sense (spinothalamic and medial lemnisci), the *ventral-posterior* (medial portion) for face sense, the *ventral-intermediate* for the cerebellar fibers which travel via the *superior peduncle* and *red nucleus,* and the *lateral* (L.G.) and *medial geniculate* (M.G.) *nuclei* for visual and auditory reception respectively. Olfactory impulses do not synapse here. The sensory receptive nuclei project in their turn to the *postcentral gyrus* of the cortex for body and face sense (see Fig. 17–2), to the *precentral gyrus* for cerebellar information, and to the *calcarine fissure* and the *superior temporal gyrus* for vision and hearing respectively. Since all thalamic projections are ipsilateral, the fibers pass to cortex of the same side as the nucleus.

In addition to the ventrolateral group of sensory receptive nuclei the thalamus has both medial and dorsal nuclei which are concerned with coordination of more than one type of sensory information, and with connections to subcortical centers. The *anterior ventral nucleus* (V.A.) receives from the globus pallidus and sends back fibers to parts of the basal ganglia, and is involved as well in the diffuse thalamic projection to many cortical areas. The *dorsolateral* and *posterolateral* nuclei receive from other thalamic nuclei and project primarily to the parietal lobe, although the posterolateral also projects to the tip of the temporal lobe. The *pulvinar* is the most posterior part of the lateral nuclear group. It is concerned with coordination of visual and auditory information and projects primarily to the parietal lobe and to the association cortex between calcarine and superior temporal cortex. The most *anterior nucleus* of the thalamus is separated from the others by the branching of the internal medullary lamina. This nucleus receives the *mammillothalamic tract* from the mammillary bodies and projects to the *cingulate gyrus.* The *medial nucleus* is divided into two parts, a medial portion and a lateral portion. The medial part receives from the midline nuclei and sends fibers to the hypothalamus, while the lateral part receives from other thalamic nuclei and projects to the frontal lobe. This projection to frontal lobe is topographical; that is, the anterior portion of the nucleus projects to the anterior frontal lobe, the posterior part to the posterial frontal lobe. Bilateral lesions of the dorsomedial thalamus in monkeys result in aimless hyperactivity, loss of fear, distractability, and a vacant facial expression.

The other major nucleus of the medial group, inside the medullary lamina, is the *central nucleus* (centrum medianum). (See Fig. 17–3.) This nucleus provides the major afferent input of the *caudate nucleus.* It projects also to putamen but not to the globus pallidus of the basal ganglia. In addition, it has connections with the main adjacent thalamic nuclei, and for this reason may be one element in the modulating effect of thalamus on cortex.

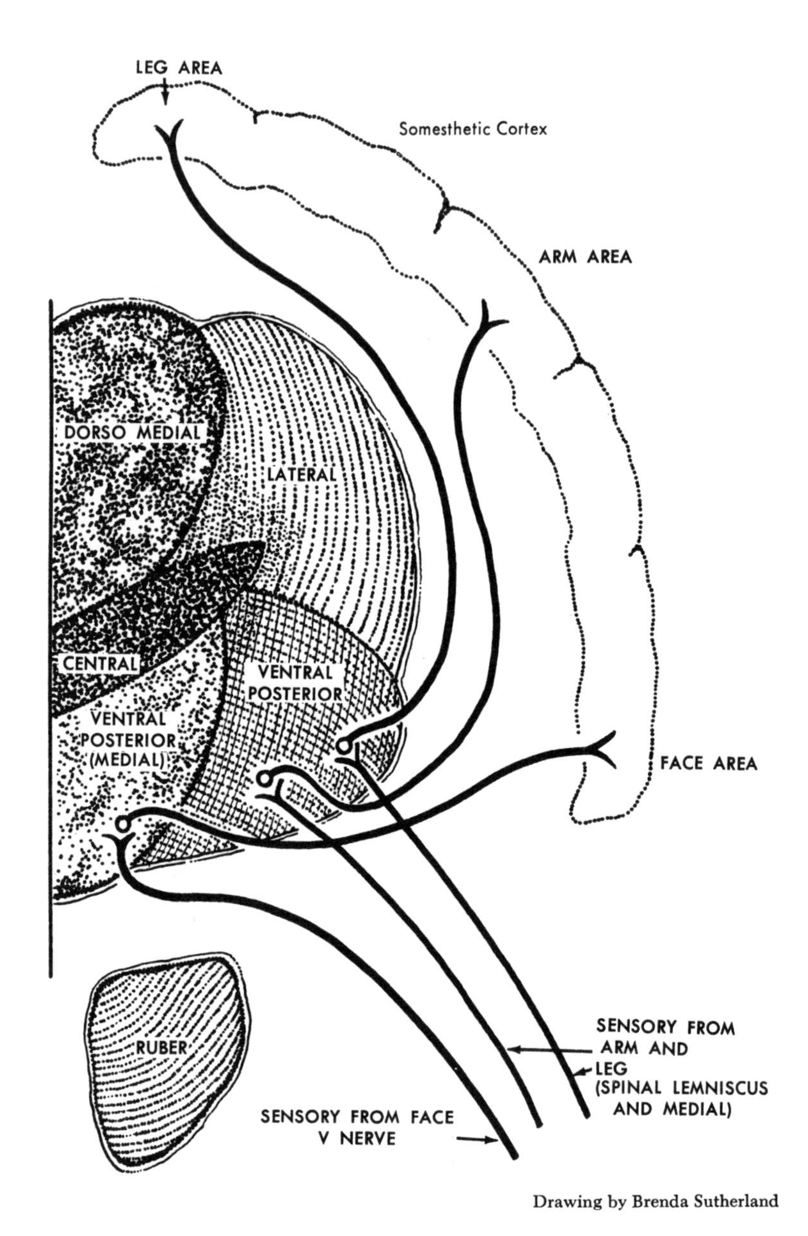

Drawing by Brenda Sutherland

Figure 17–2. Afferent Pathway to Thalamus and Cortex of Sensory Fibers from Body and Face

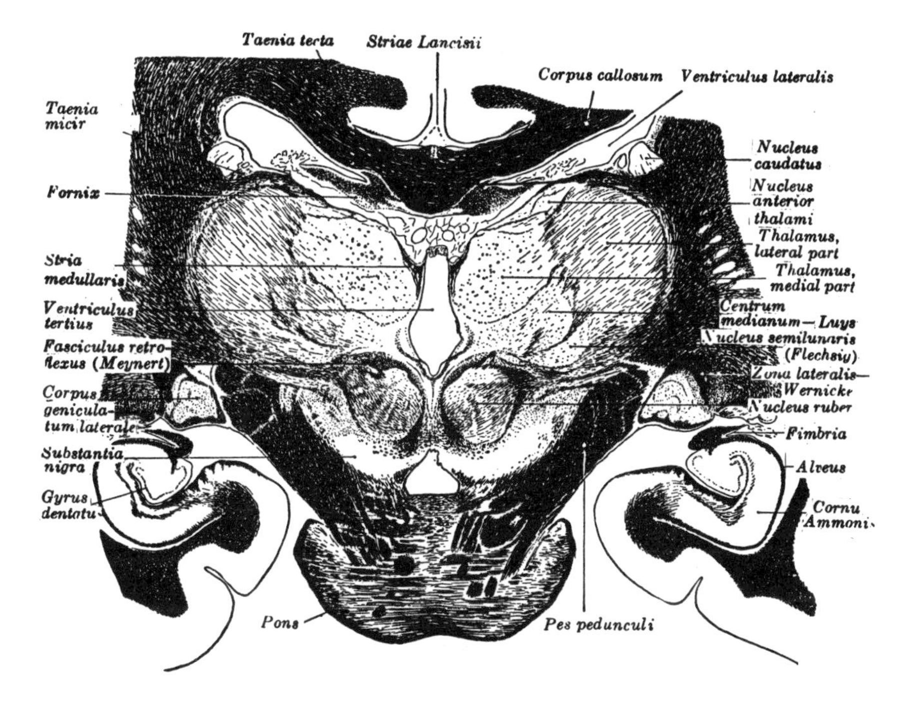

Source: S. W. Ranson and S. L. Clark, *The Anatomy of the Nervous System*, p. 301.

Figure 17–3. Nuclei of Frontal Thalamus at Level of Centrum Medianum

Other parts of the thalamic region are the subthalamus, the epithalamus, and the hypothalamus. These segments will be reviewed in other sections on the extrapyramidal system, olfactory system, or visceral homeostatic mechanisms.

In mammals and primates the primary function of the thalamus is to serve as a relay station to the cortex or to other subcortical nuclear groups. However, the animal forms below these levels, which have only rudimentary cortex or none at all, show the same relation between ascending pathways and thalamic nuclei. It is clear that in the birds, reptiles, etc. there is no cortical projection of thalamic fibers, and that the thalamus is the highest level in the ascending sensory pathway. The connecting link between the sensory and motor channels will be considered in Chapter 22 under the extrapyramidal pathways. In the lower forms, then, some form of awareness must reside in the thalamic nuclei. This conclusion is borne out not only by experiments on these animals, but by clinical cases of animals or humans born without a cortex. Even in forms which have developed thalamocortical connections, the loss of cortex does not remove all sensory experience. The ablation of the visual cortex does not remove all rod-brightness function in monkeys. The thalamus, then, can be the main sensory receptive area for primitive pain and pleasure experiences. One clinical case of a

Table 17–I

Thalamic Nuclei

Receives From	*Nucleus*	*Projects To**
	I *Ventral Group*	
Spinal and Medial Lemnisci	1. Ventroposterior	Postcentral gyrus (cortex)
Trigeminal Lemniscus	a) Medial portion	Postcentral gyrus (cortex)
Cerebellar Fibers via Ruber	2. Ventral intermediate	Precentral gyrus (cortex)
Lateral Lemniscus	3. Medial geniculate	Superior temporal gyrus (cortex)
Optic Tract	4. Lateral geniculate	Lips of calcarine fissure
Globus Pallidus	5. Ventral anterior	Basal ganglia and diffuse cortical projection
	II *Lateral Group*	
Other Thalamic Nuclei	1. Dorsolateral	Parietal lobe
Other Thalamic Nuclei	2. Posterolateral	Parietal lobe and ant. tip temporal lobe
Medial and Lateral Geniculates	3. Pulvinar	Parietal association area
Reticular Formation	4. Reticular nuc.	Diffuse cortical projection
	III *Anterior Group*	
Mammillothalamic Tract	1. Anterior nucleus	Cingulate gyrus
	IV *Medial and Midline*	
	1. Medial	
Midline Nuclei	a) Medial portion	Hypothalamus
Other Thalamic Nuclei	b) Lateral portion	Frontal lobe
Cerebellum (Interpositus)	2. Central (centrum medianum)	Caudate and putamen
Anterior Hypothalamus and Reticular Formation	3. Intralaminar nuc.	Diffuse cortical projection (limbic)
Anterior Hypothalamus and Reticular Formation	4. Midline nuc.	Diffuse cortical projection (limbic) and to medial nuc.

* For an illustration of these projections see Fig. 17–4

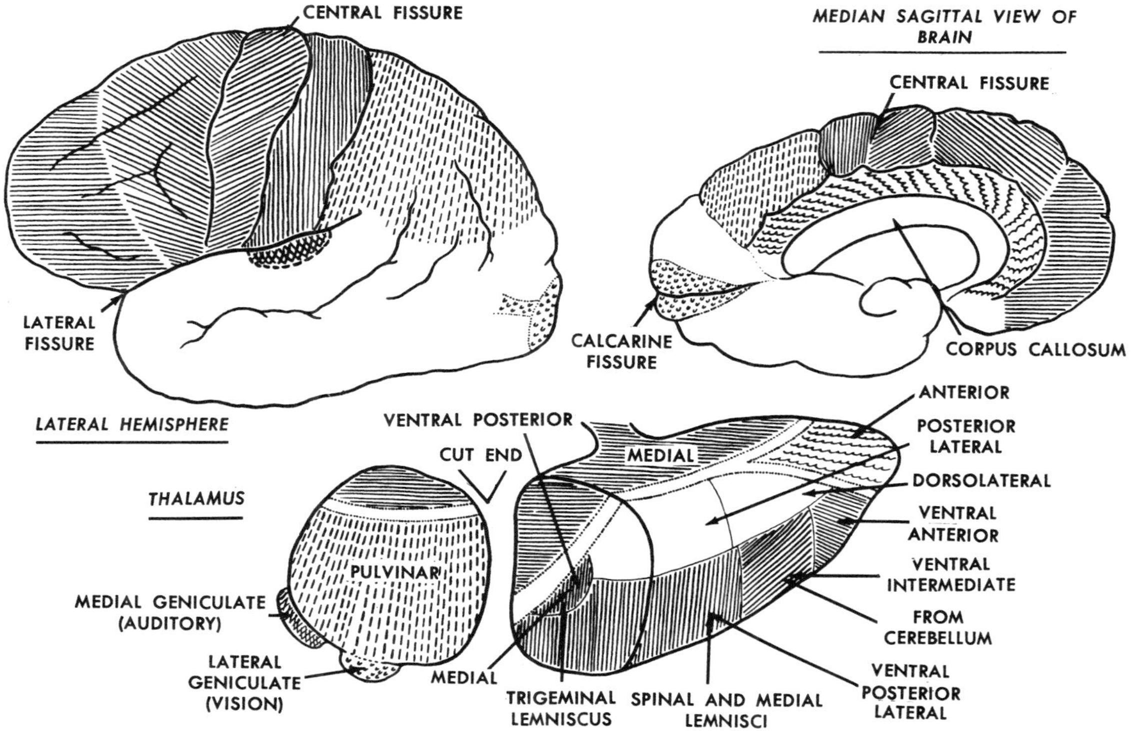

CENTRAL FISSURE

LATERAL FISSURE

LATERAL HEMISPHERE

MEDIAN SAGITTAL VIEW OF BRAIN

CENTRAL FISSURE

CALCARINE FISSURE

CORPUS CALLOSUM

THALAMUS

VENTRAL POSTERIOR

CUT END

MEDIAL

PULVINAR

MEDIAL GENICULATE (AUDITORY)

LATERAL GENICULATE (VISION)

MEDIAL

TRIGEMINAL LEMNISCUS

SPINAL AND MEDIAL LEMNISCI

ANTERIOR

POSTERIOR LATERAL

DORSOLATERAL

VENTRAL ANTERIOR

VENTRAL INTERMEDIATE

FROM CEREBELLUM

VENTRAL POSTERIOR LATERAL

Drawing by Brenda Sutherland

Figure 17–4. Thalamic Projections to Cortical Areas

thalamic child indicated fairly normal pain-pleasure responses up to six months of age. In careful studies of several children with no cortex or thalamus and only the brain stem through the mesencephalon, responses to touch on the cheek and to painful stimulation showed little if any variation from those of the normal child having a complete cortex. Even in the human, then, the thalamus must retain the basic elements of its phylogenetic function as the highest sensory coordinating center.

INTERNAL CAPSULE

The fibers contained in the cerebral peduncles on their way to pons, bulb, and spinal cord descend from the cortex by way of the *internal capsule,* which lies between the mass of the thalamus and the putamen and globus pallidus. Here too are gathered all of the axons from thalamic nuclei which ascend into the various sensory projection areas of the cortex, and the reticular activating and diffuse projection fibers which spread so widely to most cortical areas.

The internal capsule is a broad band of white fibers (myelinated) which runs from the various cortical areas ventrally and medially to the subcortical centers such as basal ganglia and pontine nuclei. The medial portion of the capsule carries predominantly the somesthetic and cerebellar radiations from thalamus to cortex, but its anterior part includes fibers projecting from medial and anterior thalamic nuclei to frontal lobes, and from frontal lobes downstream to the pons. At its caudal end the internal capsule contains both the auditory and optic radiations to the superior temporal gyrus and the calcarine cortex respectively.

The internal capsule, then, is the main highway of communication between cortex and lower centers, and as a consequence appears only in those forms where the cortex is well developed. It lies lateral to the mass of the thalamus and medial to the putamen and globus pallidus. For these relationships, see Fig. 17–5. The anterior limb of the capsule also extends lateral of the caudate nucleus. Since the putamen and globus pallidus lie largely anterior of the thalamus and the caudate nucleus more rostral still, the capsule is bent around the medial border of the globus pallidus. In longitudinal section, therefore, the internal capsule is shaped like a very flat or horizontal V, with the point coming close to the midline just anterior to the anterior thalamic nucleus. The mass of the thalamus is directly posterior, and the capsule extends laterally to separate the thalamus from the putamen and globus pallidus. The an-

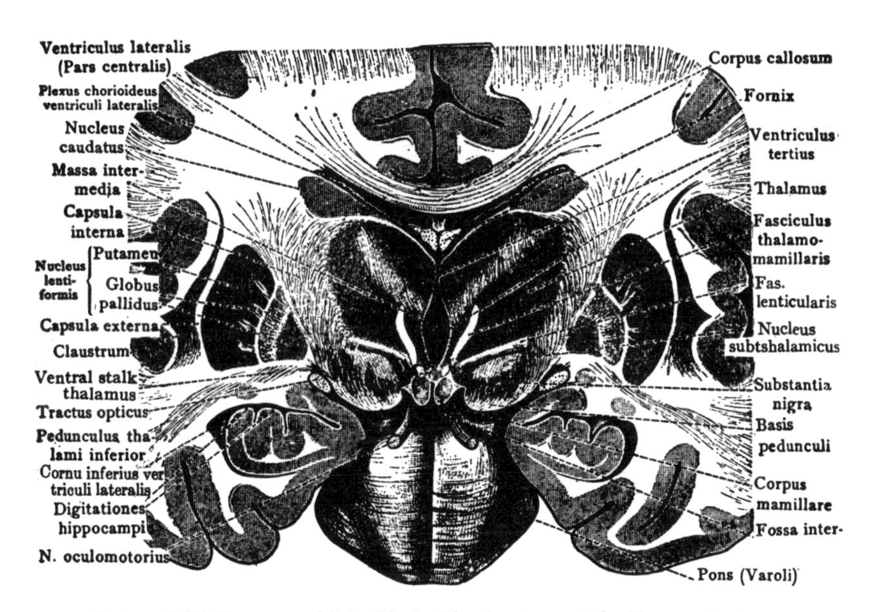

Source: S. W. Ranson and S. L. Clark, *The Anatomy of the Nervous System*, p. 315.

Figure 17–5. Frontal Brain Section Showing Internal Capsule and Peduncles

terior limb of the capsule extends laterally and anteriorly from the point of the V and separates the large caudate nucleus medially and anteriorly from the putamen and globus pallidus, which lie laterally and posteriorly. The two limbs, anterior and posterior, enclose the putamen and globus pallidus. The details of these arrangements can be seen in Fig. 17–6.

This broad band of fibers shows a separation into discrete bundles that can be identified with particular functions. The posterior limb of the capsule contains, near the knee of the V, fibers running from the motor cortex to nuclei of the cranial nerves. Thus the fibers to oculomotor (III) and to cranial nerves in the pons and medulla pass through this section. Just posterior to these fascicles course fibers from the cortex to spinal cord areas for shoulder, arm, and hand, which are, in part at least, separable one from another. Then come the fibers from the cortex to the red nucleus, and posterior to them the fibers to the lumbar enlargement of the spinal cord for the innervation of the leg and foot. The medial portion of the capsule carries the somesthetic and cerebellar

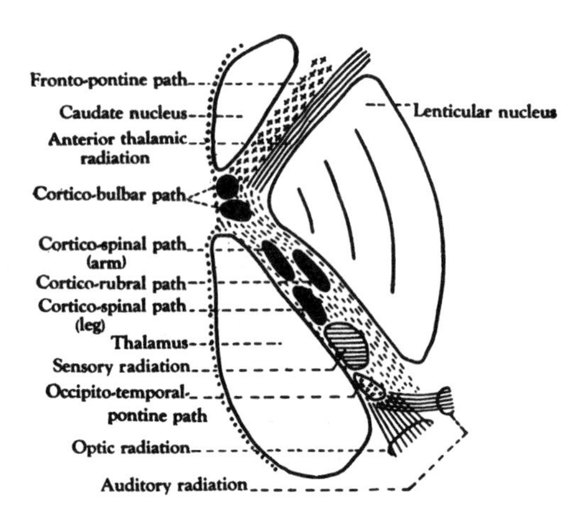

Source: C. U. Ariëns Kappers, G. Carl Huber, and Elizabeth C. Crosby, *The Comparative Anatomy of the Nervous System of Vertebrates, Including Man* (Vol. 2; New York: Hafner Publishing Company, 1960), p. 1459.

Figure 17–6. Horizontal View of Internal Capsule Showing Chief Component Pathways

radiations to the cortex. As already indicated, in the anterior limb lie both the anterior thalamic radiations to the frontal lobes and frontal lobe fibers running downstream to the pontine nuclei.

Most posterior, in the internal capsule, are the auditory radiations to the superior temporal cortex, the geniculocalcarine radiations for optic fibers to the calcarine cortex, and the posterior thalamic radiation, largely from the pulvinar to the parietal cortex. The discrete localization of the fibers in the capsule is very important clinically, for it is susceptible to damage by thromboses and tumors. Thus temporary or continuing paralysis may give an accurate indication of the location of the trouble.

The fibers of the internal capsule descending from various cortical areas to lower centers of the midbrain, pons, medulla, and cord come together ventrally in two broad bands of fibers at the base of the midbrain which are known as the cerebral peduncles. These turn caudally and become broken up into separate fascicles in the pons, where many synapse with the pontine nuclei or with cranial nerve nuclei in the pons and medulla. The remainder come together again in the pyramidal tracts, which continue into the spinal cord as the lateral and ventral corticospinal tracts.

SOURCES AND ADDITIONAL READING

The CIBA Collection of Medical Illustrations, Vol. I, *Nervous System.* CIBA Pharmaceutical Co., 1953.

Crosby, E. C., T. Humphrey, and E. W. Lauer, *Correlative Anatomy of the Nervous System.* New York: The Macmillan Company, 1962.

Ranson, S. W. and S. L. Clark, *The Anatomy of the Nervous System* (10th ed.), Chap. 15. Philadelphia: W. B. Saunders Co., 1959.

Rasmussen, A. T., *Principal Nervous Pathways.* New York: The Macmillan Company, 1945.

Ruch, T. and J. Fulton, *Medical Physiology and Biophysics* (18th ed.), Chap. 14. Philadelphia: W. B. Saunders Company, 1961. (See 19th ed., Chap. 15.)

Walsh, G., *Physiology of the Nervous System,* Chap. 11. New York: Longmans Green & Co., Inc., 1958.

Eighteen

THE RETICULAR FORMATION

The reticular formation is by definition a net-like series of short interwoven fibers and nerve cells. It extends from just above the decussation of the pyramids in the medulla rostralward through the center of the pons and midbrain, and up into the thalamus to form the reticular nuclei of the thalamus. Its general position in the medulla, pons, and midbrain is medial to the long ascending sensory pathways (spinothalamic, lateral lemniscus, etc.) but lateral to the centrally placed medial longitudinal fasciculus and tectospinal path. It is also ventral to the cranial nerve nuclei in the medulla, pons, and midbrain. In the medulla the reticular formation is made up of bilateral columns in the medial center of the right and left halves. (See Fig. 18–1.) In the pons the net-like structure of the reticular formation occupies approximately the same position as in the medulla, while in the midbrain it has become concentrated more centrally around and in the periaqueductal gray. In the thalamus, by contrast, the reticular nuclei are the most lateral of all the thalamic nuclei, being lateral to the ventral posterior and pulvinar nuclei, and forming a thin sheath on the lateral border of the thalamus. (See Fig. 18–2.)

Because it is a net-like structure of many neurons and their fibers there are relatively few clearly delimited nuclei in the reticular for-

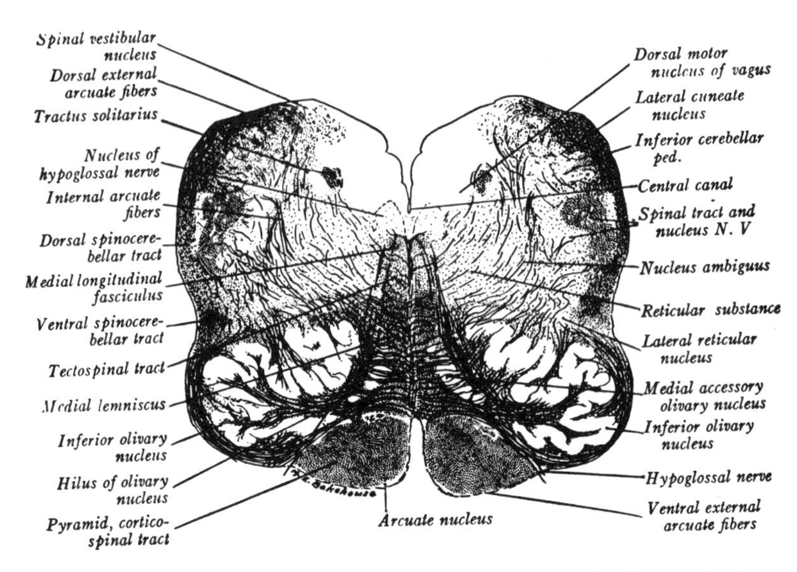

Source: S. W. Ranson and S. L. Clark, *The Anatomy of the Nervous System: Its Development and Function* (10th ed.; Philadelphia: W. B. Saunders Company, 1959), p. 210.

Figure 18–1. Reticular Formation at Level of the Medulla

mation. Even the respiratory centers in the medulla are designated by the general area at which evoked potentials are recorded. Consequently the physiological characteristics of the reticular formation are largely independent of its cytoarchitecture, although one investigator identified ninety-eight nuclear groups. Because of this generalized and undifferentiated topography the functions of the reticular formation are indicated more clearly by the pathways feeding into it and efferent fibers from it to other structures. The afferent fibers to it are: (1) spinoreticular fibers by collaterals of the main sensory bundles, (2) fibers from the principal sensory nuclei of the brain stem, (3) fibers from interstitial motor cells and the colliculi, (4) cerebellar fibers from the medial cerebellar nucleus (fastigial), and (5) corticofugal fibers from the frontal and sensorimotor cortex as well as from the cingulate gyrus, hippocampus, and entorhinal cortex.

These fiber bundles are concerned primarily with the ascending or activating function of the reticular formation. There is also a comparable descending function which will be considered below.

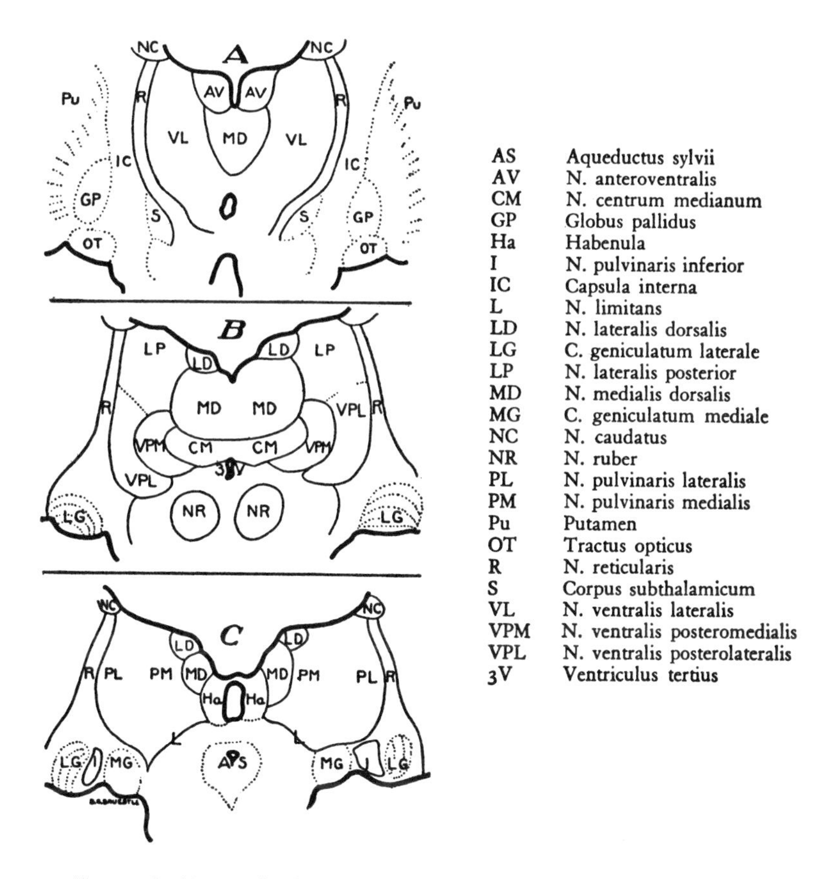

(Camera lucida drawing by A. Earl Walker, 1938.) A, Anterior thalamus with anterior and lateroventral nuclei. B, Midthalamus with posteroventral and medial nuclei. C, Posterior thalamus with pulvinar and geniculate bodies.

Source: John F. Fulton, *Physiology of the Nervous System* (3d ed., rev.; New York: Oxford University Press, 1949), p. 270.

Figure 18–2. Cross-section of Chimpanzee Thalamus Showing Principal Nuclear Masses at Three Levels

ASCENDING INFLUENCE

Attention was directed toward the reticular formation as a result of experiments showing that transection of the brain stem above the level of the colliculi resulted in a condition resembling sleep or coma. The initial explanation of this result was that it was brought about by a deafferentation of the cortex; that is, that the cortex was cut off from an afferent influx that was an essential element in arousal or wakefulness. Further studies indicated that the influx of impulses centrally through the brain stem reticular formation was strongly implicated in the arousal mechanism. As a result of this series of studies the entire mechanism was called the *reticular activating system.* The way in which the reticular activating system functions was demonstrated by the careful studies of Magoun and Moruzzi. They recorded evoked potentials in the reticular formation from excitation of somatic sensory, proprioceptive, sympathetic, vagal, auditory, visual, and olfactory conduction systems. Practically all of the major sensory pathways, then, send collaterals into the reticular formation. When this afferent influx has ascended in the brain stem it is transmitted to all areas of the cortex

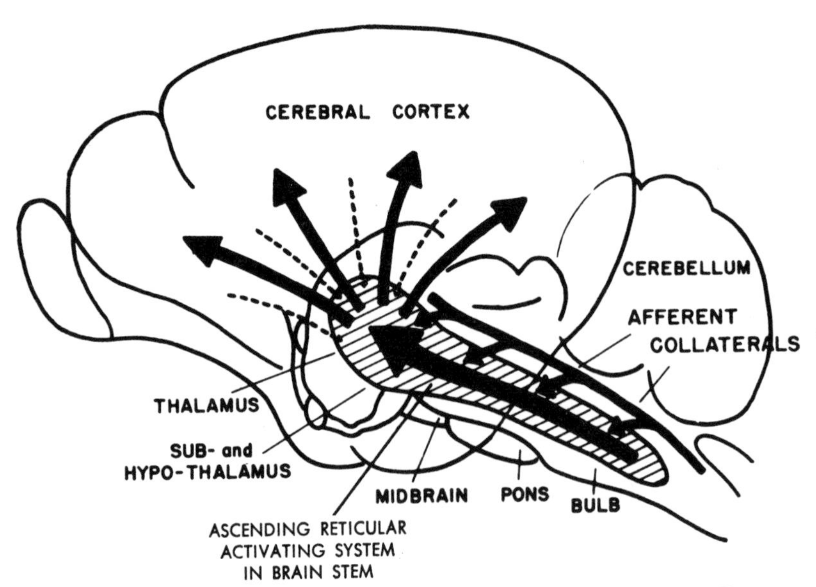

Source: T. E. Starzl, C. W. Taylor, and H. W. Magoun, "Collateral Afferent Excitation of Reticular Formation of Brain Stem," *Journal of Neurophysiology,* Vol. 14 (1951), p. 495.

Figure 18–3. Sensory Collaterals and Reticular Projection to Cerebral Cortex

by the diffuse thalamic projection system. These projections can be seen in Fig. 18–3. The area in which each sensory system is recorded is common to all modalities, and the corticofugal pulses end in the same area as the sensory modalities.

It seems clear from the work of Moruzzi, Magoun, and other workers that it is the diffuse projection to many areas of the cortex which is responsible for the arousal state, rather than the reception of impulses from the main sensory systems in their delimited cortical sensory reception sites. It is possible to record stimulation in the sensory receptor areas of the postcentral gyrus, occipital, or superior temporal areas without bringing about arousal if the pulses from the reticular activating system are blocked. Only when sensory signals result in stimulation of the reticular formation is arousal achieved. The action of anesthetic is principally to block synaptic transmission, particularly in multisynaptic reticular formation, as contrasted with fiber conduction. Because of this differential effect, transmission by the main ascending sensory fiber tracts is still possible when the somnolence, brought about by blocking of the reticular formation, is already evident. Of all the sensory systems feeding into the reticular formation the most powerful in the arousal reaction is the somatic input from the head. Touch on the face will arouse a person or animal more quickly and with less intensity of stimulus than visual, auditory, or somatic (from the body) stimulation. Visual stimulation is least effective.

ELECTROENCEPHALOGRAPHY

Electroencephalography has been widely used in connection with experiments on the arousal result of reticular stimulation. Under condition of sleep or coma the characteristic high amplitude, slow *delta* waves are recorded. Upon stimulation of the reticular formation these wave forms change to the faster *alpha* or *beta* waves of arousal or close attention or excitement. In this connection it is important to realize that there is a differential effect of slow or rapid stimulation of the reticular formation. Stimulation of 5 cycles per second will result in somnolent reaction of the animal, while stimulation at the rate of 30-90 cycles per second, even in the same location, will arouse the animal.

The reticular formation acts upon the cortex generally by a very diffuse projection system from thalamic nuclei. The cephalic conduction occurs in clearly defined fiber bundles such as (1) the lateral reticulothalamic, (2) the tegmental tract, and (3) the tectothalamic bundle to the midline and intralaminar nuclei of the thalamus. On the basis of degeneration studies, the connection between the reticular formation and the neocortex is indirect. Such studies show degeneration in the midline and intralaminar thalamic nuclei from damage to hippocampus, entorhinal, cingulate cortex, and amygdala, but not degeneration in the reticular formation. These parts of the limbic system may well be implicated in the diffuse thalamic projection system. Recent studies have indicated also that the ventral anterior nucleus of the thalamus plays a part in the diffuse cortical projection, as well as its better known function as a feedback loop to the basal ganglia.

DESCENDING INFLUENCE

The descending influence of the reticular formation is that of facilitating or inhibiting motor activity, largely at the level of spinal motor neurons. The facilitation of motor activity has been shown to arise largely from rostral segments of the central brain stem, such as tegmental and diencephalic centers. The facilitatory action, and inhibitory as well, are carried out through internuncial neurons. Because of this intervening level, sustained reticular excitation recruits an expanding pool of interneurons; and these summate their effect on more and more motor neurons, thus increasing the facilitation or inhibition.

The inhibitory action of the reticular formation arises from stimulation of lower, more caudal, reticular segments, largely in the medulla.

DESCENDING PATHWAYS

Two major descending avenues of reticular action are demonstrated by the part the reticular formation plays in the descending pathways from the basal ganglia and from the cerebellum. The extrapyramidal pathway from the basal ganglia sends fibers from the medial globus pallidus to the subthalamic nucleus and substantia nigra, as well as to the nucleus ruber. Axons of neurons in the subthalamic nucleus and substantia nigra descend to synapse in the upper reticular nuclei, specifically the *dorsal tegmental nucleus* and *central tegmental nucleus* of the pons. Fibers from these nuclei, after a second synapse, become components of the reticulospinal pathway. This series of connections is illustrated in Fig. 18–4. Axons of neurons in the nucleus ruber project to lower reticular nuclei in the medulla, specifically the *central, medial,* and *lateral reticular nuclei.* From there, after synapse, fibers enter the

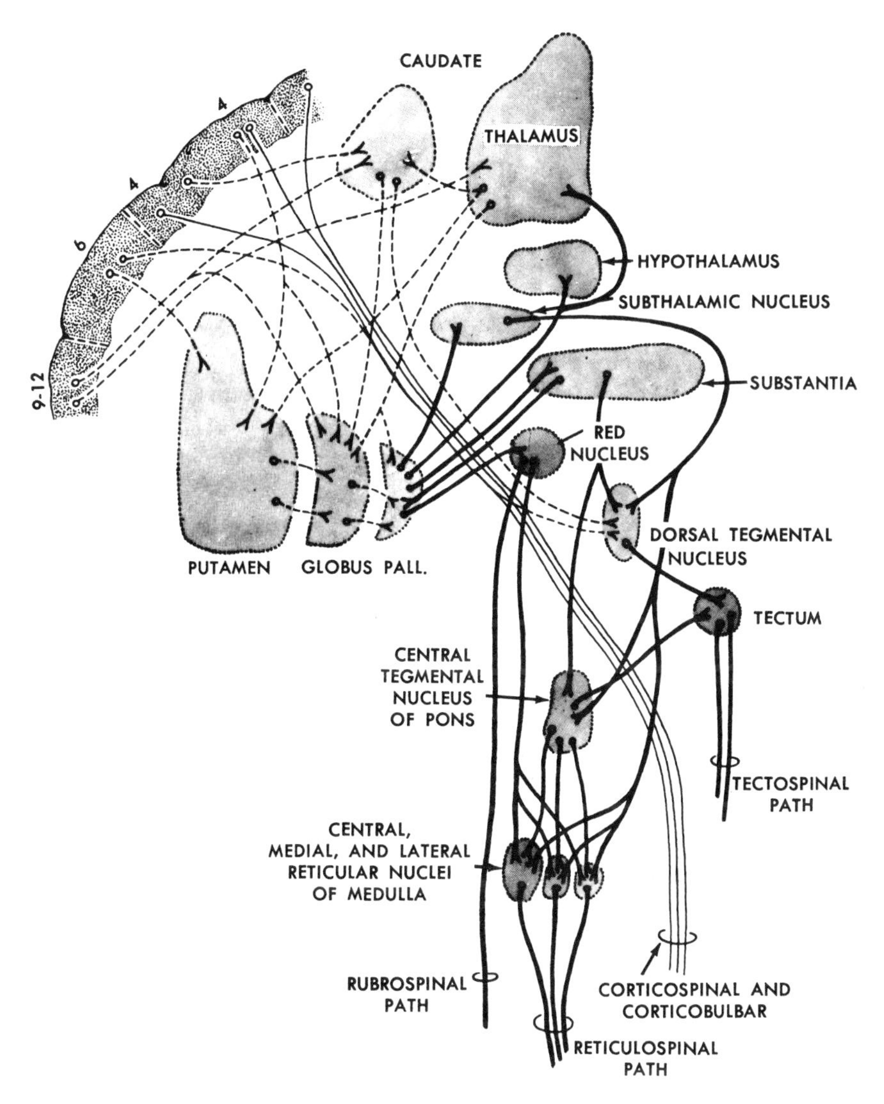

Drawing by Brenda Sutherland

Figure 18–4. Extrapyramidal Connections to Reticulospinal and Rubrospinal Tract

reticulospinal path. Another avenue from the red nucleus to the spinal cord is directly through the rubrospinal pathway. The rubrospinal path is larger than the reticulospinal in four-footed animals, whereas the reticulospinal is larger in primates. This change may be related to the development of upright posture and the consequent change in the function of the forelimbs.

The other major descending influence of the reticular formation is as a part of cerebellar mechanism. Gamma efferent pulses from the anterior horn of the cord out to the intrafusal muscle spindles are subject to reticulospinal influence. Since the excision of the anterior lobe of the cerebellum results in paralysis of the gamma efferent mechanisms, it is evident that the reticulospinal path is an avenue of control rather than a source for originating action. As was outlined under the cerebellum (Chapter 11), a gamma efferent pulse always precedes the firing of the alpha motor neuron so that the firing is modulated by proprioceptive impulses from the annulospiral endings. The medial cerebellum (the vermis) acts through the medial (fastigial) nucleus upon the central reticular formation to aid in control of postural tonus, equilibrium, and locomotor modulation of the entire body. The paravermal cerebellum, acting through nucleus interpositus and the superior peduncle, influences the lateral reticular formation for more discrete control of ipsilateral limbs. There is some evidence that the impulses from the Purkinje cells may be inhibiting or facilitating according to their rate of discharge, the slower rate bringing about inhibition. The reticulospinal activity provides more control of phasic reflexes, while the vestibular path shows more control over tonic reflexes.

The medullary section of the reticular formation has much influence on autonomic activity. The loci for inspiration and expiration are in the medulla, the expiratory center being dorsal to the inspiratory center. In addition, important influences on pressor and depressor action of the cardiovascular system originate in the medulla, the pressor locus in the lateral medial reticulum, and the depressor locus in the ventromedial zone.

It is clear that the reticular formation has important ascending and descending functions, but for the most part as avenues of passage rather than as centers of organization or determiners of reaction. Except for the autonomic centers, with their possible sensitivity to carbon dioxide, the reticular formation fits into other systems rather than forming a separate system of its own. Its dependence on the long ascending lemniscal systems is pronounced, as shown by recent experiments. Animals with lesions in the long lemniscal paths, but with the reticular formation intact, showed very deficient reactions in defense, food getting, and mating. Reactions to noxious stimuli stopped as soon as stimulation was removed. The animals, despite gross appetite and lack of reaction to shock, never learned the simplest tasks even with prolonged training. They seemed to forget from one session to the next, even when these were separated only by two hours. Errors did not disturb them as they would normal animals. The sensory inattention, lack of emotion and exploratory behavior make up a picture akin to that of an automaton. This study gives behavioral evidence that reticular pathways surviving after lemniscal lesions are capable only of diffuse arousal. The presence of rich and varied sensory stimulation is essential to develop and maintain attentive, affective, or adaptive behavior in response to varied environmental conditions.

SOURCES AND ADDITIONAL READING

The CIBA Collection of Medical Illustrations, Vol. I, *Nervous System.* CIBA Pharmaceutical Company, 1953.

Fulton, J., *Physiology of the Nervous System,* Chap. 24. New York: Oxford University Press, Inc., 1951.

Handbook of Physiology, Sec. I, Vol. II, Chap. 52, Washington, D. C.: American Physiol. Soc., 1960.

Isaacson, R. L., ed., *Basic Readings in Neuropsychology.* New York: Harper & Row, Publishers, 1964.

Ruch, T. and J. Fulton, *Medical Physiology and Biophysics* (18th ed.), Chap. 8. Philadelphia: W. B. Saunders Company, 1961. (See 19th ed., Chap. 9.)

Nineteen

THE HYPOTHALAMUS

In the floor of the diencephalon, just behind the optic chiasm and between it and the pons, lies a series of nuclei known collectively as the hypothalamus. Here are located many of the centers for initiating the complex reaction systems that maintain a *homeostatic* or physiological balance in our internal environment. Because of this function the hypothalamus is the highest level of autonomic control of bodily mechanisms. Some of these mechanisms, such as water balance, are strictly localized in particular nuclei, while others such as temperature control are more diffusely spread over an area. In most instances there will be found a different center for facilitation than is needed for inhibition of an activity. Thus in normal animals a different nucleus in the hypothalamus gives information on the condition of satiation than for the condition of hunger. The mechanisms under the control of the hypothalamus include seven: (1) water balance of the body, (2) appetite, (3) blood pressure, (4) emotional expression, (5) temperature regulation, (6) sexual behavior, and (7) the sleep-waking mechanism. For a general schema of the hypothalamus, see Fig 19–1.

WATER BALANCE

The mechanism whereby the water balance of the body is maintained is mediated by a very specialized group of cells which lie over

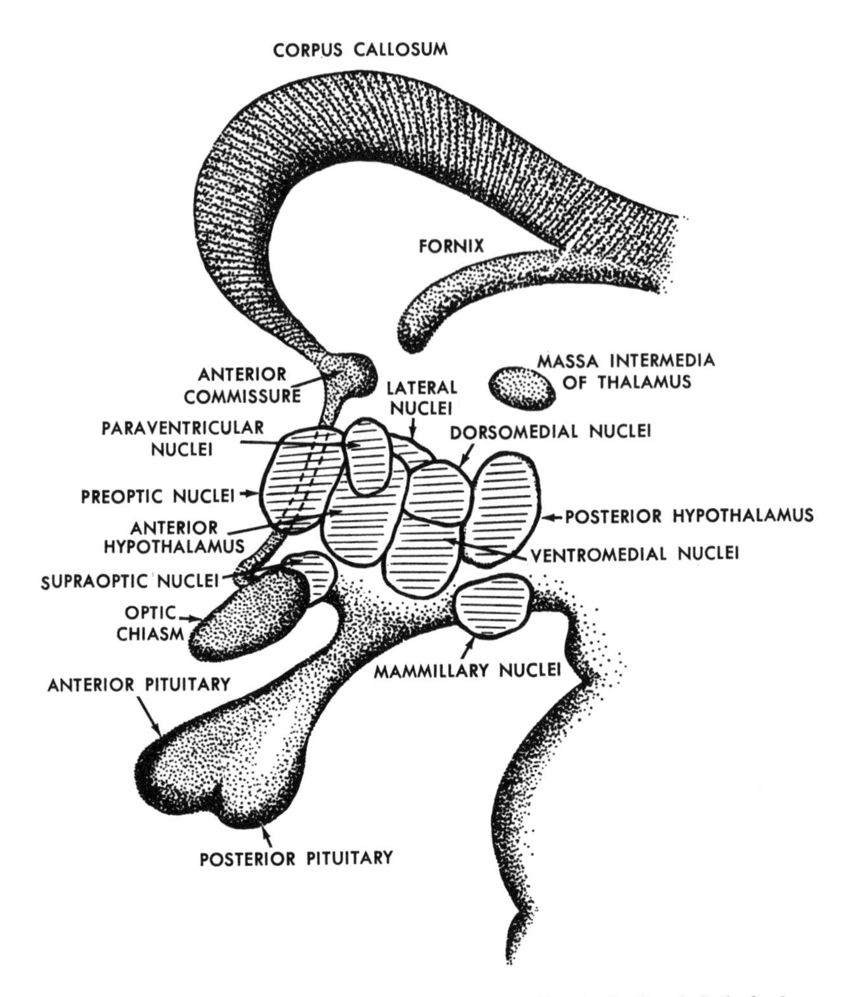

Drawing by Brenda Sutherland

Figure 19–1. General Schema of Hypothalamus Nuclei

and around the optic chiasm. The cells of this *supraoptic* nucleus are responsive to changes in the osmotic pressure of the blood as this changes with its water content. In order to carry out this task, the cells of this nucleus and some of the *paraventricular nucleus* are more closely invested with blood vessels than any other part of the brain. Some evidence suggests that the capillaries may even enter the cell bodies of the neurons. The activity essential to maintaining the water balance of the body involves first the response of the cells to changes of osmotic pressure. The response of the cells to increased osmotic pressure lies in a neurosecretory activity which results in the production and release of an antidiuretic hormone (ADH) into the blood stream. Available evidence indicates that this hormone is stored, but not secreted, in the posterior lobe of the pituitary gland. There appear to be no secretory cells in the posterior pituitary; the Gomori stainable material, indicating secretory cells, is found along the course of the nerve fibers that sweep from these two nuclei down over the median eminence and into the posterior pituitary. For the course of these fibers from the nuclei to the posterior pituitary, see Fig. 19–2. Moreover, the cells of the nuclei themselves show the same Gomori stainable material,

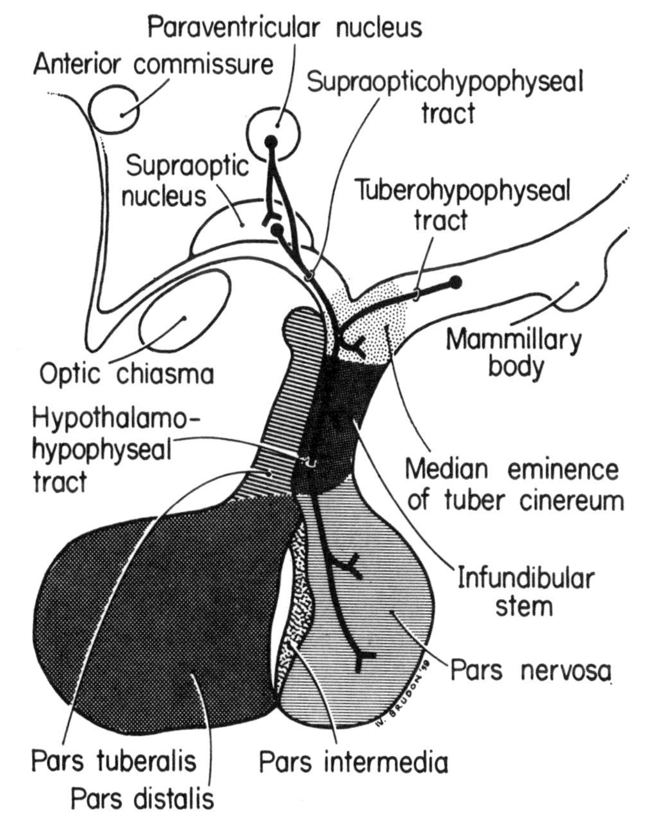

Source: Reprinted with permission of the Macmillan Company from *Correlative Anatomy of the Nervous System* by Elizabeth C. Crosby, Tryphena Humphrey, and Edward W. Lauer. © The Macmillan Company 1962. P. 324.

Figure 19–2. Parts of the Hypophysis and the Origin and Distribution of the Hypothalamo-Hypophyseal Tract

and in different amounts, depending on the current extent of secretory activity of the cells.

When the antidiuretic hormone is released into the blood stream it travels with the blood down to the kidneys. In the renal tubules the presence of this hormone promotes reabsorption of body fluids rather than their excretion as urine. The presence of ADH in the kidney changes the permeability of the membrane of the distal tubules to water, increasing the permeability to the point that water molecules escape from the tubule into interstitial fluid. In the absence of ADH the membrane of the tubule is not permeable to water, which then flows down the collecting duct and is excreted as urine. Thus when water has been ingested there is a drop in osmotic pressure, less secretion and release, less retention, and more excretion. This mechanism operates not only in water excretion but also in water intake. Microinjection of hypertonic saline solution and stimulation by implanted electrodes in the region between the column of the fornix and the mammillothalamic tract result in excessive water intake even if the animal is saturated beforehand. The response to the osmotic change by hypertonic saline takes place, at times, in an interval as short as a half minute.

When this mechanism is disturbed there may be gross maladjustment of the water balance of the organism. Tumors or experimental lesions in this area can eliminate the production of the hormone ADH. This will result in an inability of the animal to retain body fluids, a condition called "diabetes insipidus" (D.I.). Such an animal needs access continually to an adequate water supply. He has to replace continually the water excreted by his kidneys, which may be ten times the normal amount. An animal can live for a considerable period of time in this condition. Diabetes insipidus animals are sometimes produced experimentally for the study of kidney function. In experimental animals all of the secretory cells must be knocked out to produce a completely D.I. dog or cat. An animal with as little as one-eighth of its secretory cells active can produce enough hormone to result in reabsorption of body fluids.

APPETITE AND HUNGER

Appetite and hunger are also regulated by the hypothalamus. Under normal conditions the adjustment of food intake to energy requirements is very sensitive and seems to depend on caloric value or blood temperature. It is to be expected then that lesions of the hypothalamus would disturb this relationship. Lesions in or near the *ventromedial nucleus* destroy an animal's awareness of the point at which it should stop eating. The animal continues ingestion and becomes very obese—the lesion has knocked out the center giving indications of satiety. The ventromedial nucleus therefore is called the "satiety center." One of the customary concomitants of this obesity is that the animal becomes savage and loses his fear. On a number of occasions rats have been known to attack an experimenter. The dual set of stigmata—excessive eating and savageness—makes up the description of the hyperphagic animal.

Since the hyperphagic animal will not work as hard for food reward as normal animals, a different nucleus must initiate feeding response. In addition to the "satiety center" there is also a center which triggers the eating response. This is located in the dorsal part of the *lateral hypothalamic nucleus*. For the locations of these nuclei see Fig. 19–3. Stimulation of this area will start an animal eating even if well fed. A lesion in this region will conversely cause the animal or patient to refuse to eat. Despite all inducements or entreaties, this may cause starvation and death. After destruction of this portion of the lateral hypothalamic nucleus, lesions in the ventromedial nucleus will produce no alteration of the previous unwillingness to eat.

There are two theories to explain the regulation of appetite. The first is that a drop in the blood or body temperature stimulates the lateral hypothalamic nucleus and starts the eating, or alternatively the search for food. The second is that the cells of this nucleus are sensitive to changes in the blood sugar content. Hypoglycemia (low blood sugar) then will stimulate the eating syndrome. Either theory implies that the ventromedial area is responsive to a rise in blood temperature or a rise in glucose content of the blood. When the temperature rise or glucose content reaches a certain critical level the cells of the ventromedial nucleus, under normal conditions, signal a state of satiety which brings the feeding to a stop. There is obviously a close relationship between the activity of the satiation center in the ventromedial nucleus and the fullness of the stomach, but this is not a function of the hypothalamus.

TEMPERATURE CHANGES

Bodily temperature changes are subject to fairly constant regulation by hypothalamic centers. If the brain stem is transected below the hypothalamus, experimental animals become poikilothermic, and are unable, therefore, to maintain a constant body temperature during

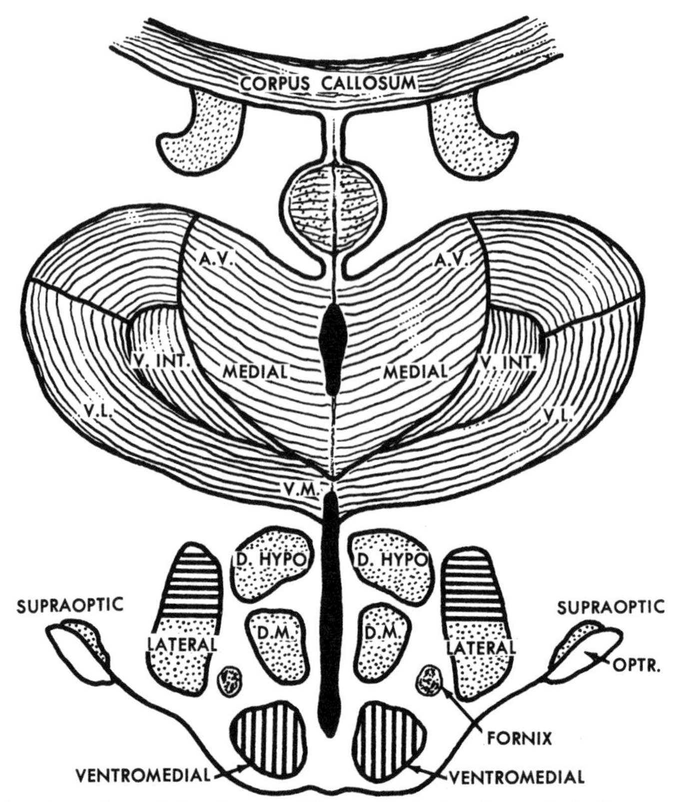

Figure 19–3. Hypothalamic Nuclei Involved in the Control of Appetite

changes of environmental temperature. Here again, as elsewhere in the hypothalamus, we find two centers complementing each other to maintain a balance. The areas of the hypothalamus influencing temperature changes extend over substantial segments of this region. In general, extensive lesions in the rostral portion of the hypothalamus and lateral to the midline will prevent an animal from cooling itself in a warm environment, but will not prevent it from raising its body temperature if the environmental temperature is cold. (For the location of these centers, refer to Fig. 19–4.) Stimulation of the medial preoptic area of the hypothalamus results in panting, sweating, and vasodilation—all necessary in the cooling reaction to excessive heat.

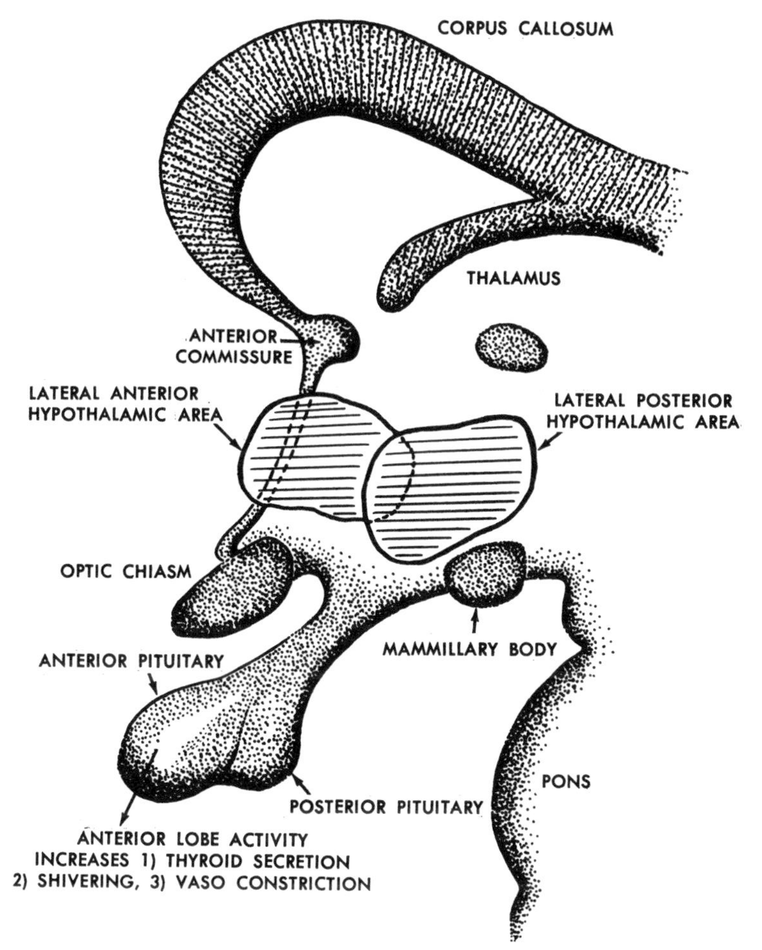

Drawing by Brenda Sutherland

Figure 19–4. Hypothalamic Regions Involved in Temperature Regulation

Opposite effects result from lesions in the posterior and lateral hypothalamus. An animal with lesions in this area can cool itself, but cannot raise its body temperature in a cold environment.

Under normal conditions the rostral hypothalamic area responds to a warm environment by initiating mechanisms for cooling the organism. These include vasodilation in the skin, sweating (which cools by evaporation), and the panting of furry animals. After rostral lesions these changes do not occur, and the body temperature rises—frequently to a dangerous and feverish degree—in response to high environmental temperature. Conversely the posterior hypothalamic centers lateral to the mammillary body normally induce changes needed to regulate body temperature against cold. These mechanisms include vasoconstriction in the skin, shivering, epinephrine secretion, and piloerection. The vasoconstriction and piloerection increase insulation against heat loss, while shivering and epinephrine increase metabolism and heat production. These automatic regulatory mechanisms do not occur if there are lesions in the posterolateral area of the hypothalamus. The animal cannot, then, raise body heat in a cool environment. Usually lesions in "the posterior portion" seem to knock out the cooling or "heat loss" centers, which are rostral, as well as the heat production mechanism. The apparent reason for this is that the posterior lesions interrupt the descending fibers from the more rostral "heat loss" centers as these pass down to the autonomic centers in the lower brain stem and medulla. When both centers are knocked out or ineffective the animal becomes wholly poikilothermic and its body temperature follows the environmental temperature for as long as the animal can stay alive.

These two centers operate reciprocally in a manner analogous to a thermostat. They either contain thermoreceptors or are activated by thermoreceptors that are extremely sensitive to slight changes around a norm of the animal's usual body temperature. Some of these thermoreceptors are clearly in the skin surface, and impulses from them reach the hypothalamic centers. Here the impulses from cold receptors connect with the posterior and lateral heat production center; warmth receptors connect with the heat loss center. There are, in addition, thermoreceptors in the head. Warming or cooling either the carotid blood (sinus) or the appropriate hypothalamic area by as little as a few degrees above or below normal blood or brain temperature will produce results comparable to those already described. In some temperature reactions the activity of both types of thermoreceptors is necessary for some adjustments, such as the shivering reaction to cold exposure.

EMOTIONAL REACTIONS

Emotional reactions of the normal animal are also initiated in part through neural activity of the hypothalamus. Visual impressions and an understanding of the significance of sensory data obviously play a part in emotional reactions, but the hypothalamus is important in the part of the emotional reaction that is dependent on autonomic circuits. This includes changes in blood pressure and blood volume, changes in rate of respiration, piloerection as an emotional reaction, and emotional sweating. All of these changes are clearly not mediated by the same nucleus but by a variety of nerve groups.

Changes in blood pressure and blood volume are just two of the changes in emotion influenced by the hypothalamus. The total pattern of either rage or fear involves a complex behavioral reaction including, in animals, arching the back, flattening the ears, hissing, spitting, or growling, piloerection, unmasking of claws, and crouching with limbs ready for the "flight or fight" of Cannon's description. These changes can be produced in animals by stimulation even when the cerebral cortex has been previously removed. The main area for stimulation of the rage reaction is the *dorsomedial nucleus* of the hypothalamus. Stimulation of this nucleus seems to have a similar effect on emotional behavior to a lesion in the ventromedial nucleus, although the latter may be accompanied, as we have seen, by excessive appetite.

If the stimulation of the dorsomedial nucleus is carried out on animals with an intact cortex the rage reaction is directed outward at some person or other animal, frequently the experimenter himself. If the stimulation is applied to decorticate animals the same overt reactions are brought about, but with one very important difference. In animals whose cortex has been removed the rage has no real direction. It is not vented at the experimenter or a neighboring animal. Because it has no natural target, this total reaction has been called "sham rage," since all the external signs of rage, save this one, are present. The reaction also is frequently brought into play by wholly insignificant stimuli, ones that normally would provoke no reaction at all. Fear reactions can also be obtained from decorticate animals, although the hypothalamic mechanism for this reaction has not been worked out completely.

BLOOD PRESSURE

The hypothalamus contains an important center for control of *blood pressure* and *blood volume*. This regulating center is located in the preoptic region between the supraoptic nucleus and the anterior commissure, and somewhat rostral to both of these points. Stimulation of this region, in an animal which has been fitted previously with flow meters around the mesenteric or renal arteries, results in immediate and substantial increases in blood pressure and blood volume. The critical area for deriving this stimulational effect is small. Movement of the stimulating electrode as much as 2–3 mm rostral or caudal will show no comparable response, even when successive stimulation is at the same depth. The normal function of the preoptic area may be the controlling of the capacity of venous reservoirs, for lesions in this region may be followed in less than 24 hours by lung hemorrhage and pulmonary edema. This result may be due to the release of cardiovascular centers from regulation by the preoptic impulses. This release allows emptying of the venous reservoirs into the pulmonary circulation.

ANTERIOR PITUITARY REGULATION

The hypothalamus is important in internal bodily regulation in more general ways than the specific mechanisms described thus far. It provides some important regulatory influences upon the activity of the *anterior lobe* of the *pituitary gland.* By means of this regulating effect it can influence the secretion of the adrenal medulla, gonadotrophic secretion, thyroid activity, etc. By its influence on the "master regulating gland" of the anterior pituitary, the hypothalamus affects all parts of the endocrine system. This influence of the hypothalamus is performed not by means of nervous connections, but by way of humoral connections with the anterior pituitary. The rich blood supply which bathes the cells of the supraoptic and paraventricular nuclei for the water balance mechanism also bathes the cells of the tuberal and posterior hypothalamic region. Here there are also neurosecretory cells which add their secretions to the blood supply of the anterior pituitary. This blood interchange between hypothalamus and anterior pituitary is known as the hypothalamic-hypophysial portal system and provides a humoral channel of connection between the posterior and tuberal hypothalamus and the anterior lobe of the pituitary (hypophysis). For an illustration of this humoral connection, see Fig. 19–5. Since pituitary-adrenal responsiveness to stress is abolished by lesions of the posterior hypothalamus, it seems clear that some substance is carried by the portal system which causes the anterior hypophysis to secrete and release its several hormones, with consequent effect on the adrenals, thyroid, gonads, and other components of the endocrine chain.

EFFERENT PATHWAYS

In addition to the hypothalamic mechanisms it is important to understand the efferent pathways open to these regulating mechanisms.

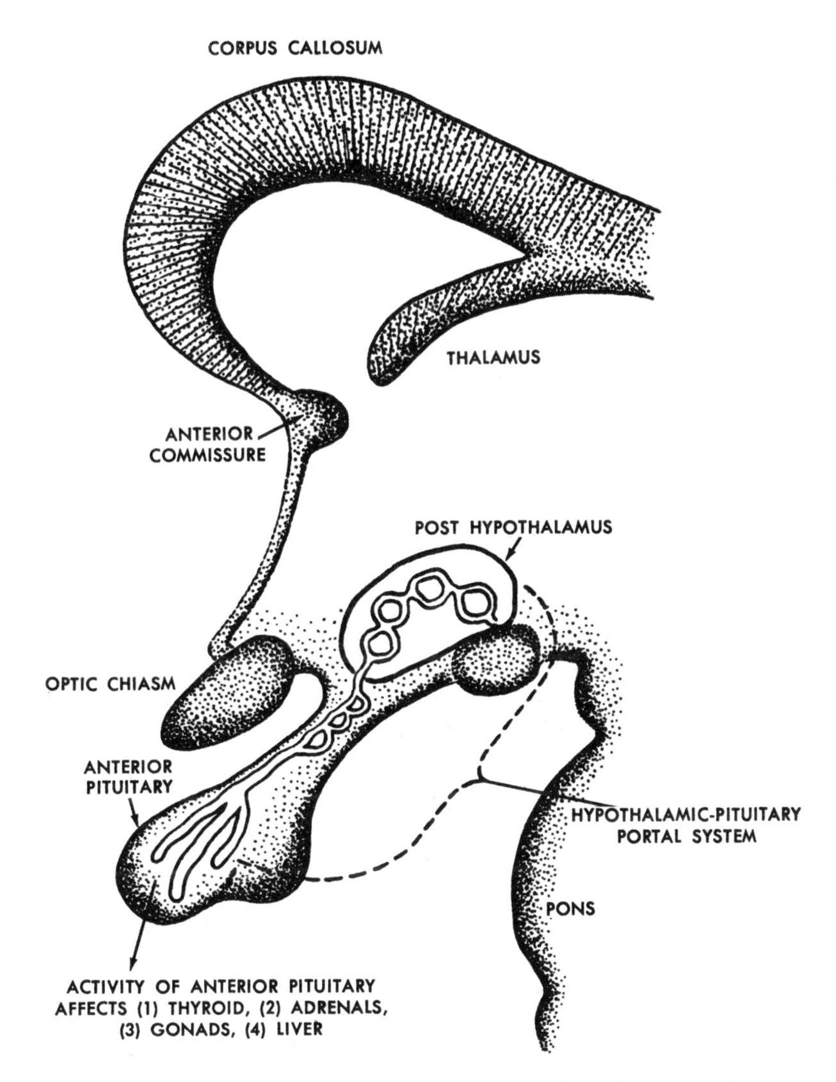

Figure 19–5. Diagram of the Hypothalamic Pituitary Portal System

The major ones include a mammillothalamic pathway from the mammillary bodies to the anterior nuclei of the thalamus, from which impulses are carried to frontal and cingulate cortex. This allows cerebral coordination. There is also a connection by *fasciculus retroflexus* between the habenula and the interpeduncular nucleus, providing for interrelations between touch-visual and taste-visceral aspects of incoming information, as in food seeking and mating. There is also a bundle which branches from the mammillothalamic tract and curves caudally as the *mammillotegmental tract* to end in the nuclei of the midbrain roof. From the *dorsal tegmental nuclei* there are connections by way of the *dorsal longitudinal fasciculus* to the visceral nuclei of cranial nerves trigeminal (V), facial (VII), glossopharyngeal (IX), and vagus (X). For an illustration of these fiber connections, see Fig. 19–6.

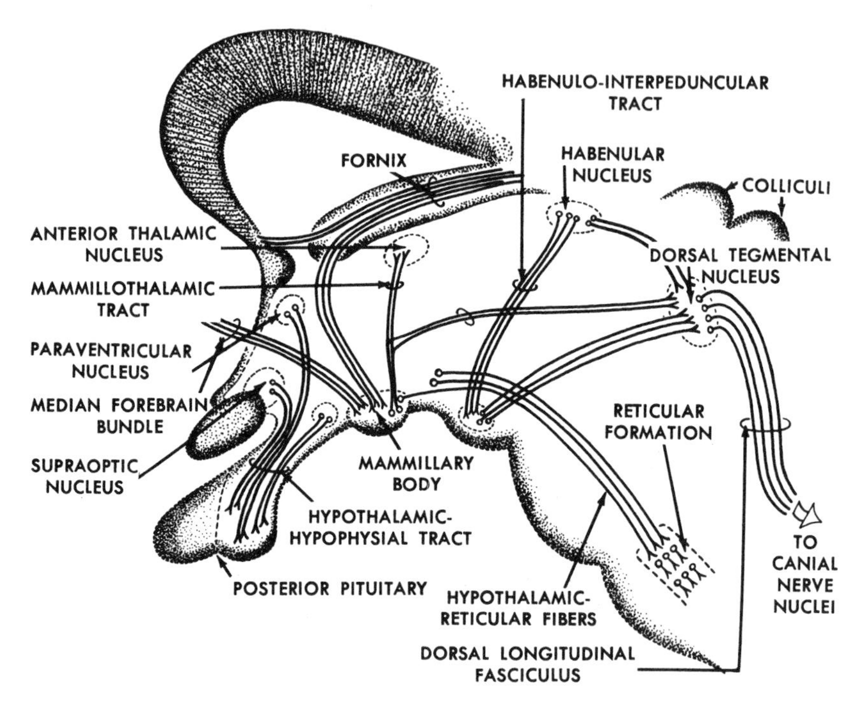

Figure 19–6. Fiber Connections of the Hypothalamus

From the posterior hypothalamus one path, which is known as the *periventricular bundle,* goes dorsally to the dorsomedial thalamic nucleus. Another branch of this periventricular bundle turns caudally from the posterior hypothalamus and runs down the brain stem as far as the vestibular nuclei and dorsal nucleus of the vagus nerve (X). The major portion of the caudally directed branch of the periventricular bundle descends to make numerous connections with the reticular nuclei and cranial nerve nuclei of the midbrain and the medulla.

It appears that all parts of the hypothalamus use these two main caudally directed channels in effecting their regulation of homeostatic or emotional mechanisms. It has been noted, for instance, that lesions in the posterior hypothalamus will at times knock out the activity of more rostral hypothalamic centers, apparently by cutting the connections between these rostral centers and the medullary or reticular nuclei. These connections are largely by means of the two caudal bundles —the periventricular bundle and the dorsal longitudinal fasciculus.

It should be clear, then, that the hypothalamus is concerned mainly with visceral adjustments to both the external and the internal environment. In interpreting experimental results it must be remembered that large lesions will interrupt many fiber pathways and neural circuits, as well as damage nuclear groupings.

The hypothalamic influences on sexual behavior and the sleep-waking mechanism have been examined under the limbic system (Chapter 16) and the reticular formation (Chapter 18) respectively.

SOURCES AND ADDITIONAL READING

The CIBA Collection of Medical Illustrations, Vol. I, *Nervous System* (Special Section). CIBA Pharmaceutical Company, 1958.

Handbook of Physiology, Sec. I, Vol. II, Chaps. 46 ff. Washington, D. C.: American Physiol. Soc., 1960.

Hess, W. R., *The Functional Organization of the Diencephalon.* New York: Grune & Stratton, Inc., 1957.

Isaacson, R. L., ed., *Basic Readings in Neuropsychology.* New York: Harper & Row, Publishers, 1964.

Ranson, S. W. and S. L. Clark, *The Anatomy of the Nervous System,* (10th ed.), Chap. 15. Philadelphia: W. B. Saunders Company, 1959.

Ruch, T. and J. Fulton, *Medical Physiology and Biophysics* (18th ed.), Chap. 10. Philadelphia: W. B. Saunders Company, 1961. (See 19th ed., Chap. 11.)

Walsh, G., *Physiology of the Nervous System,* Chap. 12. New York: Longmans Green & Co., Inc., 1958.

Twenty

THE AUTONOMIC NERVOUS SYSTEM

The previous sections have described in some detail many of the functions of the central nervous system. There are, however, some important nervous functions of biological organisms which occur adjacent to but outside the central nervous system. Practically all of these are functions of the autonomic nervous system that supplies the internal organs of the thorax, pelvis, and viscera, and the glands and blood vessels of the head, neck, and skin. This system is named autonomic because it functions without voluntary control, although conscious states can affect its functioning, as in emotional reactions.

As we have seen in the hypothalamus, there are frequently in the nervous system opposing sets of mechanisms for adjustments of temperature, appetite, blood pressure, etc. This same arrangement of contrasting mechanisms of control is also characteristic of the autonomic nervous system. There are two major divisions of this system, the *sympathetic* and *parasympathetic,* which in general have opposite functions. If the sympathetic stimulates an activity the parasympathetic inhibits or counteracts it, and vice versa. In general terms, the sympathetic division stimulates somatic activity and inhibits vegetative functions, while the parasympathetic division promotes vegetative functions and inhibits somatic functions. For a general view of the autonomic nervous system see Fig. 20–1.

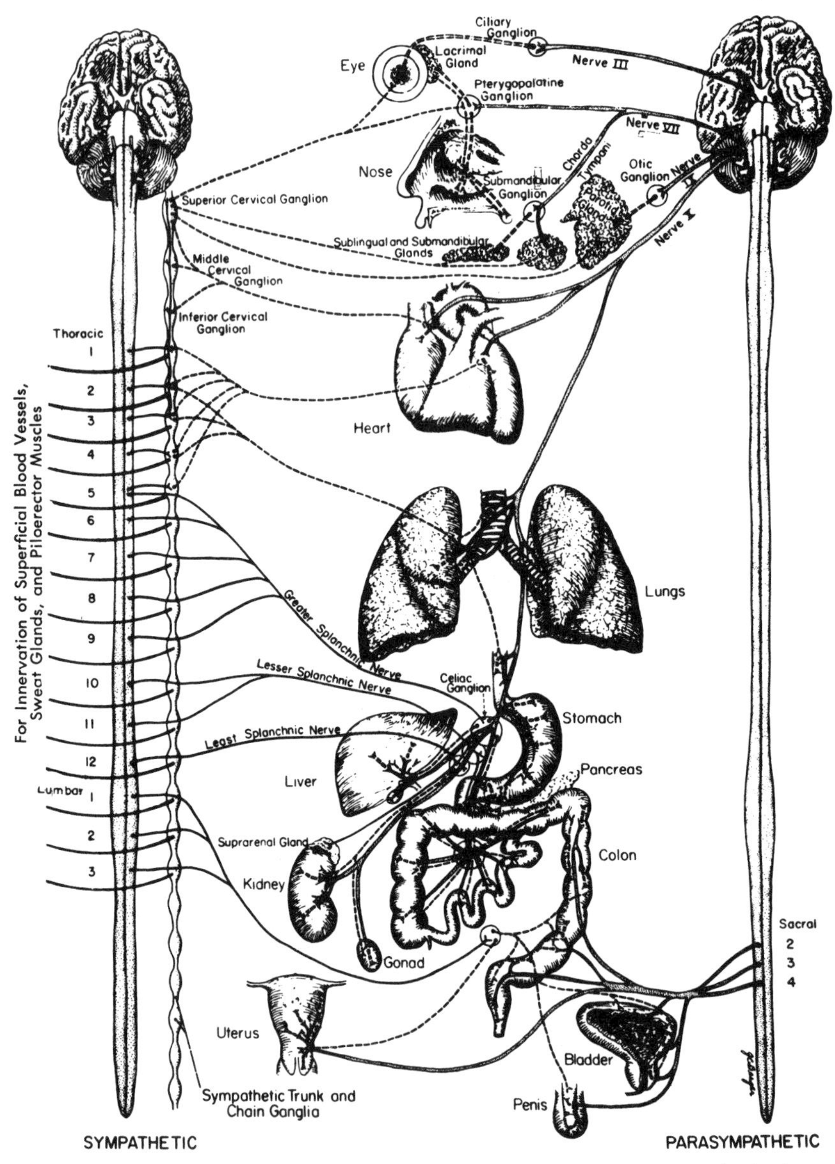

Source: *Essentials of Human Anatomy* by Russell T. Woodburne, 3rd edition 1965. Copyright 1957, 1961, 1965 by Oxford University Press, Inc. Reprinted by permission. (Modified)

Figure 20–1. The Plan of the Autonomic Nervous System; Sympathetic Nerves on the Left, the Parasympathetic Innervation on the Right (Postganglionic neurons are shown by dashed lines.)

SYMPATHETIC DIVISION

The sympathetic division is composed of a series of connected ganglia which lie alongside the vertebral column in a so-called "ganglion chain," each vertebral segment having a separate sympathetic ganglion. This chain of ganglia receives fibers from the spinal cord from the level of the 1st thoracic segment down to the 2nd or 3rd lumbar. The efferent fiber connections from the spinal cord do not extend then into the cervical level or down into the sacral. But this does not mean that these levels do not receive sympathetic fibers. The chain of ganglia extends upward, without cross connections from the cord, to form the inferior, middle, and superior cervical ganglia that supply many structures of the head and neck. The extension of the chain of ganglia, without segmental connection to the cord, into the sacral level is not as extensive as in the cervical region but does provide sympathetic innervation to the bladder, lower colon, and genitals. That portion of the sympathetic division which lies between the 1st thoracic and 3rd lumbar provides sympathetic innervation, then, to the intervening structures of lungs, heart, stomach, liver, intestines, sweat glands, and blood vessels, as well as the head and pelvic region.

PARASYMPATHETIC DIVISION

The parasympathetic division has two segments, the cranial and the sacral. The name of the segment indicates its source. While they are separated from each other by most of the length of the spinal cord, the functional effects of the two segments are very similar. The sacral segment arises from the 2nd, 3rd, and 4th segments of the sacral cord and sends fibers out to pelvic organs of the lower colon, bladder, sphincter, and genitals. The cranial segment arises as visceral roots of the oculomotor (III), facial (VII), glossopharyngeal (IX), vagus (X), and accessory (XI) cranial nerves. The 3rd cranial nerve has one component whose cells of origin lie in the Edinger-Westphal nucleus, which is adjacent to the nucleus of the oculomotor. These fibers travel to the ciliary ganglion, just back of the eye, and supply the circular muscle fibers which constrict the size of the pupillary opening. Also, the ciliary ganglion innervates the ciliary muscles, which change the curvature of the lens for accommodation to more accurate focus of images on the retina. The autonomic portion of the facial nerve (VII) supplies fibers to the submaxillary and otic ganglia for impulses to the salivary glands. In addition, rootlets from the facial (VII) supply the lacrimal glands. The 9th cranial nerve supplies fibers to some of the salivary glands. The vagus nerve (X) is the workhorse of the parasympathetic division. It supplies fibers to the pharynx, larynx, to the bronchi of the lungs, to the heart, and to the stomach, liver, pancreas, intestine, and kidney. The visceral fibers of the vagus reach down, then, to innervate all of the thoracic and abdominal structures from the larynx as far as the descending colon. One branch of the accessory nerve (XI) acts as a portion of the vagus in this visceral innervation.

Practically all of the organs supplied by the cranial and sacral portions of the parasympathetic receive opposing fibers from the sympathetic division. The glands and smooth muscles in the head, neck, and thorax receive sympathetic postganglionic fibers from the cervical ganglia—superior, middle, and inferior. The abdominal viscera receive their sympathetic postganglionic fibers in large part from the coeliac and mesenteric or other prevertebral ganglia. The pelvic organs are likewise supplied by fibers which proceed down the sympathetic ganglion chain and along the perivascular plexuses.

In contrast to the sympathetic division, the parasympathetic does not have chains of connected ganglia. Moreover, the ganglia which receive fibers from cranial or sacral segments lie close to the gland or muscle which they supply, without cross connection to other ganglia. In this way the parasympathetic action is usually discrete and limited to a single structure. For example, the ciliary ganglion which provides for lens and pupillary adjustment of the eye is close to the ganglion supplying the lacrimal glands, and yet there is no spread of nervous impulse from one to the other. This spread does occur in the sympathetic ganglia, and the effect then is more general and less delimited.

Both portions of the autonomic nervous system consist of two neuron chains. The first neuron has its cell body in the visceral efferent column of the spinal cord (intermediolateral) or in cranial nerve nuclei in the brain stem. The second neuron has its cell body in a ganglion outside the central nervous system. The axon of the first neuron synapses with the dendrites and cell body in the ganglion and hence is called preganglionic; the second neuron extends its axon from the ganglion to the effector muscle or gland and is called, therefore, the postganglionic neuron.

CONNECTIONS TO SPINAL CORD

The connections of the sympathetic division with the spinal cord are intricate, but are essential to provide the visceral effect of emotion, and of the significance of visual or auditory stimuli. These afferent and efferent fibers of the sympathetic division use routes parallel to somatic sensory and motor roots, but the efferent sympathetic (preganglionic) diverges soon after leaving the cord to form a separate bundle which connects to the sympathetic ganglion of that segment of the cord. The afferent visceral fibers from cutaneous blood vessels, sweat glands, and piloerector muscles run from the skin surface with the main sensory fibers of touch, temperature, etc. These afferent visceral fibers show the same type of unipolar cell in the dorsal root ganglia and enter the cord lateral to the main sensory fibers. The afferent sympathetic fibers continue without synapse down in the spinal gray to the *intermediolateral column* of cells in the extreme lateral part of the spinal gray. For the location of these cells, see Fig. 20–2. The cells in this column are found

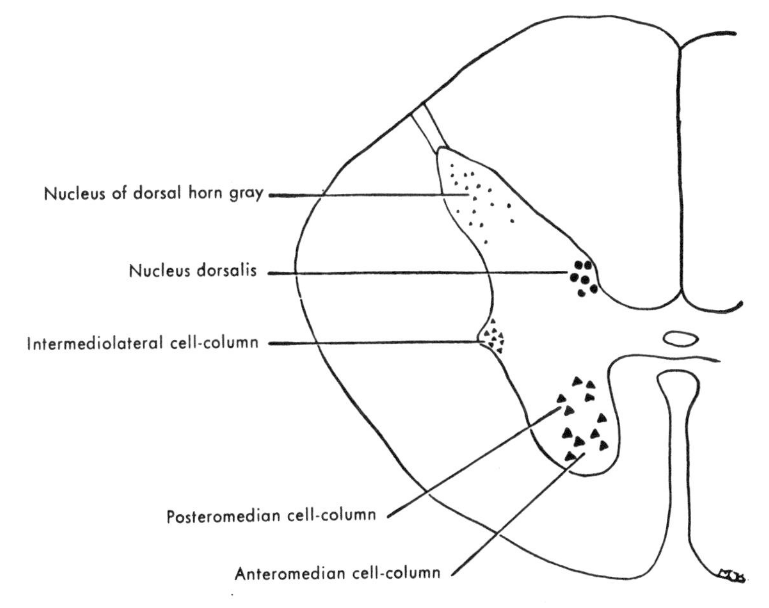

After S. W. Ranson and S. L. Clark, *The Anatomy of the Nervous System: Its Development and Function* (10th ed.; Philadelphia: W. B. Saunders Company, 1959), p. 176.

Figure 20–2. Thoracic Cord Section Showing Intermediolateral Cell Group

only in the thoracic and upper lumbar segments. The motor cells in this intermediolateral column send out axons which follow the ventral roots for a distance and then diverge from the ventral roots to enter the sympathetic ganglion. The afferent fibers from the viscera run through

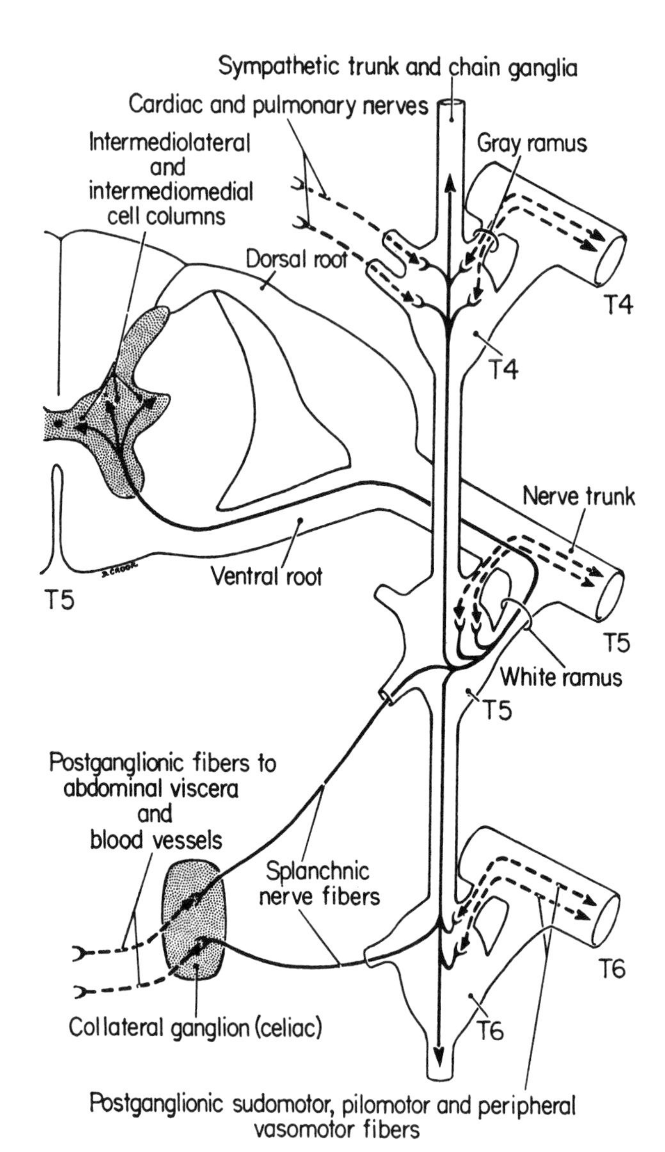

Source: Reprinted with permission of The Macmillan Company from *Correlative Anatomy of the Nervous System* by Elizabeth C. Crosby, Tryphena Humphrey, and Edward W. Lauer. © The Macmillan Company 1962. P. 520.

Figure 20–3. A Diagram to Show the General Plan of Origin and Distribution of the Preganglionic and Postganglionic Fibers of the Sympathetic Division of the Autonomic Nervous System

the sympathetic ganglion without synapse, then through the ventral root of the cord to its junction with the dorsal root. They then enter the dorsal root to run parallel to the cutaneous branch, by way of unipolar cells in the dorsal root ganglion, to the cord and to the intermediolateral column. The efferent fibers from the cells of this visceral column of the cord—when they reach the sympathetic ganglia by way of the *white ramus communicans*—may (1) synapse to travel up or down the sympathetic chain; (2) synapse to pass out the ventral motor root of the cord by way to the *gray ramus communicans,* in order to supply sweat glands, piloerector muscles, and cutaneous blood vessels in the skin; or (3) pass through the sympathetic ganglion without synapse, to end in one of the several prevertebral plexuses such as the coeliac or mesenteric. These plexuses collect a number of segmental nerves together to facilitate the massive and diffuse action of the sympathetic division. The connections just described will become clearer with an illustration. (See Fig. 20–3.)

The efferent fibers between the ventral root of the cord and the sympathetic ganglion are designated as white or gray rami communicans. These communicating branches derive their names from the presence or absence of myelin sheath around the nerve fibers. It is evident then that the fibers from the intermediolateral column out to the sympathetic or prevertebral ganglion are myelinated, while the postganglionic fibers after synapse are unmyelinated. The postganglionic branches are composed of small type C fibers (see p. 74) which conduct rather slowly and are quite resistant to asphyxiation and other toxic effects.

SOMATIC AND VEGETATIVE FUNCTIONS

In terms of functional regulation of internal bodily mechanism, the various organs of thorax, viscera, and head are supplied by both sympathetic and parasympathetic innervation. In general there is opposing action between these systems; whatever structures the parasympathetic stimulates, the sympathetic tends to inhibit and vice versa. There are exceptions, however, to this general rule and, unfortunately for simplicity, the action is not always of one kind from each division. In the heart and lungs the sympathetic stimulates by accelerating heart action and dilating the bronchi of the lungs, the parasympathetic having a reverse action. In the digestive system—stomach and intestines—the sympathetic outflow inhibits peristalsis, while the parasympathetic stimulates peristalsis and gastric secretion. These differences of function become understandable when we project them against the background of emergency action in times of danger.

The internal balancing of body needs which Cannon termed homeostasis utilizes these two opposing systems by means of a constant flow of tonic pulses to both divisions, keeping internal organs in functional balance for normal conditions. This balance is shattered when danger threatens or body needs become excessive. The blood pressure is monitored by the carotid sinus, and appropriate changes are made in size of blood vessels or rate of heart beat. Body temperature is similarly monitored by the hypothalamus, and appropriate autonomic changes are induced to conserve or lose body heat. In this way the hypothalamic and medullary centers use the autonomic nervous system to effect the changes required for homeostatic balance.

Table 20–I

Parasympathetic and Sympathetic Action

Organ	*Parasympathetic*	*Sympathetic*
Eye	Constrictor muscles of iris and ciliary muscle for accommodation	Dilator muscles of iris
Lacrimal Glands	Stimulate secretion and vasodilation	Vasoconstriction of vessels to glands
Salivary Glands	Stimulate secretion and vasodilation	Vasoconstriction and secretion
Heart	Cardiac deceleration	Cardiac acceleration and coronary dilation
Lungs	Constrict bronchi and stimulate smooth muscle	Dilates bronchi and inhibits smooth muscle
Gastrointestinal Tract	Stimulates peristalsis and gastrointestinal secretion	Inhibits peristalsis and vasoconstriction
Adrenal Medulla		Stimulates secretory cells
Urinary and Genitals	Contraction of bladder and lower colon; erection	Vasoconstriction; ejaculation of semen; inhibition of lower colon and rectum
Peripheral Blood Vessels		Vasoconstriction
Sweat Glands and Muscles of Skin		Secretion and excitation of pilomotor muscles

AUTONOMIC CENTERS IN BRAIN

The autonomic centers above the level of the spinal cord are located, for the most part, in the medulla and the diencephalon. The visceral efferent parasympathetic nuclei in the medulla are the dorsal nucleus of the vagus (X), which sends out preganglionic fibers; the nucleus salivatorius (IX) and the motor nucleus of VII for innervation of glands of the head; and the Edinger-Westphal nucleus (III) for innervation of the intrinsic eye muscles for pupillary and accommodation reflexes. For the details of this innervation, see Fig. 20–4. In addition, there seems to be a vasomotor center near the superior olive which maintains normal blood pressure.

The autonomic nuclei in the diencephalon are located in the hypothalamus, where numerous centers are located for blood pressure and blood volume, water balance, temperature regulation, etc., which have been considered in an earlier section.

The general rule that organs receive double innervation from both the sympathetic and parasympathetic does not hold true at one or two locations. The peripheral, cutaneous organs of sweat glands in particular—and possibly the vasomotor supply to peripheral blood vessels—do not have parasympathetic innervation. Any differential effect on these organs must be mediated by inhibitory fibers carried with the sympathetic, or by lack of stimulation to produce an opposite effect. The other exception is of a different sort. The adrenal medulla has no parasympathetic innervation, nor does it receive postganglionic fibers from the sympathetic. It is served only by preganglionic sympathetic fibers which branch off before the lesser splanchnic nerve synapses in the coeliac ganglion. This exception will become understandable when we consider in detail why the action of the adrenal medulla imitates the action of the whole sympathetic division.

TRANSMITTER AGENTS

One of the characteristics of the sympathetic division of the autonomic nervous system is that there is substantial persistence in its effective action. Its effective action is not of brief duration as is the somatic motor system. This persistence of action indicated a real possibility of a humoral agent which continues the action beyond the short time span of the nervous impulse. Loewi performed experiments wih two hearts connected only by a tube. Vagus nerve stimulation of the first heart resulted in a noticeable and similar inhibition on the second, showing clearly that there was a non-nervous connection between them, almost certainly humoral; Loewi called the humor "Vagusstoff."

One of the few places in the entire nervous system where the transmitter agents have been clearly worked out is in the autonomic nervous

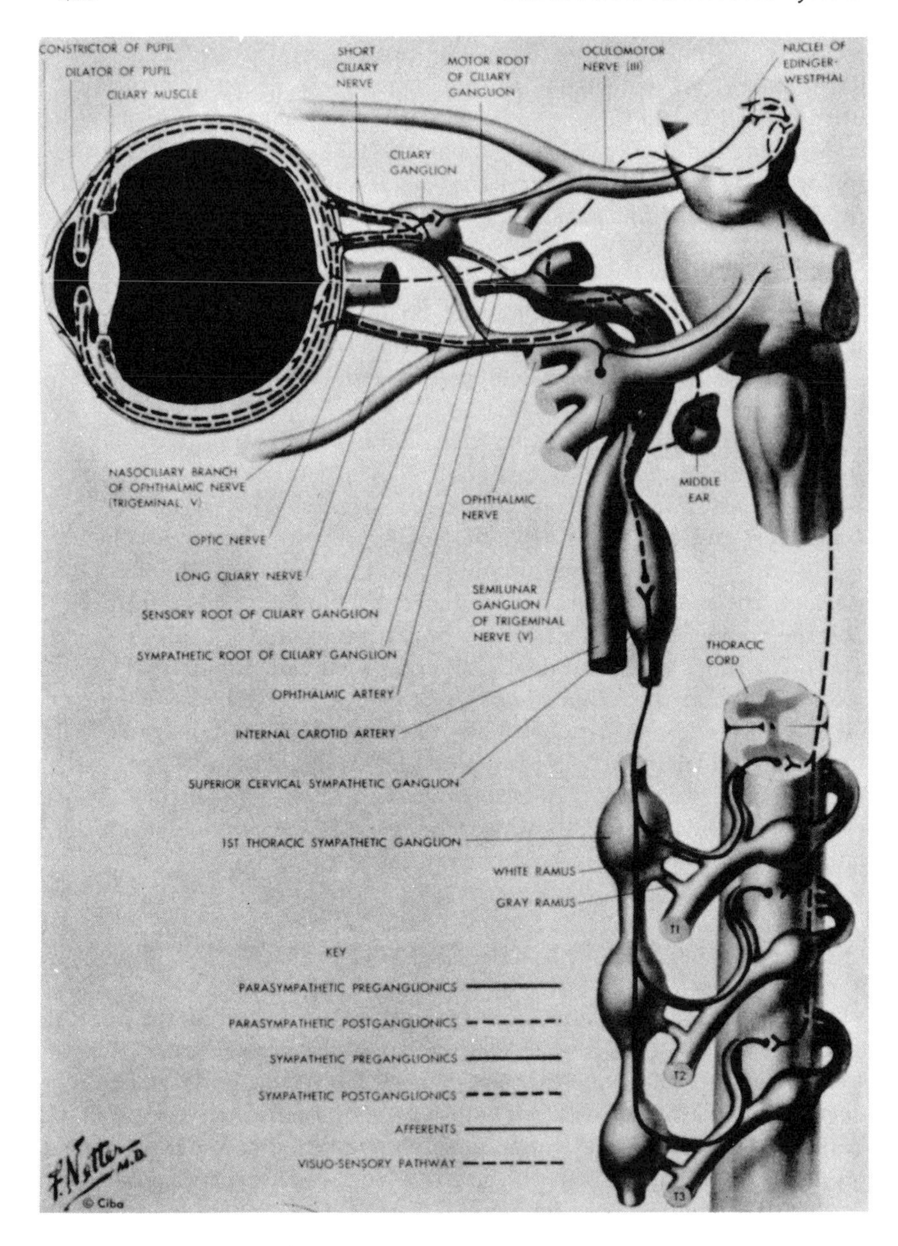

Source: *The CIBA Collection of Medical Illustrations* by Frank H. Netter, M.D. Copyright CIBA. Vol. I, *Nervous System* (Summit, N. J.: CIBA Pharmaceutical Company, 1953), Plate 65.

Figure 20–4. Innervation of Intrinsic Eye Muscles

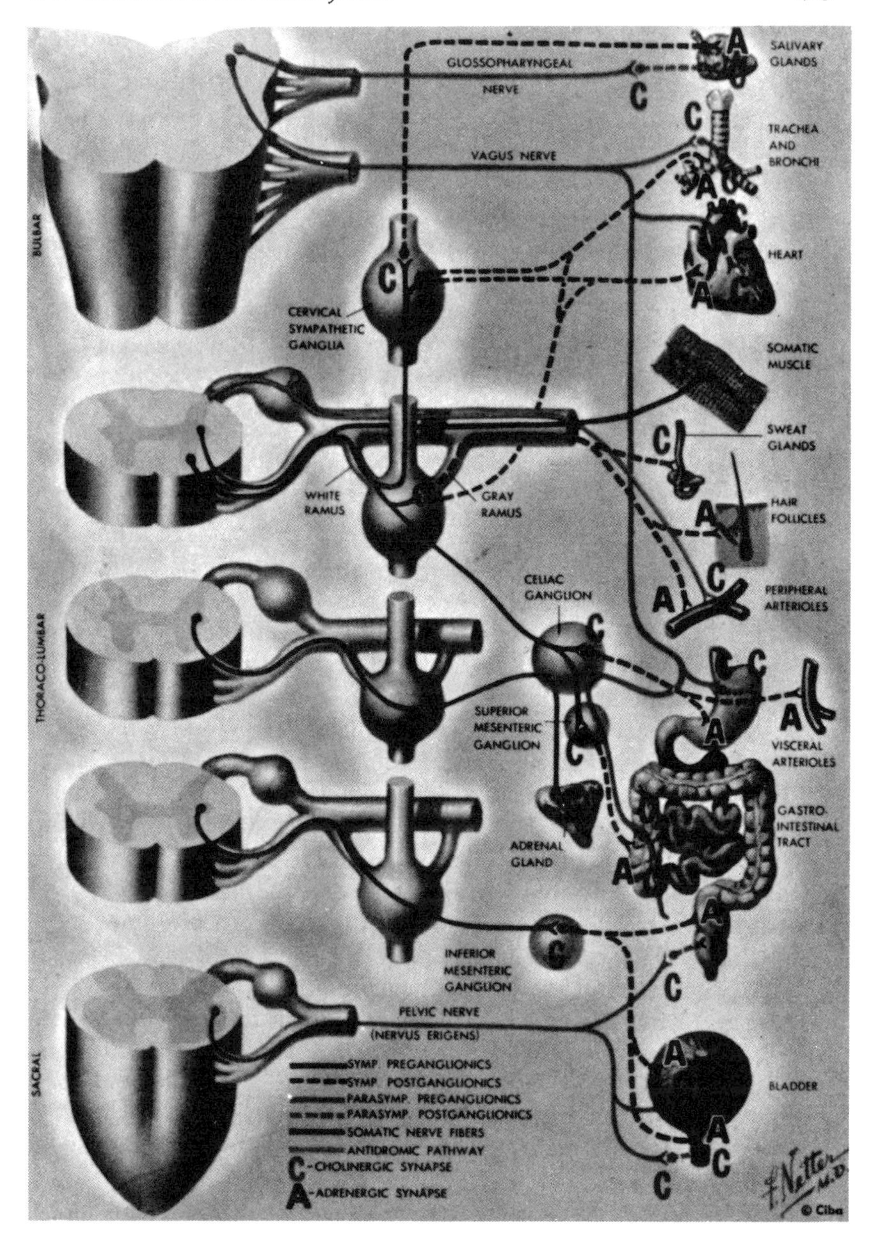

Source: *The CIBA Collection of Medical Illustrations* by Frank H. Netter, M.D. Copyright CIBA. Vol. I, *Nervous System,* Plate 56.

Figure 20–5. Schema of Cholinergic and Andrenergic Connections of Autonomic Nervous System

system. The chemical transmitter in all sympathetic and parasympathetic ganglia at the preganglionic endings is acetylcholine, and for this reason these connections are called *cholinergic*. In the postganglionic connections with glands, smooth muscle, and visceral organs or blood vessels a number of variations appear. The endings of the parasympathetic division transmit to their organs by acetylcholine again; thus they are, for a second time, cholinergic. The sympathetic division shows a sharp difference from the parasympathetic in that most of the postganglionic endings transmit by adrenalin (epinephrine or norepinephrine). These are therefore called *adrenergic* connections. For a schema of cholinergic and adrenergic endings, see Fig. 20–5. Of the sympathetic endings the two exceptions already mentioned—sweat glands and adrenal medulla—do not follow an adrenergic pattern. The terminals of these nerve fibers release a cholinergic transmitter substance at the organ surface. The exceptional circumstance of the adrenal medulla may now be understood. The adrenal medulla is stimulated by cholinergic transmitter substance, and in response gives out epinephrine into the blood stream, imitating in its effects the widespread action of the sympathetic system generally, which is mostly adrenergic.

If we look again at the differential effects of sympathetic and parasympathetic stimulation on internal organs, we can begin to understand the rationale of the differences which they exemplify in transmitter substances. Acetylcholine and epinephrine have different effects on different organs. Acetylcholine inhibits cardiac muscle, stimulates gland secretion, and stimulates smooth muscle. In contrast, epinephrine stimulates cardiac muscle, inhibits glandular secretion, and inhibits action of smooth muscle, as in inhibition of peristalsis and constriction of blood vessels. This differential action of the transmitter substances explains the complex and seemingly contradictory actions of the sympathetic division in conditions of strong emotion.

Under the influence of an emotion such as fear the homeostatic balance between these two divisions breaks down, and one becomes dominant. In a cat suddenly presented with a snarling dog, a number of visceral changes take place. As a result of massive sympathetic discharge the cat's hair stands on end (piloerection); its gastric secretion is choked off, digestion ceases, heart rate and blood pressure increase, the back is arched, claws are exposed, pupils are dilated, and blood sugar is released into the blood stream. Adrenalin is also released into the blood stream and will perpetuate these effects. These changes follow and conform to the differential effect of the adrenergic transmitter on heart muscle, smooth muscle, and glands. When the emergency is over and external calm has been restored, the control centers in the hypothalamus exert their influence on the parasympathetic division to reverse these violent reactions until normal conditions have been restored. The more prolonged effects of emotional stress come largely from the continued presence of epinephrine in the blood stream; along with excess blood sugar epinephrine takes considerable time to be neutralized or dissipated.

The hypothalamus clearly has considerable influence on autonomic functions, but how this is exercised has not yet been made evident. The main efferent pathway from the hypothalamus is from the posterior and mammillary nuclei, and passes downward to a number of centers in the reticular formation, largely in the medulla. These fibers make connection with the dorsal nucleus of the vagus, the respiratory center of the medulla, the vasoconstrictor center of the medulla, and the salivatory nuclei. Many of the reflex connections travel from the dorsolateral nucleus to the reticular formation of the medulla, down the descending tract of the ventrolateral funiculus of the cord, to make connection in the intermediolateral column of the gray matter. Most of the paths for autonomic functions are not collected into tight, discrete bundles, but the fibers are relatively diffuse and short and there are likely many synapses in the path. For more details of the relation of the hypothalamus to the hypophysis and the autonomic nervous system, the reader should refer to Chapter 19.

While the autonomic nervous system is largely free from voluntary control, it does respond to general conditions of the organism such as those which give rise to hypertension and continued high anxiety or other prolonged emotional states. Such a bodily condition inhibits the action of the parasympathetic division and maintains a continuous discharge over the sympathetic fibers. At times this hypertension results in such constriction of the peripheral blood vessels that the flow of blood is stopped. This vasospasm (Reynaud's disease) may, if unrelieved, result in decay and gangrene of fingers and toes. One of the few ways to alleviate this condition is to sever surgically the sympathetic fibers supplying the particular vessels. If the disease has not proceeded too far, the surgical cutting of the nerve fibers relaxes the smooth muscles sufficiently to permit greater blood flow to the periphery.

SOURCES AND ADDITIONAL READING

The CIBA Collection of Medical Illustrations, Vol. I, *Nervous System.* CIBA Pharmaceutical Company, 1953.

Gillilan, L. A., *Clinical Aspects of the Autonomic Nervous System.* Boston: Little, Brown and Company, 1954.

Handbook of Physiology, Sec. I, Vol. II, Chaps. 37, 38. Washington, D. C.: American Physiol. Soc., 1960.

Kuntz, A., *The Autonomic Nervous System* (4th ed.). Philadelphia: Lea & Febiger, 1953.

Ranson, S. W. and S. L. Clark, *The Anatomy of the Nervous System* (10th ed.), Chap. 7. Philadelphia: W. B. Saunders Company, 1959.

Ruch, T. and J. Fulton, *Medical Physiology and Biophysics* (18th ed.), Chap. 9. Philadelphia: W. B. Saunders Company, 1961. (See 19th ed., Chap. 10.)

Twenty-one

THE CEREBRAL CORTEX

The cerebral cortex is the highest neural center for the coordination of external events and internal reactions to them that is found in the animal kingdom. As we have seen, the extent of cortex and the dependence on its functions change materially as one ascends the phylogenetic scale. In the fish and amphibians there is no cortex and the mechanisms of adjustment for these species must, perforce, follow pathways that do not depend on cortical connections. In birds the importance of the olfactory mechanism is greatly reduced, and the thalamus and basal ganglia assume prominence in the coordination of many forms of sensory input and their coordination into a set of stereotyped instinctive reactions to seasonal changes, nesting, mating, etc. In the mammals many of the activities which are performed by the basal ganglia in lower forms are taken over in part by the cerebral cortex. This came about gradually in the phylogenetic development as the sense of vision overtook the olfactory sense as the most important sensory department, and this change in importance was a partial function of the progressive decussation of the optic fibers. Only when the visual fields overlapped, and when enough fibers remained uncrossed in the optic chiasma, was binocular vision possible. The coordination of this visual information with both auditory and somesthetic data requires a coordinating mechanism more complex than the thalamus in order to effect the "chosen" motor responses. It is for these reasons then that in the mammals, and particularly in the primates, the cerebral cortex as the "instrument of choice" has taken over many functions performed in lower species by subcortical centers. In cases of extensive decortication the subcortical centers can still carry out, after recovery, a simpler response to the same sensory input.

One other factor of growth of cortical area that changes with ascent of the phylogenetic scale is the increase in the size of the frontal lobes. In the cat and dog the area forward of the motor region is very small, consisting of only a few gyri. In some of the monkeys, by comparison, the frontal lobes are much larger and account for the forward one-third of the cortex. In humans the frontal region from the central sulcus amounts to half the lateral area of the cortex. For a general view of lateral and medial aspects of the hemispheres, see Figs. 21–1 and 21–2. As we will see, this shift in growth of frontal cortex is not unrelated to the change in character of cortical function in the three species mentioned.

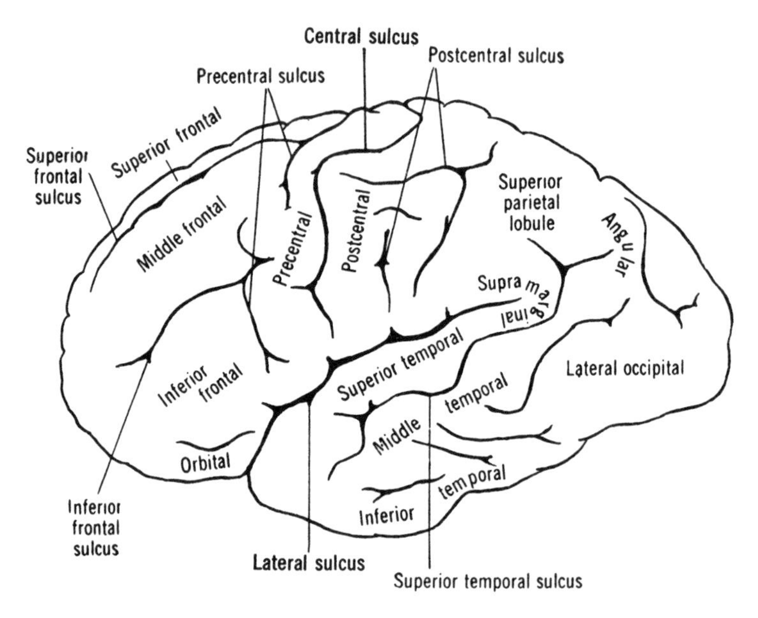

Source: Ernest Gardner, *Fundamentals of Neurology* (4th ed., Philadelphia: W. B. Saunders Company, 1963), p. 13.

Figure 21–1. Lateral Aspect of Cerebral Hemisphere

METHODS OF STUDY

One of the customary ways to study the activity of the cortex is by electrical stimulation. Stimulation studies have identified the neurons

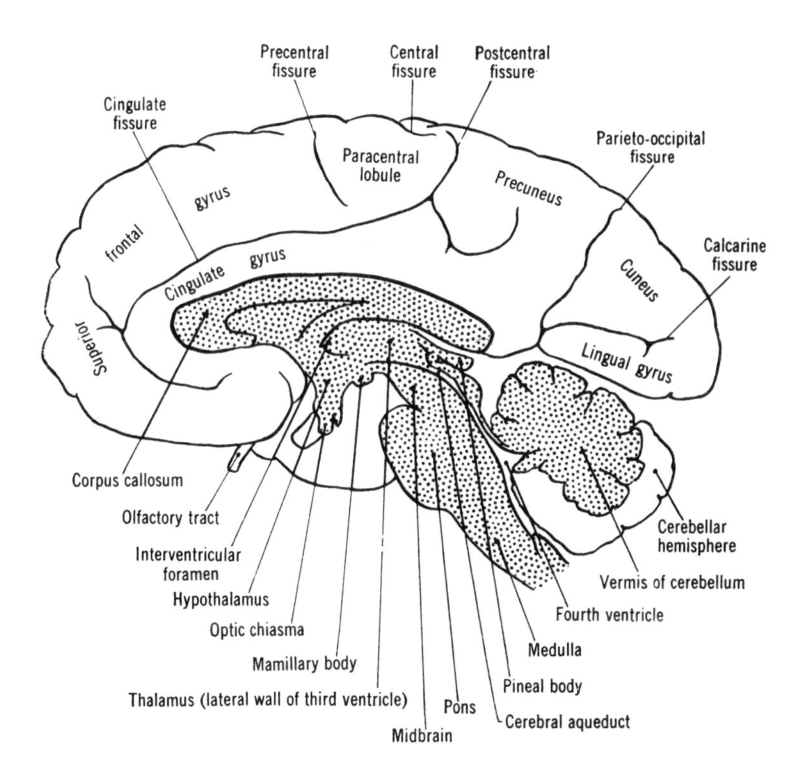

Source: Ernest Gardner, *Fundamentals of Neurology* (4th ed., Philadelphia: W. B. Saunders Company, 1963), p. 19.

Figure 21–2. Medial Aspect of Hemisphere and Brain Stem

in the motor area (Brodmann area 4) which are responsible for particular muscle movements. Stimulation of area 8 has produced coordinated movement of eyes and their opening and closing. Stimulation of the main sensory receptive areas shows no such clear response. No matter how strongly the visual area is stimulated, only a general visual "flash" results. Meaningful reception in the sensory receptive areas must come from external stimulation such as touch on a cat's paw, or light waves on the retina, or sound waves at the cochlea. While stimulation of the cortex can bring into play selected muscle groups, it cannot produce sensory "information" at the cortex, although Penfield has obtained recall of previous experiences by stimulation of the temporal lobe.

Other methods of studying cortical function are (1) ablation of restricted areas, (2) application of strychnine to cortical surface to produce strychnine spikes, and (3) the use of brain-wave patterns in electroencephalography.

1. In ablations a small area of the cortex is removed, usually by aspiration, to determine what effect this cortical loss will have on the animal's behavior or where degeneration will appear in subcortical centers. In this way ablation of the primary visual cortex (area 17) produces a blind animal, except for some minor residual thalamic function, and causes retrograde degeneration of visual projection neurons whose cell bodies are in the lateral geniculate nucleus. Ablation of the somesthetic cortex (areas 1-2-3) results in degeneration of projection neurons from the ventral posterior nucleus of the thalamus, and the loss of cutaneous sensitivity and other somato-sensory functions.

2. The reciprocal relationship between areas of the cortex has been established by localized application of strychnine to cortical areas. When strychnine application is made to one square mm. of cortical surface, there appear clearly marked electrical spikes from the firing of cells in interconnected areas of the cortex. The mapping of what areas fire or discharge other areas is called neuronography.

3. One of the most popular recent methods of studying cortical activity is by electroencephalography, or brain wave patterns. This method is based on the fact that various parts or states of the cortex show distinctively different wave patterns of electrical activity. Electrodes are placed symmetrically on both sides of the head over frontal, temporal, parietal, and occipital regions of the brain. The normal electrical activity of the brain has a very small voltage of 50 microvolts or less, but this is amplified several million times for recording purposes. The occipital cortex characteristically shows rhythmic activity of 10 cycles per second, called *alpha* waves; while the frontal and parietal cortex usually show faster *beta* waves of 20-30 per second or more. There are at least four different wave forms, manifesting differences in amplitude and frequency per second. *Delta* waves are characterized by slow oscillations of less than five cycles per second and of relatively large amplitude. Delta waves are found mainly during sleep in normal subjects, although they may occur under some stressful conditions where, for example, homeostasis and blood composition vary from normal levels. *Theta* waves, of five to seven cycles per second, are not common or evident in most normal subjects. They are thought to be associated with disturbed emotional and affective states. When present they are usually observed in frontal and temporal regions of the brain. They are found mostly in delinquent children or those with behavior problems, or in adults who manifest emotional instability associated with autonomic or visceral

reactivity. The amplitude of the theta waves is usually less than that of the delta waves. For the wave differences, see Fig. 21–3. The *Alpha* waves predominate in normal adults, during relaxed wakeful periods with the eyes closed. They have an amplitude equivalent to less than 50 microvolts, and a frequency of eight to thirteen cycles per second. The adult alpha pattern and frequency are attained by children at the age of 10 to 14 years. The alpha pattern gives way to faster beta waves in close attention or when the eyes are opened. The *beta* waves have a frequency of 18 to 30 cycles per second and a very small amplitude. The wave patterns are very stable for each individual and can be used therefore in clinical studies. The low frequency delta waves are found under deep anesthesia as well as in deep sleep. During hypnosis the pattern is like that of the normal waking EEG. Beta waves are recorded principally from the frontal lobes. A decerebrate animal shows the wave pattern of sleep, or the delta waves. Epilepsy of the *petit mal* type (minor seizure) has a very characteristic wave pattern of 3 cycles per second, consisting of a sharp fast wave followed by a slow wave (called a spike-and-slow wave pattern). These spike and slow wave patterns occur repeatedly for 10 or 15 seconds during an attack. The major or *grand mal* seizure, which involves convulsions and loss of consciousness, is initiated by increasing amplitude fast activity followed by slower waves of high amplitude.

As is indicated in the section on the reticular formation, the arousal or awakening of the cortex from sleep is accompanied by changes in the wave pattern. The slow waves (delta) and spindle formations of sleep give way to low amplitude fast activity. Diffuse cortical activation by way of the reticular formation results in a shift from the delta wave of sleep to the alpha pattern of relaxed wakefulness, and, in close attention with the eyes open, to the low amplitude fast activity, or the beta wave pattern. Brain tumors, or other pressure producing conditions in the brain, usually cause abnormally appearing slow or delta waves, often localized to the general region of the tumor or pressure.

SURFACE TOPOGRAPHY

The surface topography of the cortex has received considerable attention, particularly in the past, in order to clarify localization of function. It has been studied by Brodmann, who gave its various lobes and areas numbers; by von Bonin and Bailey, who gave letter designations to the same areas; by von Economo, who had a slightly different classification; and by many others. Although older and no longer con-

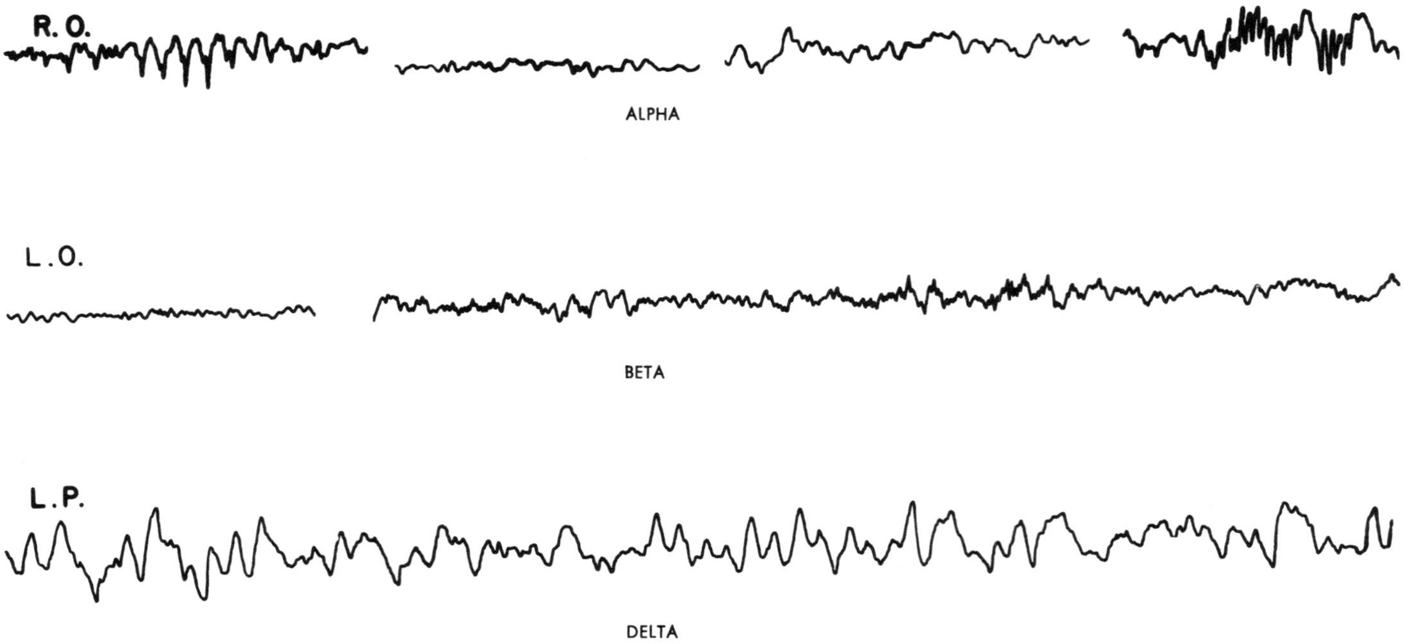

R. O.

ALPHA

L. O.

BETA

L. P.

DELTA

Source: Frederick A. Gibbs and Erna L. Gibbs, *Atlas of Electroencephalography*, Vol. 3 (Neurological and Psychiatric Disorders) (Reading, Mass.: Addison-Wesley Pub. Co., Inc., 1964), Plates 60, 11, 29, and 49.

Figure 21–3. Three Patterns of Brain Waves

sidered completely accurate, Brodmann's numbers are simpler to follow and have wide currency.[1]

The cortex is subdivided into four lobes—frontal, parietal, temporal, and occipital. The frontal lobe is anterior to the central or Rolandic fissure, and the parietal is posterior to it. For an illustration of these features, see Fig. 21–4. At the posterior pole of the brain is the occipital

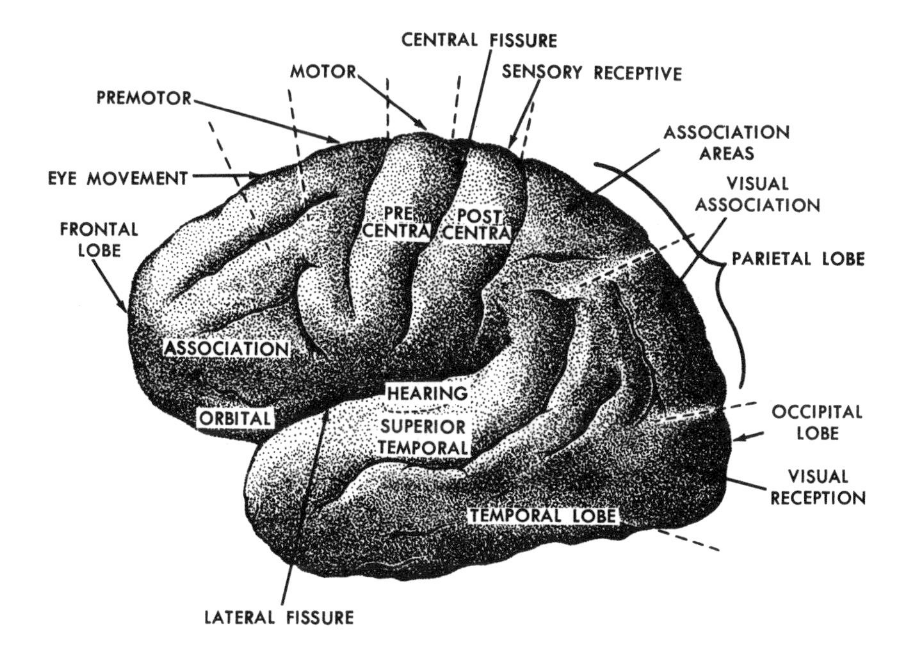

Drawing by Brenda Sutherland

Figure 21–4. Lateral Cortical Areas and Functions

lobe, and the temporal lobe is lateral and inferior to the great lateral fissure of Sylvius. One portion of the cortex, the insula, is covered up by the lower border of the lateral surface of the parietal lobe and the upper border of the temporal lobe, which meet to form the Sylvian fissure. In the depths of this fissure is the insula, an infolded section of cortex that was covered up in the enlargement of lateral parietal and temporal lobes.

[1] The order of Brodmann's numbers can be seen to jump back and forth from frontal to parietal lobe and can be confusing. The sequence of numbers merely represents the order in which Brodmann examined the cortical areas for cytoarchitectural differences.

The insula seems to be the receptive field for sensations of taste and for sensations from the alimentary canal. One of the great dividing lines of cortical topography is the central or Rolandic fissure. In general, most of the motor areas of the cortex are forward of this fissure, and most of the sensory areas of the cortex are behind or below it. Recent evidence suggests a slight amount of overlap between sensory and motor areas on the sides of the central fissure. The precentral gyrus directly in front of the central fissure is called the motor area, or area 4 of Brodmann. For the numerical designation of Brodmann's areas, see Fig. 21–5. Here there is a

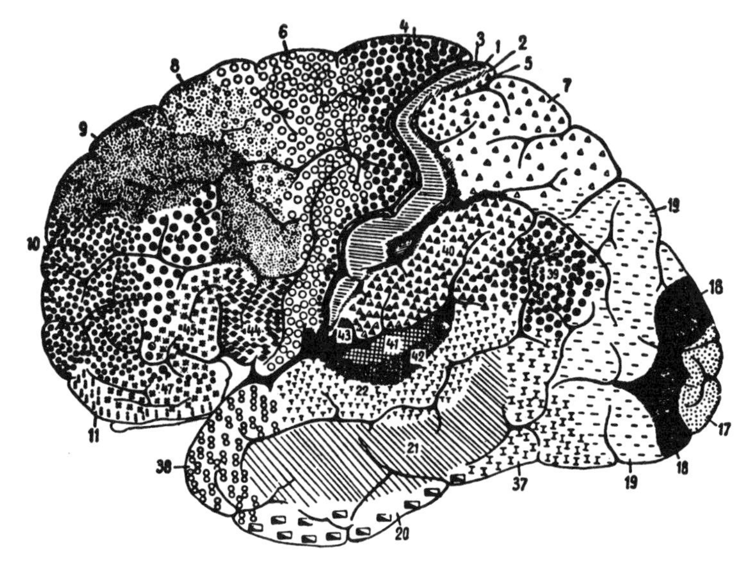

Source: *Physiology of the Nervous System* by John F. Fulton, 3d edition, 1949. Reprinted by permission of Oxford University Press, Inc.

Figure 21–5. Cytoarchitectural Map of Human Cortex

predominance of the giant pyramidal Betz cells. There are many other pyramidal shaped cells of smaller sizes in both layers III and V throughout area 4, as well as in other motor and sensory areas. The axons of cells in area 4 which are motor efferent arise in part in the Betz cells and proceed through the white matter by way of the internal capsule, through the center of the cerebral peduncles to the closely bunched pyramidal tracts of the pons and medulla. The stimulation of delimited regions in area 4 will result in movement of individual muscles in the limbs, body, or head. Contrary to the older view, there are many fibers in the corticospinals from the anterior frontal and the parietal lobes as well as from the precentral gyrus. The motor portion of the hemisphere contains only 34,000 Betz cells, whereas there are nearly 1 million fibers in each pyramid at the medullary level. The fibers which synapse in the cervical and lumbar enlargements to provide innervation to arms and legs cross at the caudal end of the medulla as the pyramidal decussation. After the decussation they travel downstream as the lateral cortico- or ventral corticospinal fibers to make contact with the ventral horn cells in the cervical, thoracic, and lumbar regions. In man 50 percent of the pyramidal fibers end in the cervical region, 20 percent in the thoracic, and 30 percent end in the lumbar and sacral levels. Since many of these fibers innervate muscles of finer and more graded muscular adjustments of tongue, lip, finger and foot manipulation, they each supply a relatively small number of muscle groups. In contrast to the gross muscular movements of the trunk in postural adjustments in which hundreds of muscle fibers work together, the movements involved in manual dexterity of handling weapons or a pen require that there be separate control of each small muscle group. This finer and more delicate control is provided by the lateral corticospinal fibers, each of which innervates perhaps 10-20 rather than 100-400 muscle spindles. A motor unit is a group of muscle fibers activated by a single motor nerve.

In addition to the crossed pyramidal pathway, there is an uncrossed portion of the corticospinal fibers that come down from area 4. This does not decussate, but travels down the cord as the anterior corticospinal tract and crosses at various levels in the cord to supply innervation to the cervical and upper thoracic musculature after a synapse in the ventral horn gray matter of the opposite side.

These fibers each supply innervation to hundreds of muscle fibers and take care of the gross muscular adjustments of bodily posture. In addition to the main motor area (area 4) there is a supplementary motor area situated on the mesial surface of area 6. Here the body musculature is represented again, and stimulation of this area results in longer lasting postural changes in limb position, involving groups of muscles operating synergically. The main projection from this area is to other motor centers, particularly the extrapyramidal system, but apparently not by way of the pyramidal pathway. For an illustration of competition for control of the motor neuron, see Fig. 21–6.

CORTICAL AREAS

The cellular surface of the cortex has been divided into a series of functionally discrete areas which are convenient for descriptive pur-

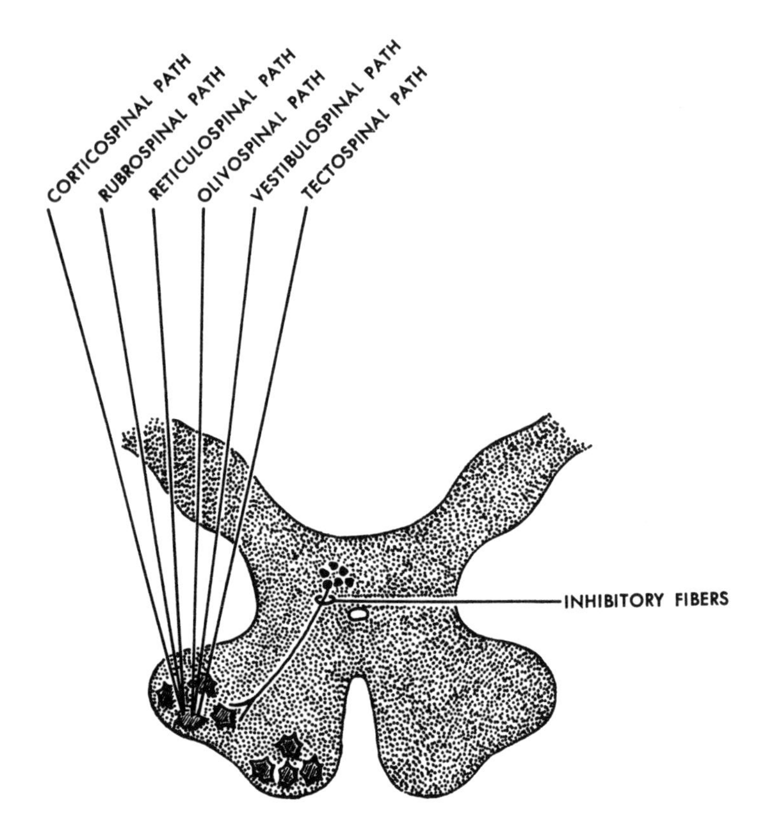

Drawing by Brenda Sutherland

Figure 21–6. Schema of Six Spinal Paths Impinging on Same Motor Neurons

poses. We have already referred to area 4 of Brodmann as the source of a large fraction of the corticospinal fibers. This area is just forward of the central sulcus. Area 6 is just in front of 4 and is the source for most of the fibers that make up the cortical originating extrapyramidal system. Forward still of 6 is area 8, which is known as the motor eye field for conjugate movement of the two eyes. From area 8 to the front pole of the cortex lie areas 9-12, which constitute the pre-frontal cortex or frontal association areas. These pre-frontal areas are considered as having rather unified action, as we will see in considering the effect of frontal lobectomies and lobotomies.

Just behind the central sulcus is the main sensory receptive area for the body senses of pressure, touch, pain, temperature, taste, and proprioception. This is the end station (areas 3-1-2 of Brodmann), in the postcentral gyrus, of the fibers which below the thalamus are the spinal, trigeminal, and medial lemnisci. In normal circumstances the sensory and motor areas of the cortex are interdependent. Response reactions are abolished by lesions of either sensory or motor areas for a particular activity. The other major sensory receptive areas are: 1) the gyri (area 17) that abut on the calcarine fissure on the mesial posterior surface of the brain, for vision; 2) the superior temporal gyrus, just below the lateral fissure, and the inside surface of the temporal lobe (area 41), for hearing; and 3) the prepyriform cortex located on the inferior surface of the temporal lobes, for olfaction.

Vestibular information ordinarily does not reach the cerebral cortex directly, but is first organized by the cerebellum and may then reach the cerebral cortex as a coordinated equilibrium and postural input. In contrast to the other sensory impulses this coordinated cerebellar information does not project on a sensory reception area for subsequent association with motor efferent cells, but is projected directly to the three motor areas already mentioned (4-6-8) for direct connection to the efferent outflow.

Some of the other numbered areas of the cortex include the parietal lobes (areas 5-7) posterior of the main somesthetic receptive area in the postcentral gyrus. The parietal lobes receive projections of coordinated sensory input from the pulvinar of the thalamus, largely for the coordination of visual and auditory information. In addition to the sensory projection areas, the parietal and temporal lobes are largely associative in function. This clearly involves coordination and some comparison. In the sense of touch, for instance, the modality itself can be distinguished at the thalamic levels, and is so sensed by lower forms. For spatial localization, however, the unimpaired functioning of the postcentral gyrus is essential. In addition, the postcentral receptive area does not give impressions of intensity. For this added quality the activity of the posterior parietal cortex must be also drawn into play. It is for this reason then that lesions in the postcentral gyrus result in loss of localization rather than loss of the touch modality as a whole.

The major cortical region not yet accounted for is the temporal lobe aside from the auditory projection area. The function of the temporal lobe is somehow different from that of other cortical centers. Aside from the auditory area on the lower edge of the Sylvian fissure, stimulation of the external sense organs results in no projection to the temporal lobe from thalamic nuclei. Its function then is largely associational and, as we will see when we consider ablations, it is important in the understanding and coordination of present experience and the recording of past experience.

Several other cortical regions should be mentioned before leaving the localization of function in cortical areas. It has been shown by stimulation experiments that the medial and basal portions of the frontal lobes give rise to visceral motor impulses. The hippocampal region has a totally different function than its earlier designation as olfactory cortex, for ablation experiments have shown a startling loss when this area is removed. The absence of the hippocampus and hippocampal gyrus on both sides makes impossible any recording of present experience as memory. The location of the hippocampus can be seen in Fig. 21–7.

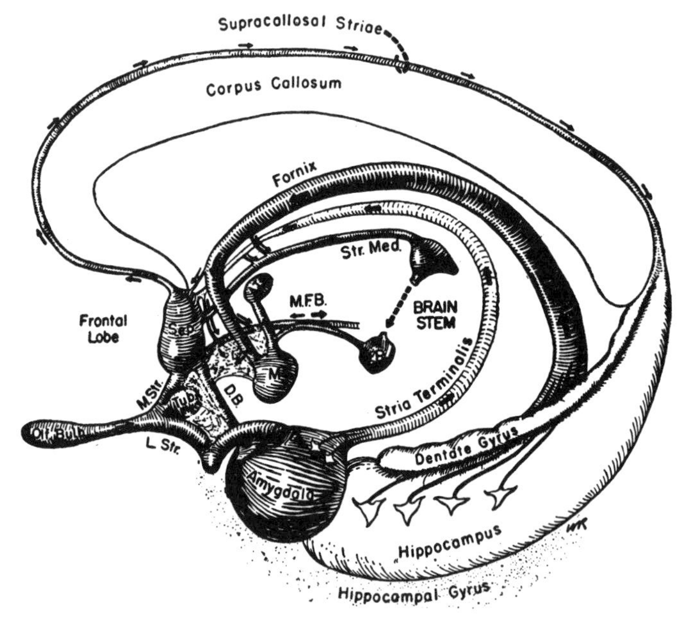

Source: Figure 2, p. 189, chapter "Psychosomatic Disease and the Visceral Brain" by Paul D. Maclean in *Basic Readings in Neuropsychology* edited by Robert L. Isaacson (Harper & Row, 1964).

Figure 21–7. Hippocampus and Related Structures

Finally there is a secondary sensory reception area hidden behind the Sylvanian fissure and across that fissure from the auditory projection area. This seems to duplicate the main sensory projection of area 3-1-2, but instead of being a contralateral projection as is the postcentral gyrus, the secondary area receives from both sides of the body. What function this secondary area has that is separable from that of the postcentral gyrus is not yet clear.

Table 21–I

Cortical Areas, According to Brodmann Numbers

Number	*Location*	*Function*
1, 2, 3	Postcentral gyrus	Somesthetic sensation from body and face
4	Precentral gyrus	Primary motor area
5, 7	Sup. parietal lobe	Association cortex
6	Anterior to precentral gyrus	Premotor area
8	Anterior to 6	Frontal eye fields
9–12	Frontal lobe	Association cortex
17	Occipital pole and midline lips of calcarine fissure	Visual cortex
18–19	Parietal lobe between 7 and 17	Visual association cortex
20	Inferior temporal lobe, pyriform and prepyriform cortex	Olfactory cortex and motivational association cortex
21	Lateral temporal lobe	Temporal association cortex
22	Superior temporal lobe	Auditory association cortex
23, 24	Superior to corpus callosum	Cingulate gyrus (limbic)
25	Inferior frontal	Inferior orbital (limbic)
26	Posterior splenium of corpus callosum	Retrosplenial cortex (limbic)
41	Superior temporal gyrus	Auditory receptive area
42	Inferior to superior temporal gyrus	Auditory association cortex
43	Lateral inferior to 1, 2, 3	Secondary sensory area
44	Anterior to lateral inferior tip of precentral gyrus	Motor speech area

The numbers on the left correspond to the numbered areas in Fig. 21–8.

MICROSCOPIC STRUCTURE

The microscopic structure of the neocortex is very similar in all species having cortex. It is composed of layers of nerve cells totalling 10–12 billion neurons and their related fibers. In the areas of the cortex which can be seen macroscopically, it is composed of six layers as shown by Nissl stain. In the oldest segment of the cortex, that of the hippo-

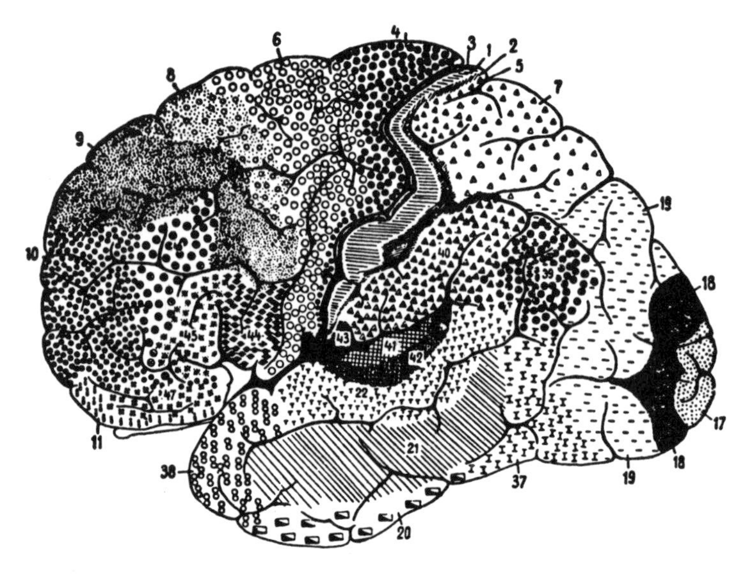

Source: *Physiology of the Nervous System* by John F. Fulton, 3d edition, 1949. Reprinted by permission of Oxford University Press, Inc.

Figure 21–8. Brodmann's Numbered Map of the Brain Surface

campal gyrus, which is buried medial to the temporal lobe, there are only three layers. On the outside surface of the main cerebral mantle is a thin layer (I) composed largely of axonal and dendritic plexuses, or feltwork. The evidence seems to indicate that the fibers making up the diffuse thalamic projection to neocortex end in layer I. The second layer (II) contains a large population of small pyramidal and granular cells. This is called the outer granular layer. The third layer from the surface (III) is sparsely filled with pyramidal and other cells. The fourth layer from the surface (IV) is called the inner granular layer and is composed of a dense population of small cells. It is here that the sensory fibers making up the thalamic radiation have their end synapse. The next layer (V) is made up predominantly of pyramidal cells. It is as axons of these pyramidal cells of various sizes that the pyramidal pathway and other efferent systems have their origin. In addition, some of the intercortical association fibers originate from cells in layer V. Below this, next to the white matter, lies the sixth layer (VI), which contains many spindle shaped cells. When impulses come into the cortex from sensory receptors by way of the thalamus and the internal capsule they end in layer IV, where the axons break up in a dense arborization of axon filaments. These spread widely in that layer and form together the end stations of the thalamic radiations. From layers III and V arise intercortical association fibers which pass out into the white matter and on to other cortical areas.

Although the microscopic structure of the cortex is similar in number of layers in all locations, marked differences exist from area to area. Regions of sensory cortex show a thicker layer IV to accommodate the incoming afferent axons, and a narrower layer V than other cortical regions. Motor cortex shows almost no layer IV, having few incoming afferents, but a large layer V to accommodate the pyramidal cells. The thickness of layers IV and V in association cortex is, in both instances, midway between that of sensory and motor cortex. (See Fig. 21–9 for the differentiation of sensory, motor, and association cortices.)

In reentering the other cortical areas the fibers move upward to arborize either between layers V and VI or between layers II and III. The motor efferent fibers arise as axons of pyramidal shaped cells, largely in layer V. These are in part from the giant pyramidal cells called Betz cells. It is possible that this size is related to the length of fiber pathway which is involved from cortex to cervical, thoracic, or lumbar spinal cord without a synapse, for innervation of limb or trunk muscles. In general, then, the incoming axons proceed farther toward the surface of the cortex than the location of the cells which are the point of origin either for association within the cortex or for efferent motor impulses. Since the axons of all efferent cortical cells travel inward to enter the white matter, the dendrites are directed toward the surface, and it is for this reason that incoming fibers proceed farther toward the surface to make synaptic contact with these dendrites. It is possible to extirpate the upper three or four cortical layers without interfering with appropriate movements. The superficial layers are important but do not affect markedly the motor response to stimulation. The extirpation of layer V, however, eliminates movement. The removal of all or part of the motor cortex does not cause memory loss in any degree. The animal attempts to respond with the other extremity.

BODY REPRESENTATION

Several aspects of the cortex proper have not as yet been examined. One of these aspects is the body representation in both precentral motor and postcentral sensory gyri. In both locations the body is represented upside down, with the face and lips at the inferior end of the gyri just

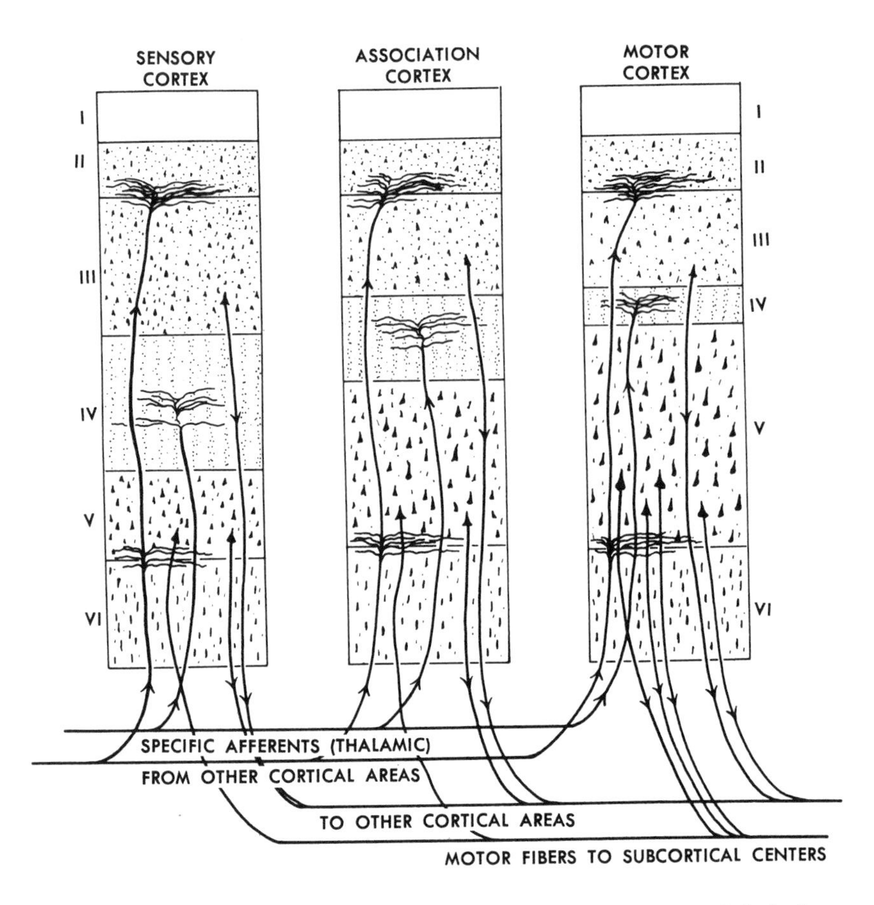

Drawing by Brenda Sutherland

Figure 21–9. Cortical Layers Showing Difference between Sensory, Motor, and Association Cortex

adjacent to the lateral fissure, and the toes and genitals—and tails in monkeys—represented by cells or fiber endings just over the lip of the median fissure. One other characteristic of this inverted sensory or motor body is that the cortical area given to a particular bodily organ or limb is a function of the number of fibers represented either as incoming sensation or as outgoing motor impulses, and not of the size of the limb or body part itself. Consequently the inverted representation is grossly distorted in shape. For a graphic depiction of this distortion, see Fig. 21–10. Large cortical areas are given over to limbs, face, hands, and lips, while only small areas are devoted to the trunk. The determining factor for the area needed on the cortical surface is the relative requirement for fine or gross control of muscle groups, and in the sensory area the detail needed in incoming sensory information. For this reason, as much of the precentral or postcentral gyrus is devoted to the thumb as to the muscles of the entire trunk.

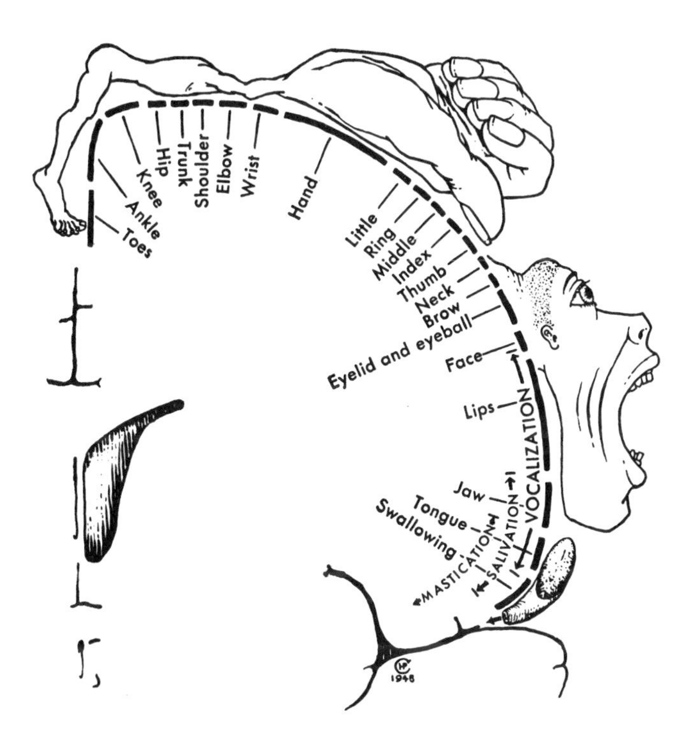

Source: Reprinted with permission of the Macmillan Company from *The Cerebral Cortex of Man: A Clinical Study of Localization of Function* by Wilder Penfield and Theodore Rasmussen. Copyright 1950 by The Macmillan Company.

Figure 21–10. Bodily Representation on Motor Cortex

ASSOCIATION AREAS

It will be observed that the sensory projections and motor areas of the cerebral cortex occupy less than one-half the total cortical area in man. There is a large expanse in the frontal, temporal, occipital, and parietal lobes from which recordings cannot be made on sensory stimulation or which give rise to no movement on cortical stimulation. These are association areas establishing relationship between sensory modalities, or between sensory input and motor reaction. An important part of most mental or emotional processes depends on the activity of the association areas. By definition, then, these association areas are tied to no sense modality; and, in fact, discrete portions of association cortex do not have separate functions. These cortical regions function as a whole, and it is for this reason that damage by lesions to association cortex depends upon the extent of the damage rather than its location. Quite extensive ablations can be effected on the frontal areas anterior to area 8 without loss of most intellectual functions. The loss from frontal ablations shows up as a reduction in ability to hold immediate past memory in attention. For this reason animals with frontal ablation have difficulty performing delayed reaction responses. There is also loss of inhibitions resulting in 1) a driven state of hyperactivity and 2) an alteration and coarsening of emotional tone, accompanied by a reduction in self-consciousness.

The parietal and occipital association areas, while not connected directly to sensory input, are so connected secondarily. The parietal areas 5-7 receive coordinated sensory information from the pulvinar and the lateral thalamic nuclei. The occipital areas 18-19 are clearly considered as visual association areas.

CORTICAL ABLATIONS

Frontal lobotomies[2] first attained prominence after a Portuguese physician successfully performed several such operations to provide relief for extremely high-tension patients. Such lobotomies have been extended and studied carefully in succeeding years. A unilateral operation has much less effect than a bilateral one—frequently only the bilateral effects a pronounced behavioral change. The behavioral changes following a frontal lobotomy are as follows:

1. There is a substantial reduction in drive. An aggressive paranoid frequently shows a reduction of anger and hostility following lobotomy. Because of this reduction the severely inhibited may find release from inhibition by a lobotomy. Some patients, after a lifetime of sexual

---

2 Ablation and lobectomy refer to the removal of tissue; lobotomy does not. Prefrontal lobectomies were performed by Fox and German before Moniz in Portugal introduced the idea of lobotomy, which involves severing the interior fibers which project to and from the prefrontal areas.

restraint, suddenly become active and unashamed in the sexual sphere.

2. Self-consciousness and concern are reduced by frontal lobotomy. The patient is less sensitive to criticism, and shows more outwardly directed behavior and social awareness, but less tact.

3. There is less depth and more superficial character to the affective life. The patient will flare up quickly but will also calm down quickly. The social effect of lobotomy is to produce not a vegetable, but in most cases a simpler, less complex individual. Sometimes this less complex person becomes less socially acceptable because of a loss of the niceties and good taste of social intercourse. The personality damage from frontal lobotomy seems to be a function of the number of fibers severed. Therefore the later practice was to limit the extent of the operation more than formerly. It has been found that a section of the inferior (orbital) surface of the frontal lobes will produce the beneficial effects without the personality damage associated with a section of the entire projection to the frontal lobe. In addition, the frontal patient sustains a reduction in reflective power and creativity. His planning is diminished, and the portion of his behavior which is dependent on sustained attention is less efficient.

Parietal lobe ablations have not had the same medical history as those of the frontal lobe, but have been performed experimentally. Ablation of the whole parietal lobe has been found consistently to remove tactile avoiding reactions and abolish instinctive grasp reactions. Operative removal of only the parietal lobe in monkeys results in a lasting withdrawal from their environment. Animals with bilateral ablation turn their back to the experimenter, and when they wish to approach him will back toward him. This is equivalent to a visual avoiding reaction. It seems clear that the parietal lobe provides for exploratory movements in space by touch or vision. This includes optic righting reflexes.

Temporal lobe ablations have been studied extensively in recent years. A large part of the temporal lobe is employed in the understanding of present experience and in the recording of past experience. Some experiments indicate that the absence of the hippocampus and hippocampal gyrus on both sides makes any recording of present experience impossible. There is, however, fairly good memory of the past except for a short period just prior to the operation. No impairment seems to appear in perception or in comprehension.

There is a difference in effect between right and left temporal lobe ablations. The left temporal ablation shows mainly a deficit in verbal memory. There is no impairment in recall of geometric drawings, but a substantial deficit appears in all verbal memory tests, particularly in recall of short passages of verse. There is also increased difficulty in learning. The right temporal ablation shows a very different pattern. Here, ablation produces no verbal loss whatever, but a clear deficit on all pictorial tests. On these same pictorial tests the parietal lobe patient makes excellent scores.

Kluver carried out a number of excellent studies of the effect of temporal lobectomies. In mature rhesus monkeys he removed the major portion of the temporal lobe, the amygdala, the uncus, the hippocampus, and the hippocampal gyrus. The behavioral changes caused by this operation can be summarized as follows:

1. *Visual agnosia*—There was no loss of visual discrimination, but loss of visual significance. The monkey was unable to tell by vision if an object was edible or dangerous.
2. *Oral tendencies*—Postoperatively the monkey had a strong tendency to examine everything by mouth. It even picked up objects by mouth rather than by hand.
3. There was a compulsion to attend to and touch everything seen.
4. A critical loss appeared in normal emotional behavior. The animal would approach any object or animal without fear. This included deadly enemies such as the snake. This followed from the loss of visual significance. In addition, there was no longer any emotional expression.
5. Sexual behavior was exaggerated and the object of attention varied. The female at times lost its maternal behavior.
6. Finally, there were important changes in diet. The animal would accept and eat meat which it normally would not use. There was also an increase in appetite and food consumption.

It can be seen that lobectomies of the temporal lobe have most profound effects on an animal's normal behavior pattern.

As Penfield has indicated, the temporal cortex plays an active role in the interpretation of the individual's present experience, and its linkage to his past experience. Patterns of past experience can be switched in to active recall by stimulation of the temporal cortex.

LANGUAGE

The temporal lobe is, aside from the auditory reception area 41, wholly associative. It is very largely involved, for example, in the associative functions needed for the complicated speech process. Language communication even in simple form involves associative functions that allow: (1) sensory representation of objects;(2) substitution of names for objects or symbolization; (3) abstraction to the extent of deriving classes of objects; and (4) further abstraction of class groupings or interrelations.

In addition to the abstraction from real objects, language involves for most people (5) vision, (6) hearing, (7) speech, and (8) written expression. Because of these eight involvements several association areas are always involved in speech understanding or production. The four areas of the dominant hemisphere which are traditionally connected with speech processes are: (1) Broca's area in the triangular portion of the inferior frontal gyrus, (2) the posterior portion of the superior temporal gyrus, (3) the angular gyrus surrounding the end of the Sylvian fissure, and (4) inferior frontal gyrus dorsal of Broca's area. The first of these, Broca's convolution, is responsible under lesion or hemorrhage for the inability to carry out the coordinated movements of lips, tongue, and vocal cords necessary for speech. After a lesion in the second area (superior temporal) a person can hear the spoken word but can no longer understand its meaning. This is sensory aphasia, or word (meaning) deafness. Lesions in the third area (angular gyrus) may result in word (meaning) blindness, in which the sight of a word conveys no meaning whatever. A fourth area, dorsal of Broca's area, on the inferior frontal gyrus and slightly rostral to it, is implicated in brain lesions affecting written expression. For the location of these association areas, see Fig. 21–11.

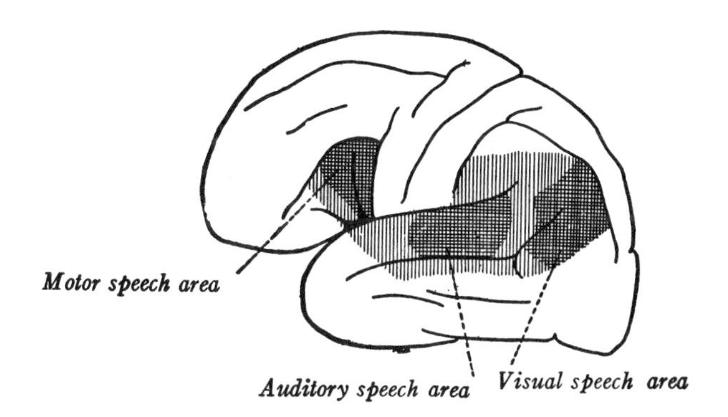

Source: S. W. Ranson and S. L. Clark, *The Anatomy of Nervous System: Its Development and Function* (10th ed.; Philadelphia: W. B. Saunders Company, 1959), p. 380.

Figure 21–11. Cortical Areas Implicated in Language Deficits

It is possible that language use activates a larger portion of the cerebral cortex than any other intellectual activity. In addition to the areas associated with aphasias, the other cortical areas involved in language use include visual cortex (area 17), somesthetic receptive cortex (areas

1-2-3), parietal lobe (areas 5-7), motor cortex (area 4), and at least temporal cortex for recorded past experience. Because of the extent of cerebral cortex involved, cerebral hemorrhage or thrombosis usually results in some loss of language function. The paralysis of the different language functions and the recovery from lesion or thrombosis may affect the parts differently. After extensive hemorrhage, for instance, it is possible to record total loss of speech production, but to see little effect on auditory or visual understanding, or written expression. The reverse may also be true: Coherent written expression may be impossible, while at the same time, the patient can dictate a perfectly grammatical letter. This separation of the different functions of language in brain damage has a parallel in the effect of a lapse of a number of years in the use of a foreign language. If the foreign language was well learned originally, reading ability may be retained with little loss after a number of years, whereas motor speech production may be very defective, and auditory understanding and written expression may be only partially lost.

INTRACORTICAL FIBERS

As we have seen, the cerebral cortex is made up of a series of cell layers approximately $\frac{3}{16}$ inch thick in all, and subdivided into sensory, motor, and association areas. Between these various areas there are connecting pathways from sensory to motor, from sensory to association to motor, and so on. The interior of the hemispheres between the cell layers and the subcortical structures of thalamus and basal ganglia is composed largely of a complex network of connecting fiber pathways. Some are short in length, connecting gyri that are adjacent or at most only two or three gyri apart; others are long fibers connecting frontal lobe to occipital or occipital to temporal. These intracortical axons are so numerous as to connect every part of the cortex with every other. The fiber tracts mentioned below are designated in Fig. 21–12.

Some of the most important fiber tracts are the following: (1) *corona radiata*, composed of incoming sensory fibers that project to postcentral gyrus, to occipital visual cortex, and to temporal auditory cortex; (2) *arcuate fibers*, connecting adjacent gyri; (3) *uncinate fibers*, connecting the orbital portion of the frontal lobe to the anterior temporal lobe; (4) *superior longitudinal fasciculus*, connecting laterally placed occipital and parietal areas to frontal cortex; (5) *superior* and *inferior occipitofrontal fasciculi*, connecting medial portions of occipital and parietal lobes to frontal cortex; (6) *cingulum*, connecting the subcallosal

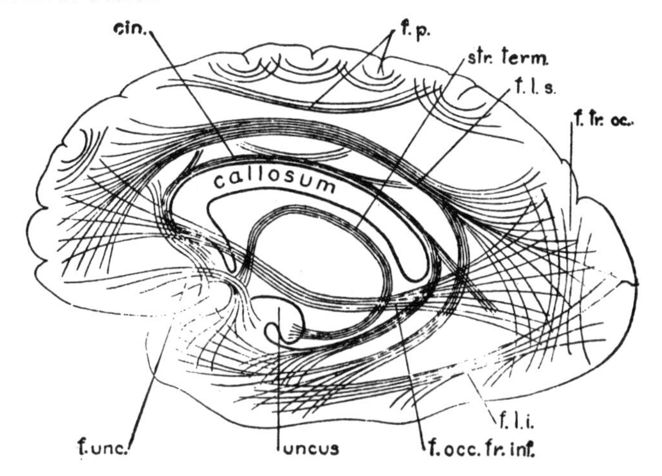

Cin., cingulum; *f.l.i.*, fasciculus longitudinalis inferior; *f.l.s.*, fasciculus longitudinalis superior; *f.occ.fr.inf.*, fasciculus occipito-frontalis inferior; *f.p.*, arcuate fibers; *f.tr.occ.*, fasciculus transversus occipitalis; *f.unc.*, fasciculus uncinatus; *str. term.*, stria terminalis.

Source: C. Judson Herrick, *An Introduction to Neurology* (4th ed., rev.; Philadelphia: W. B. Saunders Company, 1927), p. 308.

Figure 21–12. Cortical Association Fiber Pathways

frontal gyri to the hippocampal complex in the temporal lobe, arching over the corpus callosum, and then at the caudal end of the callosum turning forward inferior to the fornix and hippocampus to supply the retrosplenial cortex; (7) *inferior longitudinal fasciculus,* connecting occipital cortex to temporal pole. In addition to these longitudinal association fibers there are commissural fibers connecting the two hemispheres. The largest is the corpus callosum, whose fibers form a thick plate just above the thalamus and caudate nucleus. They connect, for the most part, homologous points in the two hemispheres. The anterior part of the corpus callosum connects the two frontal lobes. The middle portion is essential for somesthetic interconnections, while the posterior portion connects the visual cortex in the two hemispheres, which is basic to coordination of the two visual fields. The hippocampal commissure connects similar parts of the rhinencephalon in the two hemispheres. The hippocampal commissure stretches across, as a thin connecting sheet, between the hippocampi and the converging limbs of the fornix, caudal to where these limbs join to form the body of the fornix. (See Fig. 21–13.) The anterior commissure lies just above the optic chiasm and is separated from it by the preoptic nuclei of the hypothalamus. This commissure connects both the olfactory bulb and tubercle bilaterally, as well as the amygdaloid nuclei and the middle temporal gyrus.

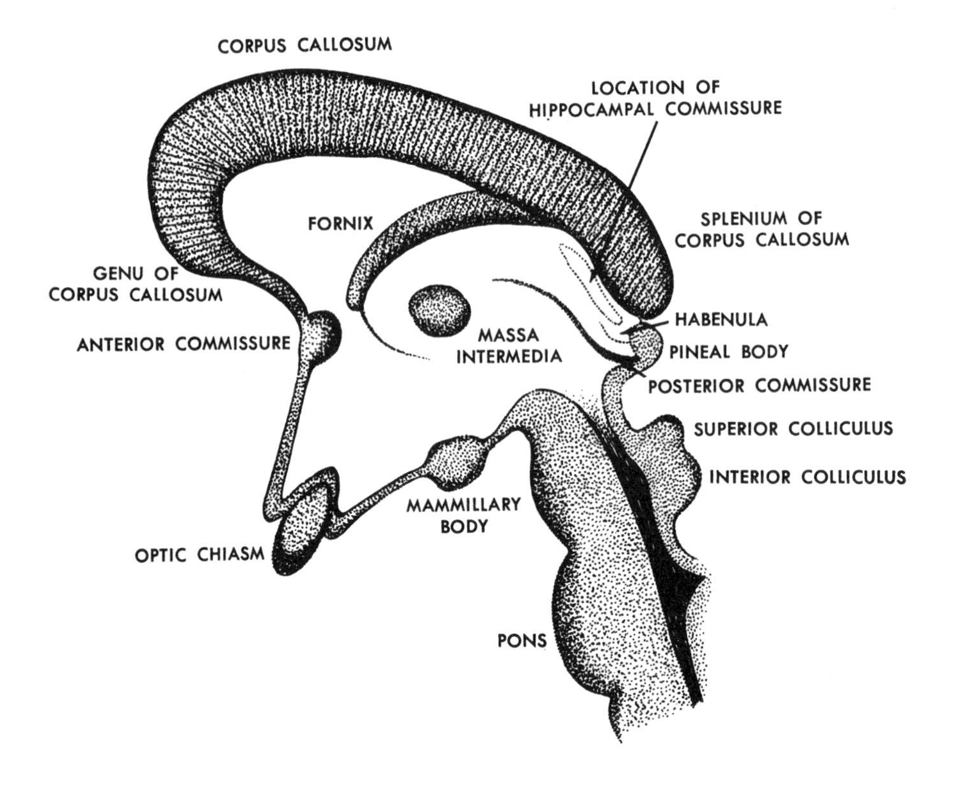

Drawing by Brenda Sutherland

Figure 21–13. Location of Corpus Callosum, Anterior Commissure, Hippocampal Commissure, and Posterior Commissure

From the description of their location, origin, and termination it should be clear that the association and commissural fibers do not serve exclusively any sensory or motor function. They connect nonsensory and nonmotor cortex, as well as sensory and motor cortex, and provide therefore the essential interconnections on which the complex cortical activity of thought and language rest.

EFFERENT FIBERS

The two major portions of the motor efferent outflow from the cortex are outlined in descriptions of the corticospinal and extrapyramidal

system which are to follow. In addition, there are other efferent pathways which are more diffuse, and which involve connections not so directly stimulating skeletal muscle as the two major motor systems. These pathways comprise cortico-rubral, cortico-bulbar, and cortico-pontine fibers. The cortico-pontine connect with pontine nuclei, and axons from these, crossing the midline, sweep up to the cerebellum as the middle cerebellar peduncle. In this way the cortex can influence the whole mechanism of posture and equilibrium. There is also, as we know, a feedback loop from the dentate nucleus of the cerebellum by way of the superior cerebellar peduncle and the thalamus to the precentral motor cortex. The cortico-bulbar connections enable events of cortical significance to influence the nuclei for respiration, heart beat, glandular stimulation, etc. The cortico-rubral fibers allow direct cortical influence on postural or locomotor movements. This influence is largely by way of the red nucleus and its connections with the reticulospinal pathway. This pathway becomes larger and more important in man and other primates than in lower animals. By contrast, in the lower four-footed animals the rubrospinal connection direct from the red nucleus is much larger, and the reticulospinal path is small.

LEARNING AND MEMORY

The examination of the anatomical and physiological mechanics of the cerebral cortex has not allowed us to touch to any extent on the more interesting cortical activities or higher mental processes. How is memory stored? In what does learning consist, etc.? It is time now to look at some of these essentially psychological considerations. The sensory input of present experience, when combined with appropriate memory, gives us our perception, for perception involves the comparison and correction of specific—and at times faulty—patterns of sensory stimulation. In addition, the extent of overlap of sensory fields and the close association between them give us some of our more complex perceptions of form and texture. Tactile or visual impulses clearly excite their appropriate memory constellations, and from this comes recognition. In some fashion from this associated memory comes organized knowledge and understanding. The rapid reactivation of memory constellations is particularly marked in visual impressions. Recognition of an airplane, with correct reference as to make, size, etc., can take place in a fraction of a second. The rapidity of this reactivation and reference makes it unlikely that it could depend on a laborious scanning process, such as one could expect in a high speed computer. As we have already seen, the symbolic construct of language involves tremendous association interrelationships. Consequently the language connections are more easily interrupted by lesion or hemorrhage. Most of the school years are involved in the building up of language organization, memory, and association. It is not surprising, therefore, that this should be the first system interrupted.

Learning and memory generally are the most difficult to explain on the basis of what is known of cerebral mechanisms. The concept of declining resistance at the synapse is totally inadequate for explaining the fact that these connections may last more than a score of years without reactivation. The time factor of persistence of memory cannot be explained by any known process of anatomy or physiology. It is clear that no limited, specific pathways are needed for learning. In addition, the effective response can use a number of efferent paths. If lesion interferes with movement of one limb, the contralateral one comes into play, without conscious thought, to effect the same response. From this lack of dependence on particular neural circuits one might begin to doubt whether the storage of memory is in the neuron at all. Certainly the flow of nervous impulse—while it is essential in intercommunication—does not appear to be primarily concerned in memory storage.

An attractive theory suggested recently by Galambos is that memory is stored not in nerve cells, but in the surrounding glial cells which form a matrix for the nervous system. There are many more glial cells than neurons in the brain, and the number of glial cells increases in direct proportion to the complexity of the nervous system; the largest number of glial cells is in man, and the number declines as one goes down the phylogenetic scale. There is, moreover, some evidence that cortical activity brings about a change in the electrical activity of the glial cells. Such a theory, if proved true, would help explain a number of things which are impossible to explain at present by the neuron doctrine.

CORTICAL ORGANIZATION

Without recourse to the glial theory of memory storage, other explanations of cortical organization have been proposed. The selective effect of particular sensory input or psychological set is well known. One reasonable explanation, by Lashley, is that an external stimulus throws the neurons involved in a coherent system into activity, whether the "system" is about chess, or sailing, or neural physiology. The billions of neurons in the cortex are organized into a large number of "trace" systems or "neuron pools," each representing one subject or a coherent part thereof. An activated "trace" system will limit the association or flow of ideas to topics related to that system. The elements of the one "trace" system are readily excitable and available to recall, while elements of other systems are held in abeyance although an intense stimulus may interrupt the dominant trace system. The blocking of other systems by a "trace" system dominating the brain field may be by the inhibition, or by preemption, of neurons which might be needed in the blocked system. Something akin to this selective activity of "trace" systems or "neuron pools" must occur to account for the complicated mental activity with which we are familiar. The experience of everyone provides support for the concept of Lashley's "trace" system so far as the factor of selectivity is concerned. When out hunting or in a sailboat race, we are seldom troubled by faulty associations. Likewise, in a final examination in chemistry we do not find the details of nervous anatomy getting in the way of the proper chemical associations. Unfortunately our information is so meager that any comprehensive theory is impossible at present.

Hebb suggested a process by which groups of neurons connect themselves in "cell assemblies." When the axon of cell A fires cell B and repeatedly takes part in firing it, some metabolic process or growth occurs so that A's efficiency in firing B is increased. This metabolic process affects the threshold for B and probably results in an increase in the synaptic vesicles or boutons active at the synapse. In this way groups of neurons, or "cell assemblies," connected by this metabolic reduction of threshold are formed, which are made active by a particular afferent impulse.

Still a third consideration for cortical organization discussed by Sholl is based on the "equipotentiality" of cortical areas and the tightness of packing of cortical neurons. Since each cortical neuron affects the activity of 4000 other neurons, on the average, the density of packing may explain why the loss of function is proportional to the amount of cortex destroyed, except in the sensory receptive or primary motor areas. These two considerations lead to an approach to cortical organization which depends on probability and statistics.

A concept of cortical organization based on probability and statistics provides no answer, however, for the selective activity of the cortex. Of the three views, only Lashley's trace system attempts to explain the selectivity of cortical associations. It is the writer's conviction that most of the attempts at theories of cortical organization have been attempts to simplify what must be an incredibly complex associational mechanism. Perhaps a theory which takes into account the full complexity of the cortex will be a more successful and adequate explanation of cortical organization.

SOURCES AND ADDITIONAL READING

Beach, F. A., D. O. Hebb, C. T. Morgan, and H. W. Nissen, eds., *The Neuropsychology of Lashley*. New York: McGraw-Hill Book Company, 1960.

The CIBA Collection of Medical Illustrations, Vol. I, *Nervous System.* CIBA Pharmaceutical Company, 1953.

Fulton, J., *Physiology of the Nervous System,* Chaps. 15, 17–20, 22. New York: Oxford University Press, Inc., 1951.

Handbook of Physiology, Sec. I, Vol. II, Chaps. 54, 55. Washington, D. C.: American Physiol. Soc., 1960.

Isaacson, R. L. ed., *Basic Readings in Neuropsychology*. New York: Harper & Row, Publishers, 1964.

Penfield, W. and T. Rasmussen, *The Cerebral Cortex of Man*. New York: The Macmillan Company, 1950.

Ranson, S. W. and S. L. Clark, *The Anatomy of the Nervous System* (10th ed.), Chaps. 16, 18. Philadelphia: W. B. Saunders Company, 1959.

Ruch, T. and J. Fulton, *Medical Physiology and Biophysics* (18th ed.), Chaps. 11, 14, 21. Philadelphia: W. B. Saunders & Company, 1961. (See 19th ed., Chaps. 12, 15, 23, 24.)

Sholl, D. A., *The Organization of the Cerebral Cortex*. New York: John Wiley & Sons, Inc., 1956.

Walsh, G., *Physiology of the Nervous System,* Chaps. 7, 8, 10, 12. New York: Longmans Green & Co., Inc., 1959.

Warren, J. M. and K. Akert, *Frontal Granular Cortex and Behavior*. New York: McGraw-Hill Book Company, 1964.

Twenty-two

THE PYRAMIDAL AND EXTRAPYRAMIDAL MOTOR SYSTEMS

Although the sources of information about the outside world and from our bodies by way of our sense organs are many and varied, the avenues of control of voluntary and involuntary movement in response to afferent stimulation are few indeed. A superficial count shows at least twelve different kinds of sensory receptors: four in the skin, three distance receptors in the head, and four different proprioceptive receptors—one each in muscle, tendon, and joint, and one for equilibrium. Aside from taste these constitute the sources of incoming information upon which we act. By contrast, there are only two major motor pathways aside from connections fitting into these pathways, such as from the cerebellum. These motor pathways are the corticospinal, with its branchings in the pons and to the cranial nerves, and the extrapyramidal system, which is more diffuse and is composed of short links into which the cerebellar influence can be injected, as in the reticulospinal. Since muscles and glands are the only effector organs we possess, this paucity of pathways together with the autonomic nervous connections may be considered sufficient.

CORTICOSPINAL TRACT

The corticospinal tract is the great motor system of voluntary control. It begins in the precentral motor cortex (Brodmann area 4), although there are clearly components that come from premotor (area 6) as well as from the postcentral region of the parietal cortex. A substantial part of this pathway arises then in the giant Betz cells of area 4, but also

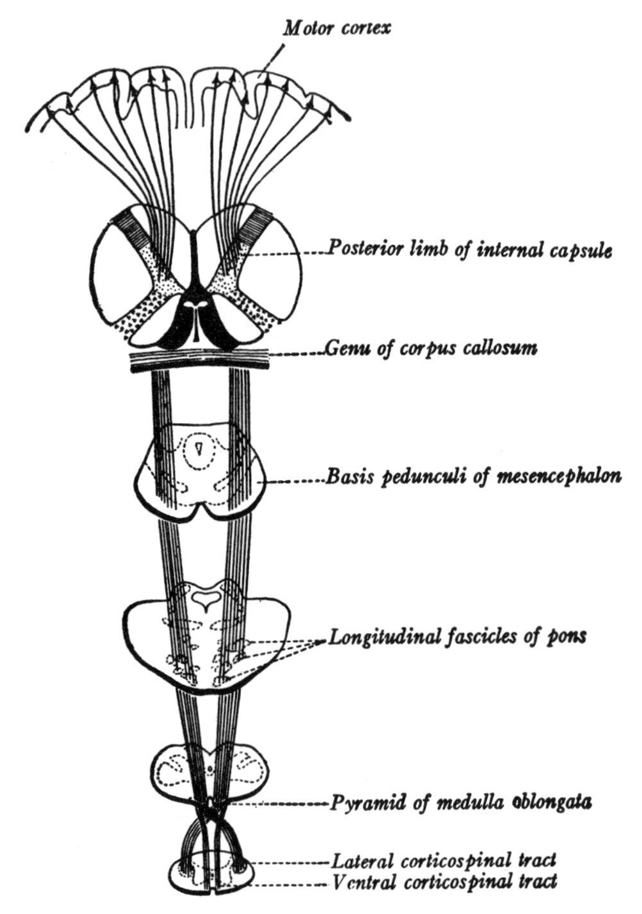

Source: S. W. Ranson and S. L. Clark, *The Anatomy of the Nervous System: Its Development and Function* (10th ed.; Philadelphia: W. B. Saunders Company, 1959), p. 397.

Figure 22–1. Entire Length of Corticospinal Pathway

from other smaller pyramidal cells here and elsewhere. The pyramidal motor system proceeds ventrally through the internal capsule and enters the cerebral peduncle at the base of the mesencephalon. For the entire corticospinal path, see Fig. 22–1. The corticospinal tract traverses the pons as a series of separated longitudinal bundles, or fascicles, giving off branching collaterals or a series of separate direct fibers to the motor nuclei of the cranial nerves—particularly III, IV, V, VI, and VII. The direct separate fibers are known as the *corticobulbar* path. These connections enable a person or animal to respond by facial muscle, eye movement, or glandular activity to cortical direction. Collaterals or separate direct fibers also occur in the medulla to connect with the cranial motor nerve nuclei of X, XI, and XII.

In addition to the collaterals to cranial nerve nuclei the corticospinal pathway includes fiber bundles which end in the nuclei of the basilar portion of the pons to connect with the pontine neurons. These fiber bundles are therefore called *cortico-pontine.* Aside from these collaterals and terminal bundles the corticospinal path proceeds through the pons without interruption, and then becomes consolidated into the pyramids on the ventral surface of the medulla. At the caudal end of the medulla most of the corticospinal fibers (80 percent) cross the midline in the pyramidal decussation and move dorsally and laterally to take up a position in the lateral funiculus of the spinal cord as the lateral corticospinal tract. Of these crossed fibers 50 percent end in the cervical and 30 percent in the lumbar enlargements for synaptic connection with the motor neurons innervating arms and legs. The corticospinal fibers which do not cross in the pyramidal decussation continue down the spinal cord in the ventral funiculus of the same side as the *ventral corticospinal* path. The ventral corticospinal tract does not continue much below the midthoracic level. The fibers in this tract cross the midline a few at a time down to midthoracic levels and make synaptic connection with motor neurons in the anterior gray of the cord. The ventral corticospinal pathway was once thought to innervate largely the trunk musculature, but this is now in doubt.

The direct voluntary pathways, then, are the related group of corticobulbar, corticospinals (including collaterals to cranial nerve nuclei), and corticopontine for cerebellar connections.

EXTRAPYRAMIDAL PATHWAYS

By definition the extrapyramidal system includes all nonreflex motor pathways not included in the corticospinal or pyramidal system. The major subcortical centers of the extrapyramidal system are the basal ganglia located anterior and lateral to the mass of the thalamus. Phylogenetically the basal ganglia must perform all the motor functions of animal species which possess little or no cerebral cortex. In birds, which have a highly developed striatum and little if any cerebral cortex, the upper and lower striatum can regulate their behavior, and they can even exhibit some learning without cerebral cortex. Complex instinctive actions such as mating, nesting, and flying require the hyperstriatum but not the cortex. As the cerebral cortex developed it brought into being a second source of motor impulse, the corticospinals, or alternatively, a cortical origin for extrapyramidal impulses. In higher mammals the striatum is not a dependency of the cortex, although with connections to it, but a discharge path for thalamic reflexes. For the relation of the basal ganglia to the thalamus, see Fig. 22–2.

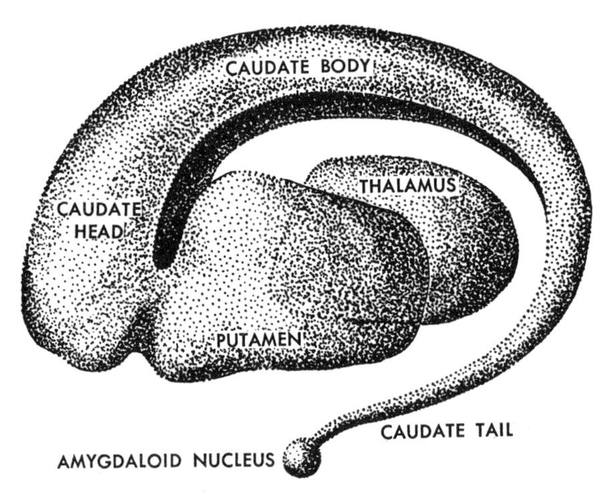

Drawing by Brenda Sutherland

Figure 22–2. Basal Ganglia and Thalamus

BASAL GANGLIA

The basal ganglia are composed of the *caudate nucleus, putamen,* and *globus pallidus.* The globus pallidus has two parts, lateral and medial, separated by a medullary vellum. Fibers entering the globus pallidus have their first synapse in the lateral portion, while the efferent fibers to thalamus and brain stem nuclei arise from the medial globus pallidus. Thus the cortical areas such as 6, to some extent 4, and a few others send fibers to putamen and caudate nucleus. From there the connections go to the lateral and then to the medial globus pallidus. From the medial portion of the globus pallidus the connections fan out to the thalamus, hypothalamus, subthalamic nucleus, and substantia nigra. The globus pallidus is regarded as the center for producing automatic and associated movements and their control. Many other interconnections exist, including those from thalamus to caudate and putamen, from caudate and putamen to substantia nigra, and from interpositus nucleus of cerebellum to centrum medianum of thalamus, which in turn provides the main afferent input of the caudate nucleus and to the putamen. Another connection runs from caudate to pallidum to thalamus to cortex (area 4) and back to nucleus ruber. The efferent motor pathways to the body from this complex system are from subthalamic nucleus and substantia nigra to reticular nuclei and reticulospinal path, and from nucleus ruber down the rubrospinal or reticulospinal path. For the complexity of extrapyramidal connections, see Fig. 22–3. The subthalamic nuclei and substantia nigra project to upper reticular and tegmental nuclei, while nucleus ruber projects both to lower reticular nuclei of the medulla and by the rubrospinal path.

LESIONS OF BASAL GANGLIA

Experimental lesions of the basal ganglia in animals do not seem to produce additional deficit in voluntary movement after cortical ablation. They do not seem then to operate independently of the cerebral cortex as a parallel motor path. Cortically induced movement is modulated or arrested by stimulation of the basal ganglia, indicating a most intimate connection to the cortical areas as part of a modulating feedback mechanism, or else as a source of first-priority claim on the motor neurons of the spinal cord and brain stem. Studies of damage to the basal ganglia indicate a confused and unclear picture. After lesions, there may be exaggerated movements and poverty of movement, slow writhing movements (athetosis), involuntary jerky movements (tics and choreas) which do not impede the most delicate voluntary movement, and wild flinging movements (ballismus). What the critical nuclei are in these pathological instances is not clear, for the area of damage is often too widespread and unspecific. It is possible that the connections of the basal ganglia with the thalamus, cortex, lower midbrain nuclei, inferior olive, and the converging influences on the final common path

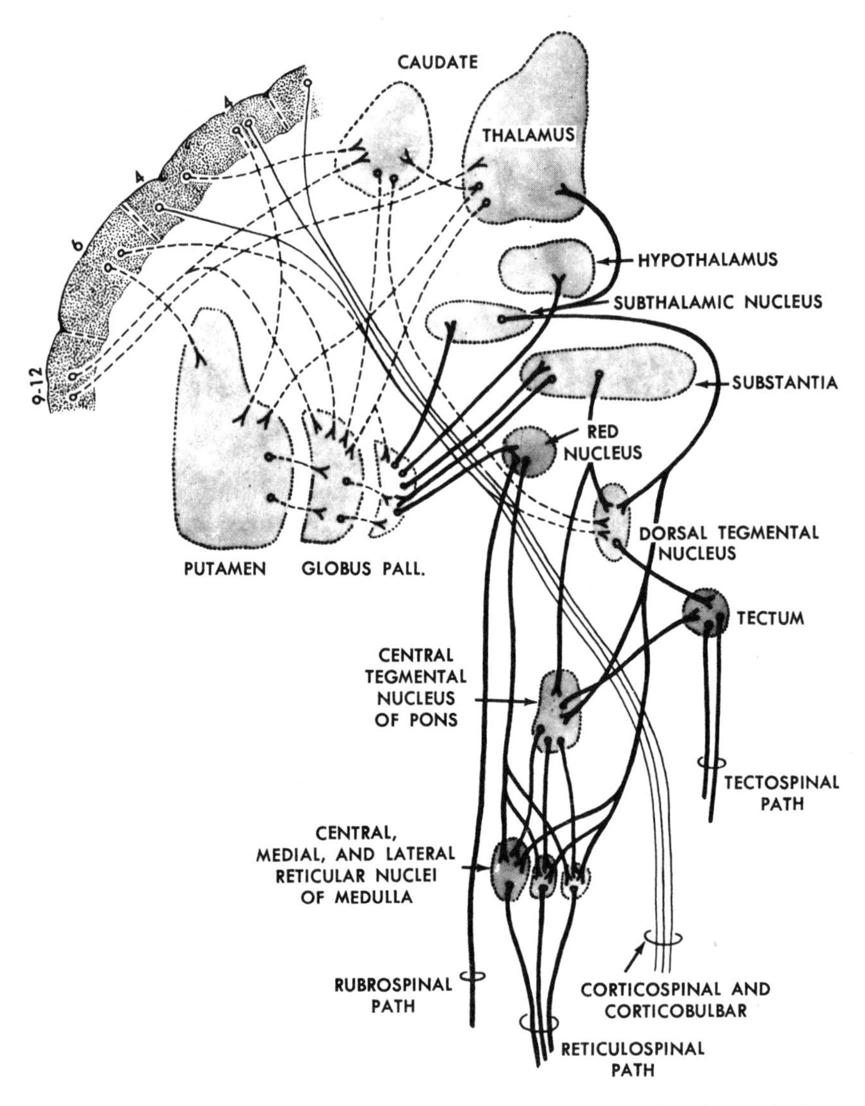

Drawing by Brenda Sutherland

Figure 22–3. Afferent and Efferent Pathways of the Extrapyramidal Motor System

are too complex to yield either a simple or a unitary answer. As large as the entire caudate nucleus is—head, body, and tail—we know almost nothing about its function except from a few experiments on the large head of the nucleus. A definite tail of the caudate nucleus may be lacking in rats, and is very attenuated in cats.

Experiments have shown that stimulation of the caudate results in slow turning movements of head and neck, while rotating movements such as those during fighting or mating may be brought about by stimulation of the basal ganglia. Occasional children born without cerebral cortex known as anencephalic monsters, and some born without basal ganglia, have shown gross movements of adjustment in postural reactions, yawning and stretching, and oral responses to fingers above reflex levels which must in part be carried out either by the basal ganglia or the subthalamic, nigral, or rubral nuclei.

It is evident then that an important role of the extrapyramidal system is the regulation of posture and locomotion. Large turning movements, as well as rolling in animals, are brought about by stimulation of the upper segments of this system. In this regulation of posture and locomotion the extrapyramidal system and the cerebellum must combine. Since they both synapse in rubral and reticular nuclei, such cooperation is facilitated. As was indicated under the section on the midbrain, the integrity of the nuclei ruber and subthalamicus are essential for normal and accurate locomotion, since they stimulate the contraction of the distal flexor muscles.

SOURCES AND ADDITIONAL READING

The CIBA Collection of Medical Illustrations Vol. I, *Nervous System.* CIBA Pharmaceutical Company, 1953.

Fulton, J., *Physiology of the Nervous System,* Chaps. 20, 21. New York: Oxford University Press, Inc., 1951.

Handbook of Physiology, Sec. I, Vol. II, Chaps. 34, 35. Washington, D. C.: American Physiol. Soc., 1960.

Ranson, S. W. and S. L. Clark, *The Anatomy of the Nervous System* (10th ed.), Chap. 19. Philadelphia: W. B. Saunders Company, 1959.

Riley, H. A., *An Atlas of the Basal Ganglia, Brain Stem, and the Spinal Cord.* New York: Hafner Publishing Co., Inc., 1960.

Walsh, G., *Physiology of the Nervous System,* Chap. 10, New York: Longmans Green & Co., Inc., 1959.

Twenty-three

BLOOD SUPPLY OF THE BRAIN AND CEREBROSPINAL FLUID

The nervous system is not an independent system, as some persons may have supposed, but is connected to the major sources of bodily metabolism and receives its nourishment therefrom. In fact the brain and spinal centers are particularly sensitive to any malfunctioning of the blood circulation, which picks up oxygen from the lungs, distributes it to nervous and other tissues, and removes carbon dioxide and other waste products. Nervous tissue in particular cannot continue to live for more than a very few minutes without blood supply, and the oxygen which it provides.

The blood supply of the brain and upper levels of the spinal cord comes from the internal carotid artery and vertebral artery for the brain, and from branches of the vertebral artery for the upper spinal cord. Lower levels of the cord receive their blood supply from vascular vessels in the thoracic, lumbar, and sacral regions. The internal carotid artery separates from the common carotid artery at the location of the carotid body. It ascends rostrally to enter the skull on the under surface of the brain, forward of the anterior-posterior midpoint, at the level of the optic chiasm. Here it branches to form the anterior and middle cerebral arteries. The anterior cerebral artery flows forward and upward, supplying by arterioles and capillaries the medial surface of the frontal lobes and the medial surface of the brain back to the preoccipital notch, and up over the medial edge of the superior brain surface. The middle cerebral artery, which is more extensive, moves laterally from the region of the chiasm, supplying the inferior portion of the frontal lobes and the frontal pole of the temporal lobe. (See Fig. 23–1.) Its main

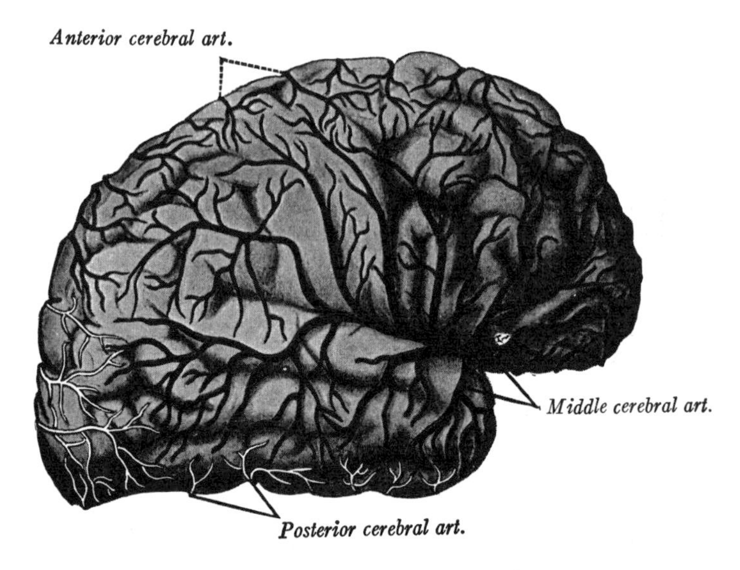

Source: S. W. Ranson and S. L. Clark, *The Anatomy of the Nervous System: Its Development and Function* (10th ed.; Philadelphia: W. B. Saunders Company, 1959), p. 79.

Figure 23–1. Arteries of the Lateral Surface of the Cerebral Hemispheres

branch moves laterally in the Sylvian fissure to spread widely over the lateral surfaces of the frontal, parietal, and temporal lobes. In this course it supplies branches to internal capsule and basal ganglia. It is this branch, called the lenticular striate artery, that is particularly susceptible to cerebral apoplexy (to be described in Chapter 24).

The vertebral arteries branch from the subclavian arteries and ascend through the foramina of the upper six cervical vertebrae, wind around the articular process of the atlas, and, now from behind, are able to enter the skull by the foramen magnum. Inside the skull the two vertebral arteries join to form the basilar artery, which follows the median cleft of the pons and brain stem until it branches into the posterior cerebral artery and the superior cerebellar artery just caudal to the pituitary and mammillary bodies. Before reaching its final branching the basilar artery supplies the cerebellum by means of the anterior inferior cerebellar artery, which serves mainly the anterior portion of its ventral surface, and the superior cerebellar artery, which curves back between the cerebrum and cerebellum to supply its superior surface. Before the vertebral arteries join to form the basilar, the posterior inferior cerebellar artery branches off to serve that portion of the cerebellum.

The posterior cerebral artery (see Fig. 23–2) forms the final division

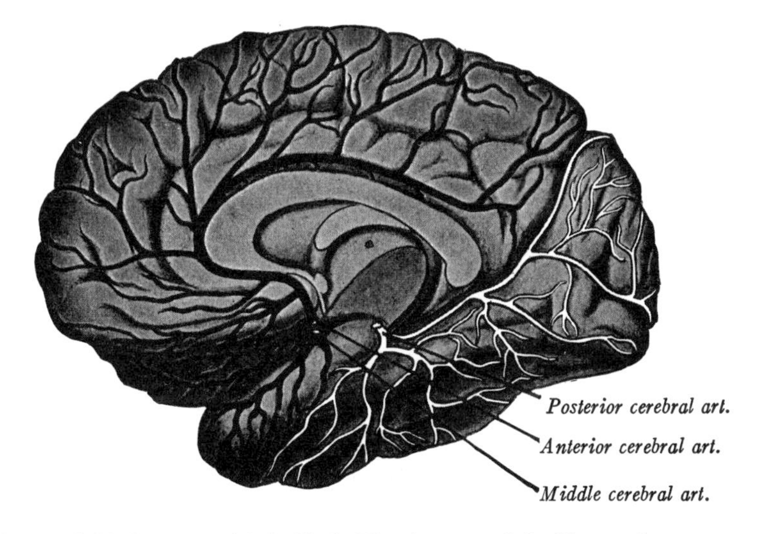

Source: S. W. Ranson and S. L. Clark, *The Anatomy of the Nervous System.*

Figure 23–2. Medial Brain Surface and Arteries Serving It

of the basilar artery and sweeps laterally and up around the brain stem to supply the inferior surface of the temporal lobe and the mesial surfaces of the occipital and temporal lobes, and to supply the adjacent superior and lateral cortical surfaces.

On the ventral surface of the brain the two divisions of internal carotid and basilar arteries are joined by small communicating branches, the posterior communicating arteries, and the two anterior cerebral arteries are joined by an anterior communicating artery. Thus there is formed around the optic chiasm and the pituitary a complete circle of blood vessels—named after its discoverer—the circle of Willis. (See Fig. 23–3.) This complete circle of blood vessels can cause difficulty when experimenters are trying to cut the optic chiasm in making a split-brain preparation.

The branchings of the main arterial supply described above become finer arterioles, and these by subsequent branchings form the fine capillaries through whose thin walls oxygen, carbon dioxide, nourishment, and waste products pass to keep in healthy condition the metabolism of the nervous cells and other structures. After the oxygen and nourishment have been taken up by the nerve cells, and the waste products given back to the blood stream, the capillary flow enters the venous system. The cerebral veins in general parallel the course of the arteries and will not be described in detail here. The brain cavity has, however, several large venous sinuses which should be mentioned. The cavernous sinus, just lateral to the optic chiasm, and the transverse sinus on the posterior floor of the skull serve the inferior brain vessels; the superior sagittal sinus provides a large venous reservoir which extends down part way into the midline sulcus dividing the two hemispheres.

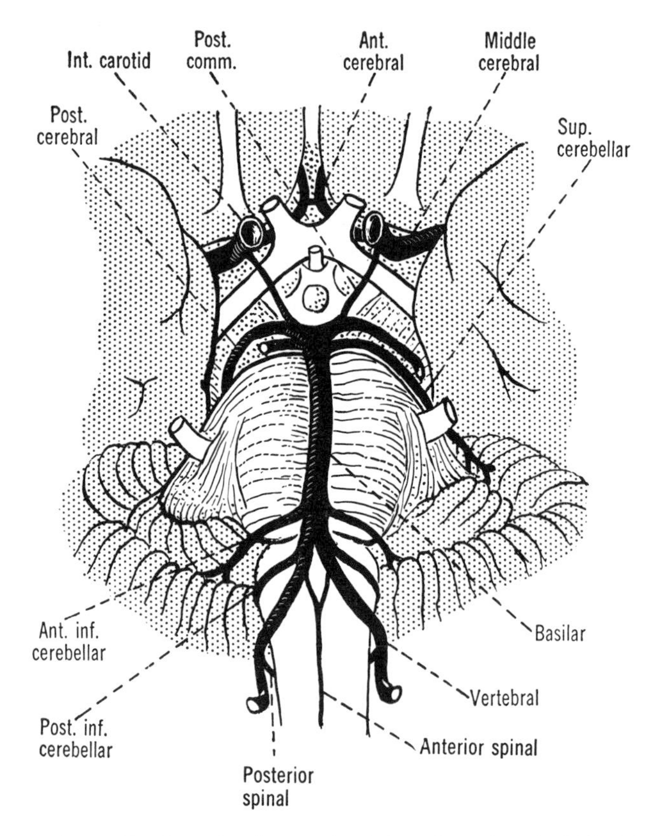

Source: Ernest Gardner, *Fundamentals of Neurology* (4th ed.; Philadelphia: W. B. Saunders Company, 1963), p. 42.

Figure 23–3. Arterial "Circle of Willis" on Base of Brain

CEREBROSPINAL FLUID

The cerebrospinal fluid is a blood plasma filtrate formed largely by the choroid plexuses in the ventricles. There are plexuses in both of the lateral ventricles, and in the III ventricle and IV ventricle. The cerebrospinal fluid fills the subarachnoid space between the dura mater and the pia mater over the entire central nervous system, as well as the ventricles and the central canal of the spinal cord. A slow circulation of the cerebrospinal fluid is maintained by the greater pressure at the choroid plexus, where it is formed, than at the arachnoid villi, where it is absorbed back into the venous system. The fluid circulates from the lateral ventricles to the 3rd ventricle, then through the cerebral aqueduct into the 4th ventricle. The 4th ventricle is continuous with the central canal of the spinal cord. In addition, the 4th ventricle has median and lateral apertures whereby the fluid flows into the subarachnoid space. It circulates in the subarachnoid space around the brain and spinal cord before being absorbed back into the venous system. For the details of cerebrospinal fluid circulation, see Fig. 23–4.

The cerebrospinal fluid, surrounding as it does the brain and spinal cord, provides an important cushioning effect to the nervous system from blows or accidents. In addition, the cerebrospinal fluid is important in disease. Cerebrospinal fluid may be tested for pressure or withdrawn for analysis of cell or electrolyte content, by a puncture by hypodermic needle below the end of the spinal cord; that is, at the 4th or 5th lumbar segment. This is known as the lumbar puncture. Increased cerebrospinal pressure may give evidence of tumors; the fluid may be tested for syphilitic or other infections. Procaine may be injected into the spinal cord for spinal anesthesia.

Whether the cerebrospinal fluid has an important part in the nutrition of the brain or in transfer of materials which result from metabolic activity of the brain and spinal cord is as yet uncertain. There is a definite barrier, known as the bloodbrain barrier between the blood circulation and the cerebrospinal fluid. The chemical compositions of the blood and cerebrospinal fluid are different in some respects, the latter being normally clear fluid and free of blood except after rupture of the walls which separate them. Large molecules of certain substances found in the blood stream are not supposed to be able to penetrate into the cerebrospinal fluid. The large protein molecules are of this type, especially those of RNA and DNA, which are recently thought to be involved in learning and memory.

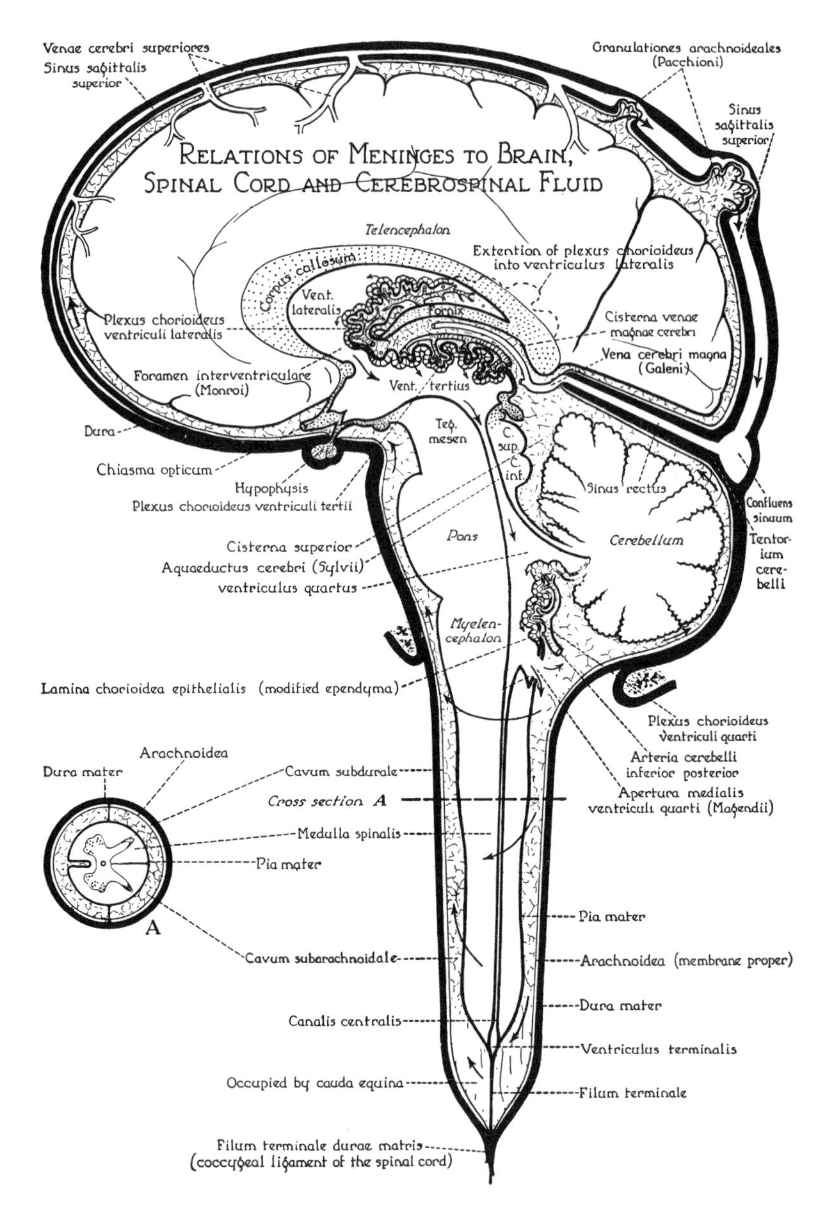

Source: Reprinted with permission of The Macmillan Company from *The Principal Nervous Pathways* (3d ed.) by Andrew Theodore Rasmussen. Copyright 1932, 1941, 1945 by The Macmillan Company. (Labeling altered slightly.)

Figure 23–4. Saggital View of Brain and Spinal Cord Showing Circulation of Cerebrospinal fluid

SOURCES AND ADDITIONAL READING

Gardner, E., *Fundamentals of Neurology,* Chap. 4. Philadelphia: W. B. Saunders Company, 1963.

Handbook of Physiology, Sec. I, Vol. III, Chaps. 60–62. Washington, D. C.: American Physiol. Soc., 1960.

The CIBA Collection of Medical Illustrations, Vol. I, *Nervous System.* CIBA Pharmaceutical Company, 1953.

Ranson, S. W. and S. L. Clark, *The Anatomy of the Nervous System* (10th ed.), Chap. 3. Philadelphia: W. B. Saunders Company, 1959.

Twenty-four

EFFECTS OF DISEASE, DESTRUCTION, AND DEGENERATION OF NERVOUS TISSUE ON BEHAVIOR

The nervous system functions remarkably smoothly during most of the life span of animals and man. However, accidents and disease can cause spectacular changes in both function and performance. The sudden decline, for instance, of the neighborhood trampolines was not unrelated to some severe accidents of both inexperienced and experienced trampoline users. In some instances, particularly inept falls have so twisted the vertebral column in the neck as to squeeze the spinal cord and result in nearly total paralysis from the neck down—some of the victims have never recovered. Likewise, accidents from shallow water diving or whip lash injuries in auto collisions give rise to jamming of the cervical cord and brain stem with similar resultant damage. It is important, then, in trying to understand nervous function to examine the effect of disease and destruction upon it.

DEGENERATION

The adult nerve cell cannot divide mitotically. The nervous system cannot, therefore, replace any cells which may be destroyed by accident, lack of blood supply, or disease processes. Some cells die under normal conditions during a life span. Nearly one-fourth of the neurons in the brain, cord, and peripheral ganglia are lost by the eighth or ninth decade of human life. This helps to explain the diminished sensitivity of touch, taste, or vision in old age, as well as tremors and weakness of the motor apparatus. While a neuron, once destroyed, cannot be reconstituted, the axonal processes of some cells, after being sectioned, can be restored and in favorable circumstances reconnect the neuron and the structure innervated. Cells and processes confined to the central nervous system generally do not survive the cutting of the axon.

When an axon in the peripheral nervous system is cut, there is a characteristic disappearance of the Nissl substance of the cell body, and its nucleus shifts toward the periphery of the cell. These changes are more severe the closer the cut is to the soma of the neuron, and are more noticeable in cells with abundant Nissl substance. When section of an axon occurs, the terminal parts beyond the cut swell for several days and then disintegrate and break up into platelets of unconnected tissue. The swelling and degeneration proceed from the terminal end toward the cut. If the axon is myelinated the myelin also breaks down in a few days. The neurilemma cells then multiply very rapidly and move into the degenerating tissue. They act as phagocytes in this process and ingest the disintegrating axis cylinder and myelin. All the remains of the axis and myelin are removed by phagocytosis, and only the rows of neurilemma cells formerly surrounding the myelin are left. For the illustration of degeneration and regeneration, see Fig. 24–1. Similar changes occur a short distance proximal of the cut; this is known as retrograde degeneration. The degenerating myelin differs chemically from the normal, and if treated with potassium dichromate will stain black with osmic acid. This reaction is utilized in the Marchi stain for degenerating fibers. The Nauta silver stain is now used also for this purpose.

After the neurilemma-derived phagocytes have cleaned up the degenerated axis and myelin a reverse process frequently takes place in the peripheral nervous system. Several weeks after the injury there is a gradual reconstruction of the cell, the nucleus moves back to a more central position, and the Nissl substance becomes reconstituted. In the

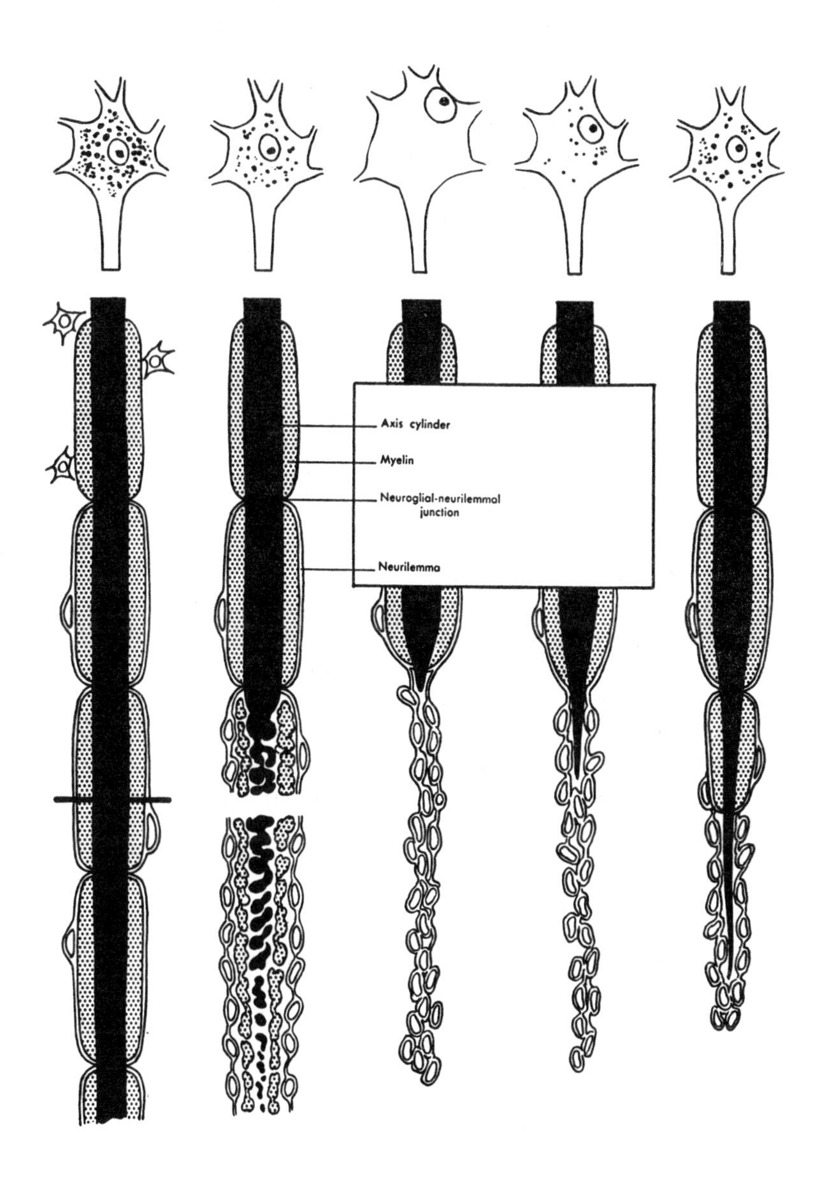

Source: Ernest Gardner, *Fundamentals of Neurology* (4th ed.; Philadelphia: W. B. Saunders Company, 1963), p. 82.

Figure 24–1. Schematic Representation of Degeneration of Myelinated Fibers

axon the severed tip above the cut begins to grow distally as a series of growing tips within the confines of the neurilemma sheath and cells. Such growth will not occur if the cell body does not survive and begin to reverse the chromatolysis of the Nissl substance. The axon regenerates at the rate of a few millimeters a day initially, and then more slowly. The myelin is formed around the axis cylinder by the activity of the neurilemma interacting with the axis cylinder. The neurilemma sheath, or Schwann cells which remain after degeneration, forms a tube down which the axis cylinder grows, and, if all circumstances are favorable, reestablishes synaptic contact with the structure previously innervated.

As already indicated, regeneration does not occur in the brain and spinal cord to any significant degree. The dense glial and collagenous scars which characterize central nervous system lesions are major factors in preventing regeneration, the scars acting as a block to distal outgrowth. Further, the lack of neurilemma in the central nervous system provides no core or tube for the axon tip to follow in its growth.

A peripheral nerve cut severs hundreds of fibers. Degeneration goes on at the same rate in all, but regeneration is faster in nonmyelinated than in myelinated fibers. At times there is a spread of axonal branching from neighboring nerve fiber to the denervated area, and this goes on at a faster rate than the regeneration. For this reason the reinnervation occurs much faster than regeneration alone would permit.

There is an amazing capacity for regeneration in cold-blooded animals. While regeneration is limited to the peripheral nervous system in birds and mammals, it is not so limited in fish, amphibia, and reptiles.

LESIONS

Damage to the nervous system, whether accidental or intentional, brings about major changes in nervous function. Ablation of the occipital poles of the rhesus monkey results in a blind animal except for some reflex reaction to visual stimuli. The same is true of the somesthetic receptive area, or the auditory receptive area. If, however, there is interruption of both voluntary and reflex reactions to visual stimulation, we may conclude that the damage has occurred between the eye and the reflex centers in the superior colliculi. In fact, the extent of damage which shows up in a clinical examination frequently indicates clearly where the lesion is. A lesion in a restricted area of motor cortex may result in paralysis of a hand or lower leg only. In experimental lesions it is possible to limit the cortical ablation so that in monkeys, for example, only the tail is paralyzed. As has already been indicated, lesions occurring in the internal capsule cause paralysis of various parts of the body in accordance with their location in the capsule. This type of lesion, occurring prior to decussation of the corticospinal fibers, affects the opposite side of the body. Among the major sites of lesions are the long ascending sensory and descending motor paths, and a number of the diseases to be considered later involve such lesions.

The occurrence of lesions in the nervous system frequently involves what has been named "release phenomena," the release showing the absence of a normal inhibitory control and the dominance of a facilitatory pathway. This release phenomenon is seen clearly in decerebrate, spinal animals where the extensor reflex is dominant. It is also seen when lesions occur in the basal ganglia. Lesions in the head of the caudate nucleus or putamen frequently result in coarse, irregular, jerky movements called the chorea syndrome, or tic. Lesions in the subthalamic nucleus may result in wild flinging movements known as ballismus. Similarly, intention tremor during voluntary activity occurs after lesions in the dentate nucleus of the cerebellum or its fiber connections to the nucleus ruber.

Both clinical and experimental lesions in parts of the nervous system have proved immensely valuable as a major means of identifying the functions of the various nuclei and fiber pathways.

SPINAL SHOCK

One of the most severe lesions which can occur in the nervous system is the complete section of the spinal cord or brain stem. Such section results in a severe depression of the normal reflex activity below the cut, as well as permanent loss of voluntary motor activity dependent on the ascending sensory information. The period of depressed activity varies with the species of animal. Frogs recover most of their reflex activity quickly, but dogs and cats may require days for recovery. In humans the recovery from shock is even slower. At the end of the period of shock the reflex activities begin to reappear. The animal responds to pain by withdrawal of a limb, the rectal and urinary reflexes resume activity, and the animal begins to function on a reflex level below the point of transection. But since the connection with the higher centers is lost, the reflex responses are frequently exaggerated. The flexor reflexes, which are initiated by higher voluntary centers, give way to an exaggerated extensor reflex pattern which is characteristic of decerebrate rigidity. For an example of this rigidity, see Fig. 24–2. A decerebrate

Source: Figure 4, Lewis J. Pollock and Loyal Davis, "The Reflex Activities of a Decerebrate Animal," *J. Comp. Neur., 50*: 384

Figure 24–2. Exaggerated Extensor Tonus of Decerebrate Rigidity

animal, properly supported from falling, may continue in a standing position for hours.

Several months after spinal section the withdrawal reflexes become exaggerated and spread to visceral and autonomic outflow. Thus vigorous scratching of the plantar surface of the foot results in extreme withdrawal, as one would expect. It also results in sweating and contraction of the bladder and rectum. The autonomic reflexes in man are more completely suppressed than are somatic reflexes. For the first month or two the skin is very dry and pink. It is warm and pink from vasodilation caused by paralysis of the vasoconstrictor mechanisms. Reflex sweating does not appear till the third month after the injury. The bladder and rectal functions are gravely interfered with by spinal transection, and the reflexes which allow control of evacuation are abolished. There is some return of reflex function after the third week. During the intervening period great care is needed in removal of urine and feces to avoid infection—stagnant urine which was not removed has led, at times, to peritonitis. If lower spinal centers are released from forebrain control in a monkey by snipping the descending fibers seriatim, the degree of shock is never as great as when all pathways are cut at once.

Many experimental transections are supratentorial in the dog or cat for a particular reason. The centers for respiration are located in the medulla, and unless these are kept connected to the cord and the cranial nerves the animal will die shortly from asphyxiation.

SECTION OF CORPUS CALLOSUM

Transection of the corpus callosum separates the two hemispheres of the cerebral cortex. It will be remembered that this broad band of fibers connects homologous points in the two hemispheres. Under normal conditions cats with an intact callosum cannot be taught conflicting patterns of discrimination with the two eyes trained separately. Animals with section of the callosum and the optic chiasm, however, can perform conflicting discriminations easily. Furthermore there is no sign of difficulty or evidence of conflict in learning the conflicting patterns. But suppression of hemispheric interplay by callosal section does not erase any already impressed training or transfer. And because the section of the callosum affects both hemispheres equally, the operation does not upset their dynamic balance or interfere with synergic movements and rhythmic activities.

EFFECT OF DISEASE ON NERVOUS FUNCTION

A number of well known diseases involve interference with the functioning of the nervous system, or have a serious effect upon its normal operation.

Poliomyelitis

Poliomyelitis is caused by a virus which brings about gradual destruction of parts of the nervous system. The virus is found all over the world, and the risk of the bulbar form of this disease is increased by tonsillectomies in the summer and early fall.

The changes in the nervous system are brought about by minute capillary hemorrhage and the infiltration of lymphocytes which choke the small blood vessels. The vascular deficit affects particularly the anterior horn cells in the lumbar and cervical enlargements which provide innervation to arms and legs. In this disease the motor neurons in the anterior horn of the spinal cord show progressive chromatolysis and shrinking of the nuclei. This process is illustrated in Fig. 24–3. The cell

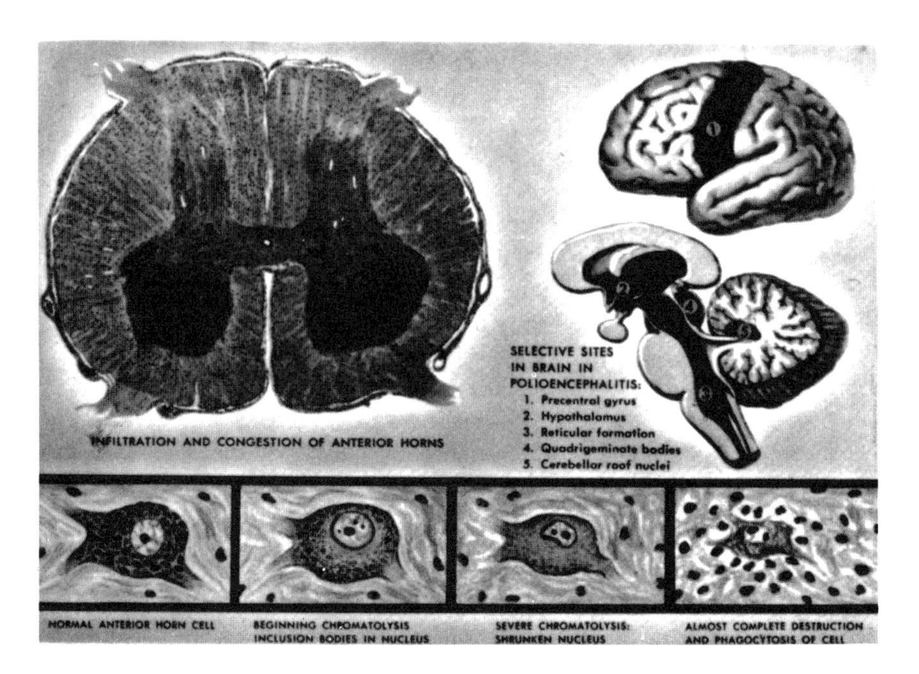

Source: *The CIBA Collection of Medical Illustrations* by Frank H. Netter, M.D. Copyright CIBA. Vol. I, *Nervous System* (Summit, N. J.: CIBA Pharmaceutical Company, 1953), Plate 93.

Figure 24–3. Sites of Anterior Poliomyelitis Attack and Chromatolysis of the Motor Neuron

then is in process of a degeneration which extends to the axonal fibers going out to particular muscle groups. Finally the motor neurons disappear, and paralysis occurs in the muscles previously innervated by them.

The disease has three forms which are progressively more serious:

1. *Abortive*—The onset is sudden, the symptoms being cough and gastrointestinal complaint, followed by restlessness or somnolence and a stiff neck. This stage lasts for only a few days and is followed by either complete recovery or the development of the paralytic form.

2. *Paralytic*—The person with this form is acutely ill, with symptoms of headache, stiff neck, pain and tender muscles, and enlarged spleen and lymph nodes. Paralysis follows in a few days after the above symptoms, *as the neuron cannot stand anoxia* for more than a short while.

The paralysis involves mainly the lower limbs, less often the arms, rarely the trunk or sphincters. The spinal fluid shows a substantial increase in the number of lymphocytes.

3. *Bulbar*—In this form the lesions or degeneration occurs at levels above the spinal cord. The degeneration may occur in the motor area of the cortex, or in the basal ganglia, hypothalamus, reticular formation, colliculi, or cerebellar nuclei. This form shows ocular or facial palsy, speech disturbance, and difficulty in swallowing. Paresis of diaphragm, neck, intercostal muscles, and abdominal muscles is less frequent, but when it does occur it frequently results in respiratory arrest, which is obviously always fatal. This form clearly affects the motor nuclei of the cranial nerves rather than anterior horn cells. Its fatality rate may run as high as 25 percent. This, then, is the fatal form of the disease, whereas the other forms are paralytic or even less severe.

Hypertensive Apoplexy

Many of the diseases which affect the functioning of the nervous system are of vascular origin. One of the best known of these is hypertensive apoplexy. In general apoplexy is an effusion of blood into brain tissue brought about by a rupture of the vascular wall. The rupture may occur at any time but is more common after violent exertion, traumatic experience, or emotional tension. The rupture also may occur during sleep. After the age of 40 apoplexy is a common cause of death. Anything which elevates blood pressure, such as repressed drives or anxieties, will result in vascular hypertension which may invite rupture at a weak spot. This disease shows two forms, benign and malignant:

1. *Benign*—The vascular ruptures are mild and infrequent. The terminal arterioles become deficient in blood and minor hemorrhages occur. The patient complains of faintness, dizziness, headache, and forgetfulness. Later there may be disturbances of motor, sensory, or speech function. Restoration of function follows improved cerebral circulation. Vascular scars of this benign form are found in many persons who develop the malignant form.

2. *Malignant*—This may occur years or months after the mild form. The vascular rupture is explosive. See Fig. 24–4 for the most frequent locations. It may displace and destroy parts of the internal capsule, causing paralysis of muscle groups or of a whole side. If the rupture is into the ventricles it is rapidly fatal. The patient is unconscious, with death or recovery frequently in 36 hours. There may be facial weakness or

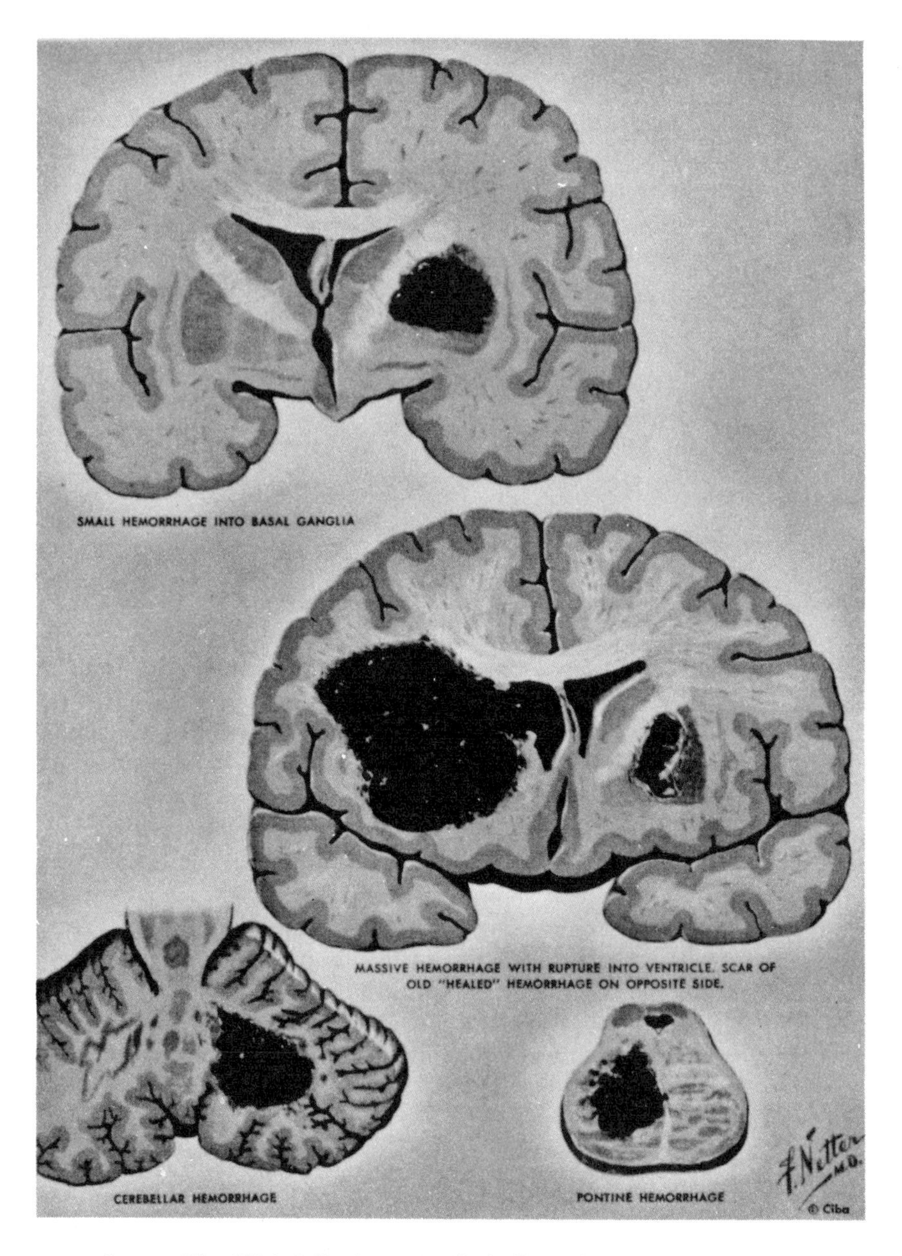

Source: *The CIBA Collection of Medical Illustrations* by Frank H. Netter, M.D. Copyright CIBA. Vol. I, *Nervous System*, Plate 86.

Figure 24–4. Effusion of Blood in Hypertensive Apoplexy

aphasia and, as was indicated in the discussion of the internal capsule, the paralysis may point to the location of the hemorrhage. Recovery is slow, requiring from six to eight weeks for resumption of function; while recovery from aphasias may never be complete. In patients with extreme hypertension the incidence of apoplexy may be substantially reduced by bilateral section of the sympathetic ganglion chain supplying the smooth muscles of the small blood vessels.

Multiple Sclerosis

Multiple sclerosis is a disease of unknown origin which occurs mainly in young people. It is most common among females from age 13 to 30, and is found most frequently in cool, moist areas of the temperate zone. The disease begins with destruction of the myelin sheath, the insulating fatty covering over the nerve fiber. With removal of the myelin the nerve fiber can still transmit impulses, but imperfectly as compared to normal healthy conditions. As the disease progresses the nerve fiber itself degenerates, leaving sclerotic *plaques,* or scars, in various parts of the nervous system. These plaques are found most frequently in the cervical enlargement, the pons, the cerebellum, the basal ganglia, and the medulla, as well as the spinal cord. They are customarily found in several places in the same patient, hence the term multiple. The disease shows periods of decline and periods of recovery, but because nervous tissue is destroyed in both the motor and sensory pathways there is a slow, progressive deterioration, sometimes for 20 to 30 years. The ataxic and spastic gait which is common among patients with multiple sclerosis is understandable if one reviews the locations of the sclerotic plaques. In many patients the degeneration occurs in the posterior columns of the spinal cord, which convey muscle sense and two-point touch to the brain. In others the lesion may occur in the medullary pyramids or cerebral peduncle, which are on the corticospinal motor pathway for muscular control. The character and location of the sclerotic plaques can be seen in Fig. 24–5. In both cases, in late stages of the disease, the pathways for information and for motor control are lost. Abnormalities of gait and movement are therefore inevitable. In the advanced stages the symptoms of tremor, nystagmus, and scanning speech are common. In the last stages, so much nervous tissue is destroyed that there is deterioration of mind and personality. Recent clinical evidence indicates a possible link between the measles virus and multiple sclerosis. A large percentage of sclerosis patients in one study showed measles antibodies in the spinal fluid.

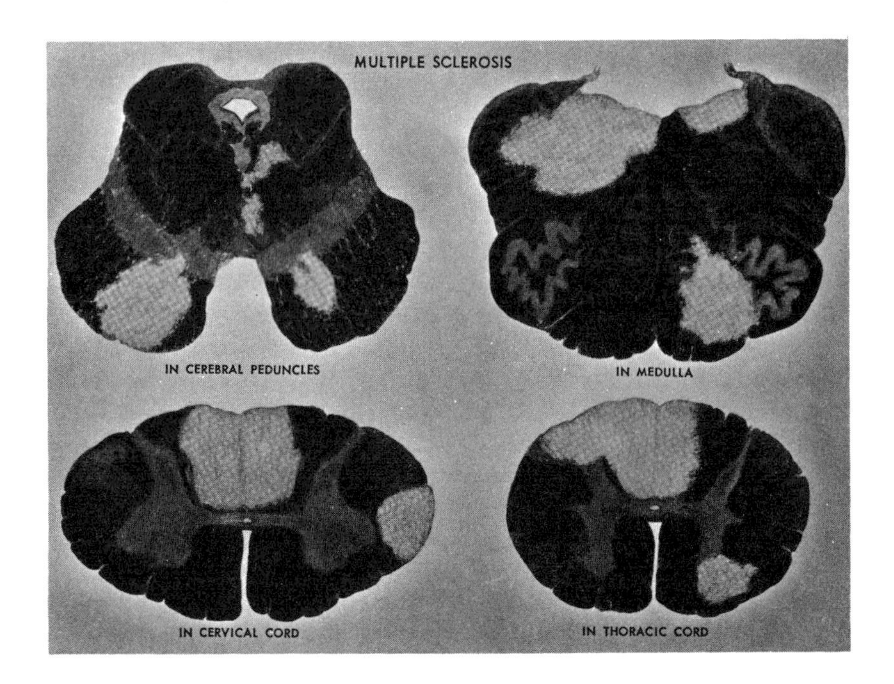

Source: *The CIBA Collection of Medical Illustrations* by Frank H. Netter, M.D. Copyright CIBA. Vol. I, *Nervous System*, Plate 104.

Figure 24–5. Character and Location of Sclerotic Plaques in Multiple Sclerosis

Neurosyphilis

Neurosyphilis is the response of the brain and spinal cord to the syphilitic spirochete. This disease causes inflammation of nerve cells and interstitial tissue, producing small lymphocytes as well as giant cells. These developments lead to degenerative lesions which frequently occur in the posterior columns of the cord, which is the cortical pathway for muscle sense. It also affects the optic nerve, resulting in impaired vision. In addition, the knee and ankle jerk are absent. *Tabes dorsalis* sequel to syphilitic infection, which shows the above characteristics, occurs predominantly in males at a period of 5 to 15 years after the primary infection.

General paresis, which is the other form taken by the disease, is characterized by degeneration of the brain and meninges with atrophy of cortical cells. It is also accompanied by proliferation of astrocytes which replace nerve cells. This form of the disease has a particular affinity for the frontal lobes. It shows symptoms of headache, personality changes, delusions of grandeur, and disturbed emotional responses. It is a progressive disease ending in total dementia.

Brain Tumors

It is impossible to describe the neural involvement of all types of tumors. The gliomas, which are the largest group, are therefore selected for presentation here.

The cardinal signs of brain tumor (gliomas) such as headache, vomiting, and papilledema—are due to increased intracranial pressure. The two most critical forms of gliomas are astrocytoma and glioblastoma (spongioblastoma).

1. *Astrocytoma* is a slow growing tumor, well differentiated from adjacent brain tissue. It accounts for 40 percent of all gliomas, and they are found most frequently in the lateral cerebellar lobes of children or temporal or frontal lobes of adults. The disturbed brain functions are caused by both intracranial pressure and displaced brain structures. Because of the tumor's slow growth the normal signs of headaches, etc. from increased pressure may be postponed for some time. The brain adjusts itself to the tumor growth so that signs of increased intracranial pressure do not show up until the tumor is well advanced. Surgical removal provides much relief; irradiation is of little benefit.

2. *Glioblastoma. Glioblastoma multiforme* is the most malignant form of this disease and occurs exclusively in the cerebral hemispheres. It occurs more often from 40 to 55 years of age than at any other period. It originates in the cerebral white matter, where the cells multiply rapidly. They advance to the cortical surface, where the gyri and intervening fissures are pushed aside and flattened, while the surface blood vessels are displaced. The rapid growth results in cerebral edema, areas of degeneration, and scattered hemorrhages. The clinical picture changes rapidly with increased intracranial pressure to show sudden convulsions, mental and intellectual impairment, followed by paralysis and coma. Surgical removal only infrequently results in complete recovery.

Herniation of Lumbar Intervertebral Discs

Many cases that in earlier years were called lumbago or sciatica have been shown to be due to herniation of intervertebral discs. The cause of this difficulty is usually trauma or injury or violent exertion. A bulge, or herniation, occurs at the weakest point of the joint capsule, resulting in back pain from pressure on the nerve roots. If the herniation fails to improve with rest, the continued pressure and irritation may result in leg pain, numbness, and "sciatica." This stage is accompanied by a tilt of the trunk and partial disability. If the compression is unrelieved and the pressure on the nerve roots increases, the sciatic nerve pain becomes intense and the patient may become seriously disabled. If unrelieved, this condition may lead to muscle atrophy and paralysis. Bed rest, traction, massage, and exercise frequently give much relief. In extreme instances an interlaminar operation may be necessary, to remove the protruding disc, or the ruptured parts of it.

This condition may be simulated by congenital defects or by the presence of tumors, so that care is needed in its diagnosis.

Paralysis Agitans

Paralysis agitans, which is characterized by tremor of resting muscles, lack of facial expression, and a flexed body attitude, is classified as senile if occurring after 50 years of age. Behaviorally the patients exhibit a shuffling gait, a bent and rigid posture together with head shaking and "pill rolling" tremors of the fingers. Another form of the disease affecting young persons but with similar behavioral manifestations is called "juvenile" or "encephalitic." Most cases of the encephalitic form show prior encephalitis or influenza or recurrent fevers. Paralysis agitans in either form is a progressive disease slowly resulting in weakened muscles; eventually the patient is incapacitated.

In all cases of paralysis agitans there is disease and damage to the basal ganglia. The disease affects chiefly the caudate, putamen, globus pallidus, and substantia nigra. While these parts are affected most, all parts of the basal ganglia system are affected or diseased to some degree. In terms of the connected stages which have been shown to be characteristic of the basal ganglia system, this is easily understood. A lesion at any synaptic point interrupts the motor control.

Degenerative changes are prominent in the senile form so that the motor cells of the basal ganglia disappear, being replaced by glial cells. There is also much demyelination. In the encephalitic form the cell loss occurs as a result more frequently of infiltration of the brain tissue by lymphocytes. This infiltration gives rise to degenerative changes similar to those found in the senile form. Either form of paralysis agitans is a progressive disease with no real cure. A patient may find relief from drugs and rest, since fatigue exacerbates the disease condition. In the end, after many years, death usually comes from some other disease condition.

Vasospasm— (Raynaud's disease)

Raynaud's disease is a disorder of the peripheral vascular system. The disorder consists in a painful paroxysm of cutaneous vasoconstriction. In this vasospasm the caliber of the peripheral blood vessels is greatly reduced from their normal size. If no relief from this excessive constriction is provided, the blood flow may be restricted for a period sufficient to result in gangrene.

This disease affects most frequently the fine blood vessels in the fingers and toes. In persons susceptible to it, the paroxysm is usually brought on by exposure to intensive cold or emotional stress. In addition, long continued and unrelieved emotional stress alone can have similar results.

It is not certain that vasospasm results from excessive discharge of the sympathetic division of the autonomic nervous system, although the initiation by emotional stress would implicate the sympathetic impulses. Vasospasm may be reduced to allow near normal blood flow by a change of climate or reduction of tension. Nevertheless, when no further relaxation of the smooth muscles served by the vasoconstrictor fibers is possible, surgical relief is the rational procedure. Since impulses in the sympathetic fibers regulate vasoconstriction of the cutaneous vessels, surgical interruption of these fibers increases the flow of blood through the skin. The surgical procedure consists in transection of the sympathetic fibers in the preganglionic or postganglionic segment. On occasion the postganglionic section results in denervation sensitivity to epinephrine, which is usually produced as a result of both cold and emotional stress. This hypersensitivity to epinephrine may result in severe vasospasm even after the operation. The indicated treatment then is preganglionic section, severing the preganglionic fibers in the upper thoracic levels for the hand and in the upper lumbar levels for the feet. Such treatment may give the relief that is needed for normal activity. In chronic cases of Raynaud's disease anatomical changes in the blood vessels may eventually prevent dilation of the arterioles, even in the absence of vasoconstrictor nerves. In such cases the operation on the sympathetic fibers is of no value or relief.

Other Pathological Conditions

Other pathological conditions which affect the nervous system could have been included. Several of these have been omitted either because of vagueness in the description of the causative agent, or because the term covered so many different disease conditions. Encephalitis, for instance, usually involves inflammation of the brain but also includes forms caused by poison or hemorrhage. Cerebral palsy is a term too broad for limited description, as it is defined as "any one of a group of conditions affecting control of the motor system due to lesions in various parts of the nervous system, and arising usually as a result of birth injury or congenital defect." Epilepsy or other convulsive states also could have been described. But here again, no clear pathological changes in the nervous system can be adduced in all cases. Abnormalities are seen in the electroencephalogram (EEG), but even changes in the pattern of brain waves are not uniformly found. The most nearly uniform condition associated with epileptic attack is a shift from an acid to an alkaline balance in the cerebral cortex. But it does not seem certain that such a shift occurs in every instance of seizure, or is progressively more striking in the cases of *grand mal* than in those of *petit mal.*

SOURCES AND ADDITIONAL READING

The CIBA Collection of Medical Illustrations, Vol. I, *Nervous System.* CIBA Pharmaceutical Company, 1953.

De Jong, R., *The Neurological Examination* (2nd ed.). Hoeber-Harper, 1958.

Isaacson, R. L., ed., *Basic Readings in Neuropsychology.* New York: Harper & Row, Publishers, 1964.

Ranson, S. W. and S. L. Clark, *The Anatomy of the Nervous System* (10th ed.), Chap. 21. Philadelphia: W. B. Saunders Company, 1959.

Ruch, T. and J. Fulton, *Medical Physiology and Biophysics* (18th ed.), Chap. 7. Philadelphia: W. B. Saunders Company, 1961. (See 19th ed., Chap. 8.)

Twenty-five

CONCLUSION

The student who has perused this volume thus far will have seen a number of aspects of the nervous system unfold in connected sequential order. Information about internal or external conditions affecting an animal's welfare begins in the delicate sensory receptors in the skin, in muscle and tendon, in the head, and in internal organs. The transduction of these external or internal influences, light rays, or sound waves, etc. into coded nervous impulses brings this datum of environmental information into the transmission and conduction system of a connected network of nerve cells.

At the level of spinal reflexes many responses and adjustments to the incoming information are possible. Avoidance of pain, elaborate posturing of urination and defecation, and even a part of the coordinated movements essential to copulation are all part of this reflex range of activity. When, however, reflex reaction is no longer adequate for survival or other strong motivation, the other levels of the nervous system are brought into play. The spinal pathways from the body lead upward to a number of coordinating centers of first magnitude. The medulla, just above the spinal cord, is dominated by the visceral centers for controlling and modulating heart beat and respiration. It also provides an avenue of passage for the nerve bundles to the cerebellum and other higher centers. The cerebellum should be considered along with equilibrium and proprioception, since it coordinates both, as well as initiating the gamma efferent system. With its six channels of input the cerebellum monitors and modulates most of the automatic body and muscle movements, including muscle tone. Intimately related to cerebellar function is the pons, since its basilar portion contributes the cortical component to the cerebellar functions. The pons is also an important center for the auditory pathways and reflexes. The midbrain, which connects with the pons, is dominated on the dorsal surface by the inferior and superior colliculi, reflex centers for hearing and vision respectively. In its ventral portion the midbrain contains components of the motor systems in the cerebral peduncles, the red nucleus, and the substantia nigra.

Feeding into the thalamus, rostral of the midbrain, are two very important distance receptors—vision and hearing. The other distance receptor, olfaction, is laid down before the thalamus develops, and has a separate series of connections which provide part of the basic data to which the limbic system reacts. The thalamus is a most important integrating center. It has connections with the hypothalamus, limbic system, and lower centers; it has connections with the basal ganglia for thalamic reflexes; and perhaps most important of all are its interactions with and regulatory influences upon the cerebal cortex. It is the last sensory relay station to cerebral cortex. Articulating into the thalamic complex in its ascending activity is the reticular formation of the brain stem, which is important in sleep-wakefulness, alertness, and attention. In addition the reticular formation is an important component in extrapyramidal motor activity.

The hypothalamus and the autonomic nervous system join together in the homeostatic reactions of the organism in relation to fear, hunger, rage, blood pressure and volume, and temperature regulation. It is because of this joint activity that the hypothalamus is called the head ganglion of the autonomic system. One of the more complex systems which connect to the hypothalamus is the limbic system. This system is concerned partly with motivational reinforcement of behavioral patterns. Perhaps for this reason, it includes that portion, the hippocampus, which is essential for the fixing of present experience in memory.

The cerebral cortex, as the highest coordinating center in mammals, dominates all other nervous activity and makes other systems ordinarily subordinate to it. On the basis of this supremely plastic organ, man has developed language and other higher mental processes. Much of this expanding knowledge of cortical function has come as a result of newer methods of study. Cortical ablation and lesions have given way to intracellular recording and stimulation, both electrical and chemical. New techniques, comparable in impact to electron microscopy and electroencephalography, may open up areas of information about the nervous system of which we are, at present, ignorant. By such new methods the complex processes of language and visual interpretations may become clearer, although certainly not less complex.

Still in the future is knowledge about neural integration and the coding of information. Perhaps these may be illuminated by increasing information about protein synthesis, as in RNA or DNA, which have proved so critical in establishing the genetic pattern. Or the correct theory may depend on the awesome complexity of the cerebral cortex, as in vision, where the geniculates and the occipital cortex provide many times the complexity of interconnections that was believed possible a decade ago.

Some people have thought that the new field of psychocybernetics might provide some important answers. It seems doubtful, however, whether a mechanical study of feedback systems can provide useful information about the nervous systems. Computer engineers would like to know, for their own use, how the nervous system carries out its complicated and intricate feedback of information, and even of attitude and intention. Whatever the future holds in new information about nervous function, a thorough understanding of the principal psychological processes, auditory and language deficit, clinical behavior anomalies, and many other attributes of human and animal behavior cannot be developed or maintained without a knowledge of nervous function and nervous integration.

Glossary

Ablation—Removal of tissue, by cutting, cauterization, or by aspiration.

Absolute refractory period—The brief period following excitation of a neuron during which no response can be evoked.

Accommodation—Change in shape of the lens for sharp focus at different distances.

Acetylcholine—Chemical transmitter substance at some neuromuscular and synaptic endings.

Acuity—Fineness of sensory discrimination.

Adaptation—Reduction in sensory response as a result of continuous stimulation.

Adrenal cortex—Outer layers of adrenal glands, secreting steroids.

Adrenal glands—Endocrine glands situated above the kidneys.

Adrenalin—Hormone of the adrenal medulla; epinephrine.

Adrenal medulla—Endocrine gland separate from the cortex; secretes epinephrine and norepinephrine.

Adrenergic—Adjective applied to substances or nerve endings which produce the effect of adrenalin, or which respond to it.

Afferent—Conducting of nervous impulse from periphery centralward, for example from sensory ending to the CNS into a nucleus, opposed to efferent.

Agnosia—Inability to recognize objects, as visual agnosia.

Ampulla—Enlargement of the semicircular canals containing the vestibular receptor cells.

Anion—The negative ion, which moves toward the positive pole.

Annulospiral ending—Receptor in muscle spindle, for stretch.

Anosmia—Inability to smell one or more substances.

Anoxia—Oxygen deprivation.

ANS—Autonomic nervous system.

Antidiuretic hormone—Hormone of the posterior pituitary, inhibiting excretion of urine.

Antidromic—Nerve impulse moving from axon to cell body, or opposite to normal direction; discharge of cell body through excitation of axon rather than dendrites.

Aphasia—Language deficit in recognition or production.

Aqueous humor—Fluid which fills space between cornea and lens of eye.

Arachnoid—Delicate, cobweb-like meningeal layer, containing blood vessels.

Archicerebellum—Oldest part of the cerebellum.

Astrocyte—Neurological cell of star shape.

Auditory ossicles—Three small bones of middle ear, connecting tympanum to oval window.

Autonomic nervous system (ANS)—That portion of nervous system innervating internal organs, smooth muscles, and glands.

Axon—Neuronal fiber conducting impulse away from cell body to other neurons or glands, or to muscle end plate.

Basal ganglia—Caudate nucleus, putamen, and globus pallidus.

Beta rhythm—Oscillations in EEG of about 18-30 per second.

Binaural—Both ears, as binaural stimulation.

Bipolar cells—Cells in retina connecting rods and cones with ganglion cells.

Brain—CNS above the level of spinal cord, and enclosed in cranial vault.

Brain stem—The brain exclusive of cerebral and cerebellar hemispheres.

Brightness—Light-dark aspect of visual sensation.

Cation—The positive ion, which moves toward the negative pole.

Cauda equina—Bundle of lumbar and sacral spinal nerves, below end of spinal cord; resembles horse's tail.

Caudal—Toward tail end of animal.

Central nervous system (CNS)—Portions of nervous system lying within skull and spinal column.

Cerebellum—Coordinating center for posture and equilibrium, situated above pons and medulla.

Cerebral cortex—Superficial layers of cerebral hemispheres.

Cerebrum—Most dorsal and rostral parts of brain, above the level of thalamus and basal ganglia.

Chiasm—Crossing of visual fibers from nasal retina only. Juncture of optic fibers from the two eyes on inferior brain surface.

Cholinergic—Substances or nerve endings whose effects are mediated by acetylcholine.

Cholinesterase—Enzyme which breaks down acetylcholine.

Choroid—Middle coat of eye, containing blood vessels.

Choroid plexus—Vascular structures in ventricle of brain which secrete cerebrospinal fluid.

Chromatolysis—Loss of Nissl substance in neuron cell body.

Ciliary muscle—Internal eye muscle which changes shape of lens.

CNS—Central nervous system.

Cochlea—Auditory portion of inner ear.

Colliculi—Four prominences on dorsal surface of midbrain, the more rostral called superior, the more caudal inferior.
Complementary colors—Colors which produce gray when mixed.
Cone—Receptor for color and daylight vision.
Convergence—Turning eyes inward, to focus on near object.
Cornea—The front, outer coat of eye, transparent to light.
Crista—Bell shaped mass of receptor cells in ampulla of semicircular canals.
Cupula—Gelatinous mass covering the crista of semicircular canals.
Curare—Drug which blocks neuromuscular transmission, and paralyzes striated muscle.
Cutaneous—Pertaining to the skin, and superficial layers of body surface.

Decerebrate rigidity—Extreme extensor tonus following section of brain stem.
Delta rhythm—Slow rhythm in EEG, characteristic of sleep.
Dendrite—Fiber conducting toward the cell body.
Dermatome—Skin area supplied by single spinal nerve.
Diabetes insipidus—Inability to retain body fluids, through excessive excretion by kidneys.
Diencephalon—Rostralmost part of brain stem, thalamus, hypothalamus, and basal ganglia.
Dorsal—Toward the upper surface; toward the back in four-footed animals.
Dorsal root—Bundle of afferent nerve fibers entering the dorsal or posterior spinal cord.
Dorsal root ganglion—Enlargement of dorsal root by cell bodies of afferent neurons.
Dromic— (Nerve impulse) moving from dendrites to cell body to axon.
Dura mater—Tough opaque membrane between brain and skull; the outermost of three layers investing the brain and spinal cord.

Ear, inner—Part of ear set in skull, containing cochlea and vestibular organ.
Ear, middle—Chamber between eardrum and inner ear, containing the ossicles.
EEG—Electroencephalogram.
Efferent—Conducting nervous impulses away from a nucleus, as from spinal cord to muscle.
Electroencephalogram (EEG)—Recording of electrical activity of brain.
Endocrine gland—Gland which secretes hormone into the blood stream.
Endolymph—Liquid filling the cochlea and vestibular organs.
Epilepsy—Convulsive disorder frequently with loss of consciousness and change in EEG pattern.
Epinephrine—Hormone of the adrenal medulla; adrenalin.
Eustachian tube—Tube connecting middle ear and throat.
Excitation—Response to stimulation, opposite of inhibition.
Extensor—Muscle or movement which extends a part of body.
External auditory meatus—Outer ear, channel for sound waves to reach eardrum.
Extrapyramidal—Motor pathways or nuclei not in pyramidal system.

Fasciculus—Bundle of nerve fibers, usually with common function.

Final common path—Single connection to muscle by way of motor neuron, convergent influence upon final efferent segment.

Flexion reflex—Reflex bending of limb.

Flexor—Muscle or movement which bends a joint.

Flower spray ending—Receptor in muscle spindle.

Fovea—Central depression in retina; spot of most accurate vision.

Funiculus—One of the segments of white matter of spinal cord, as posterior, lateral, and anterior.

Ganglion—Group of nerve cells, usually outside the CNS.

Ganglion cells—Third-order neurons in retina; their axons form optic nerve.

Gastrointestinal tract—Digestive tract from mouth to anus.

Gland—Organ specialized for secretion.

Gray matter—Cell bodies and unmyelinated parts of the CNS which appear pink in live animals.

Gyrus—Outward fold of brain surface between adjacent fissures.

Harmonics—Overtones, multiples or submultiples of fundamental tone.

Homeostasis—Maintenance of various kinds of internal equilibrium, or balance between opposing systems, chemical or neural.

Hormone—Chemical substance secreted in an endocrine gland.

Hue—Color dimension of visual sensation.

Hypoglycemia—Blood sugar level which is below normal.

Hypophysis—Pituitary gland.

Hypothalamus—Most ventral part of diencephalon, beneath the thalamus.

Incus—Intermediate middle ear ossicle; the "anvil."

Inhibition—Prevention of response to stimulation; opposite of excitation.

Iodopsin—Photosensitive pigment in cones of retina.

Iris—Plates of muscles surrounding pupil of the eye and controlling its size.

Kinesthesis—Muscle-tendon-joint sense.

Knee jerk—Patellar reflex, initiated by sharp tap on patellar tendon beneath knee cap.

Labyrinth—Intricate inner ear structure.

Lemniscus—Band of second-order neurons carrying sensory information to thalamus.

Lens—Transparent, adjustable structure within the eye which focuses light rays on retina.

Lesion—Delimited destruction of nervous tissue.

Leucotomy—Removal of delimited core under cortical tissue.

Lobectomy—Excision of a lobe.

Lobotomy—Incision into a lobe, cutting the fibers.

Macula—Receptor region in saccule and utricle.

Malleus—Auditory ossicle next to tympanum; the "hammer."

Medulla oblongata—Portion of brain stem next above spinal cord.

Meissner's corpuscle—Encapsulated end organ for touch in the skin.

Membrane, basilar—Membraneous part of spiral cochlea on which rests the organ of Corti.

Membrane, Reissner's—Thin membrane dividing scala media from scala tympani, in cochlea.

Membrane, tectorial—Gelatinous structure overlaying hair cells of organ of Corti.

Micron (μ)—Millionth part of a meter, one thousandth of a millimeter.

Microtome—Adjustable sliding knife used to cut thin microscope sections for slides.

Midbrain—Portion of brain stem between pons and thalamus.

Millimicron ($m\mu$)—Millionth part of a millimeter.

Modalities—Different sensory modes or departments, for example vision, audition.

Motor nuclei—Group of efferent cell bodies within the CNS.

Motor unit—Single efferent nerve fiber and associated muscle fibers.

Muscle spindle—Effector-Receptor structure in muscle, important in neural feedback of information regulating adjustment of muscular contraction.

Myelin sheath—White fatty sheath covering axons; provides white matter of spinal cord and brain.

Nasal mucosa—Membranous lining of nasal passages.

Neocortex—Most recently evolved portion of cerebral cortex.

Neurilemma—Thin sheath covering neurons outside the CNS, except at their terminations.

Neuroglia—Supporting nonneural cells of the CNS.

Nucleus (nervous system)—Group of cell bodies within the CNS, having the same or similar functions.

Occipital—At back of head, as opposed to forehead.

Olfaction—Sense of smell.

Olfactory epithelium—Layer in upper nasal passages containing olfactory receptor cells.

Optic chiasm—Crossing of the nasal fibers from each retina.

Optic disk—Exit of the optic fibers from eye; blind spot, with no visual receptors.

Organ of Corti—Structure resting on basilar membrane in cochlea of inner ear and containing sensitive hair cells for audition.

Oval window—Membranous covering of cochlear duct, to which stapes is attached; transmits pressure waves from middle ear bones to inner ear fluid.

Overtones—Frequencies of sound waves which are whole-number multiples of the fundamental.

Oxytocin—Hormone of posterior pituitary which excites smooth muscle such as in uterus.

Paralysis, flaccid—Paralysis with flabbiness of muscles.
Paralysis, spastic—Paralysis with extreme tonus of muscles.
Parasympathetic nervous system—Portion of the ANS stimulating vegetative functions, cranial and sacral regions of neuraxis.
Peripheral nerves—Afferent and efferent nerves outside the CNS.
Peristalsis—Progressive waves of contraction moving down the gastrointestinal tract.
Photopic vision—Cone vision; daylight vision.
Pia mater—Innermost of three membrane layers covering brain and spinal cord, transparent and adherent to the CNS.
Pilomotor response—Erection of hairs on surface by contraction of smooth muscle attached to the base of hair.
Pituitary, anterior—Anterior portion of small endocrine gland on floor of brain case; secretes six hormones.
Pituitary, posterior—Posterior portion of small endocrine gland on floor of brain case; innervated by hypothalamus.
Pons—Portion of brain stem between medulla and midbrain.
Postcentral gyrus—First convolution of cerebral cortex posterior to central fissure.
Postganglionic neuron—Neuron of ANS which originates in outlying ganglion and terminates in an effector organ.
Preganglionic neuron—Neuron of ANS which originates in CNS and terminates in an outlying ganglion.
Premotor area—Cerebral convolutions lying just anterior to motor area.
Proprioception—Sensation from muscles, tendons, joints, and semicircular canals, utricle, and saccule.
Psychosomatic disorder—Physical disorder which has a psychological origin.
Pupil—Opening through which light is admitted to interior of eye.
Pyramidal tract—Bundles of nerve fibers running through pyramids of medulla; the corticospinals.

Receptor—Cell differentiated from others in being sensitive to certain stimuli.
Reciprocal innervation—Double innervation, excitatory and inhibitory so that when a muscle is excited, its antagonist is inhibited.
Reflex—Simple, innate response to a particular stimulus.
Reflex arc—Simplest neural link between receptor and effector by way of the CNS.
Reflex, pupillary—Change in size of pupil because of change in illumination.
Reflex, righting—Reflex tending to orient an animal upright in relation to gravity.
Relative refractory period—Period following absolute refractory period, when neuron can be excited only by intense stimulation.

Reticular formation—Diffuse central core or column of gray matter extending from lower medulla to diencephalon.

Retina—Innermost coat of the eye, containing visual receptors and bipolar and ganglion cells.

Reverberating circuit—A closed CNS circuit in which nerve impulse may persist without added stimulation.

Rhodopsin—Photosensitive pigment of rods of retina.

Rod—Visual receptor for low illumination; produces gray and white sensation only.

Rolandic fissure—Main fissure dividing frontal from parietal lobe; known as central fissure.

Rostral—Toward head end of animal.

Round window—Small membrane covered opening at opposite end of cochlear duct from oval window.

Ruber—A midbrain nucleus concerned with locomotion.

Saccule—Vestibular receptor site for lateral tilting.

Saturation—Purity of hue; lack of white.

Sclerotic coat—Tough outer coat of eyeball.

Semicircular canals—Canals set in three planes to receive sensation of acceleration and deceleration.

Spasticity—Abnormally high muscle tone, due to disorder of CNS.

Sphincter—Muscular ring that relaxes and contracts, opening and closing an orifice of the body.

Spike potential—Brief wave of negative potential which is recorded as nerve impulse passes a point.

Spinal animal—Animal whose spinal cord has been separated from the brain.

Spinal reflex—Reflex obtainable when only the spinal cord is intact.

Stapes—Middle ear ossicle adherent to oval window of inner ear; the "stirrup."

Striated muscle—Muscle with horizontal striations, usually attached to skeleton; voluntary muscle.

Sulcus—Grooves between gyri on cerebral and cerebellar cortex.

Summation, spatial—Adding the effects of several subthreshold simultaneous impulses, in order to cross synapse.

Summation, temporal—Adding the effects of several subthreshold, successive impulses, in order to cross synapse.

Sylvian fissure—Lateral cerebral fissure dividing temporal from other lobes.

Sympathetic nervous system—Portion of ANS connecting with thoracic and lumbar cord, with ganglion chain adjacent thereto.

Synapse—Functional connection between two neurons.

Taste buds—Structures in surface of tongue containing sense organs of taste.

Tectum—Roof of midbrain; the colliculi.

Thalamus—Large group of nuclei in diencephalon.

Timbre—Quality of a sound differentiated by the voice or instrument producing it.

Tonus—Continuous slight tension in smooth or striated muscles; tone.

Topographic organization—Maintenance of spatial relationships from receptor to cerebral or other central structures.

Tumor—Abnormal tissue growth in an animal; may be benign or malignant.

Tympanum—Large membrane closing off external auditory meatus; the eardrum.

Unipolar cell—Neuron with one common extension from cell body for afferent and efferent fibers.

Utricle—Receptor site for sensation of forward and backward tilt.

Vagus—Cranial nerve X, serving heart, stomach, and intestines.

Ventral—Toward the belly side of an animal.

Ventral horn—Gray matter in ventral part of spinal cord; anterior horn.

Ventral root—Motor fibers leaving the spinal cord.

Ventricle—Cavity in interior of brain containing cerebrospinal fluid.

Vestibular sense—Sense of equilibrium, with receptors in semicircular canals, utricle, and saccule.

Visual acuity—Fineness of visual discrimination.

Visual angle—Angle in the eye formed by lines projected from the edges of an object to the lens.

Vitreous humor—Viscous fluid filling the chamber between lens and retina.

Index

Index of Illustrations